HORSE OWNERS GUID
NATURAL HOOF CARE

Horse Owner Commentaries

Jaime Jackson's *Horse Owners Guide to Natural Hoof Care* is a wonderful book, many thanks. How I care for my horses has really changed. After two years of horseshoes and an uncomfortable horse, I said "Enough." The tremendous changes I saw in my horse's hooves in the few weeks after his last set of shoes were removed was a real shock and wake-up call to me! My good horse BJ is now turning 6 years old and a real pleasure to ride! Many times I have to hold him back and he is much more willing to move, it's a complete turn around. I've had horses in the past with the same "problem" BJ had, wish I could go back and give them a natural approach to living conditions all horses need. – RP

I have your book, *HOG*, and have been practicing your trimming guidelines for most of this year. The change in my clients' horses is even hard for me to believe. I can say now that I have seen some close to perfect feet. Before this I had only seen one horse with feet this pretty and well-developed. – JR

Finally! A book that explains the mechanics of the hoof and hoof maintenance in laymen's terms. I've always wanted to educate myself about hoof maintenance, but was unable to find anything that was "readable." And, of course, farriers are reluctant to explain their methods and reasons for doing things the way they do. – PB

May I also send my thanks to Jaime and Co. for publishing his knowl-

edge and instructions on hoof trimming. My horse too, sends his thanks! – LSH

Thanks so much for helping all of us care for our horses' feet naturally and improve their quality of life! I send anybody I can recruit your way and always highly recommend the *HOG*. I own other books as well but have found it to be by far the most useful. – KG

I know you hear this all the time but Jaime's book is just such a lifesaver for people all across the country (and probably around the world too!). I find some of them doing a pretty good job having read his book. Jaime has always been way ahead of his time. In the future of hoof care, well after our time on earth, I'll bet the *HOG* will be standard reading in farrier science classes and vet schools. – LS

Please express my thanks to Jaime for his dedication to barefootedness. My 3 horses are doing extremely well and so are my friends' horses. With Jamie's books and video and my natural trimmer's personalized instruction we are all very comfortable caring for our own horses. My horses actually prefer me doing their feet rather than having a farrier come. I can really see a difference in their way-of-going. I always thought shoes were a bad idea, but everyone told me I was crazy. I will continue to tell people about our success stories and hopefully once they are aware and investigate this avenue they will realize

how much healthier their horses can be. – JB

Thanks. I am having such a good time reading and watching the video by Jaime that I have gotten a little on the impatient side to get after this trimming! – WS

My search has led me to study the research you have done on the hooves of the wild Mustang and the parameters for the natural trim. I have read two of your books and also have viewed the trimming video. As a result of the knowledge you have bestowed upon me, two of my foundered horses are walking normally again and also I am helping two other horses in my neighborhood one of which has foundered very severely. All of my horses are now barefoot and our two riding horses are doing great even riding in very rocky soils along the Colorado River without boots. – KL

Jackson's books, which I have learned a lot from together with his video I bought from you, are fantastic. If it is possible, I would like to thank Mr. Jackson for making it possible to learn. – HM

I read your books with great interest. As a physician I have some background in mammalian anatomy and physiology. Your descriptions of the very complex equine hoof mechanism could rival that found in modern medical textbooks. Absolutely terrific! – BM

Wild stallion of the west surveying his kingdom . . .

With flowing tail, and flying mane,
Wide nostrils never stretched by pain,
Mouths bloodless to the bit or rein,
And feet that iron never shod,
And flanks unscarred by spur or rod,
A thousand horse, the wild, the free,
Like waves that follow o'er the sea.
                              Lord Byron

HORSE OWNERS GUIDE

to NATURAL HOOF CARE

JAIME JACKSON

STAR RIDGE PUBLISHING
HARRISON, ARKANSAS

Cover: The author at work.

Frontispiece: Undisclosed location in wild horse country.

Printed in the United States of America.

First printing, April 1999

ISBN 0-9658007-6-8

Star Ridge Publishing
P.O. Box 2181
Harrison, AR 72601
1-870-743-4603
1-870-743-1637 (FAX)
www.star-ridge.com

Neither the author, Star Ridge Publishing, nor any individual or organization quoted in this Guide accept responsibility for any applications or misapplications of the ideas or procedures presented herein. The publisher presumes in all instances that horse owners will solicit the services of qualified hoof care providers. Natural hoof care is a sophisticated and highly technical process that should only be practiced by qualified natural hoof care practitioners trained in high performance barefooted trimming methods, or by persons under their supervision.

I SHOULD HAVE LIKED to draw the attention of the whole learned fraternity of blacksmiths, who mutilate horses, the world over. The hoofs were as solid and as sound as ivory, without a crack or wrong growth of any sort. It is noticeable that the equine race, in its wild state, has none of the ills of the species domesticated. The sorrows of horse-flesh are the fruits of civilization. By the study and imitation of Nature's methods, we could greatly increase the usefulness of these valuable servants, and remove temptation from the paths of many men who lead blameless lives, except in the single matter of horse-trades. - W.E. Webb (1872)

(Above) W.E. Webb. *Buffalo Land: An authentic Narrative of the Adventures and Misadventures of a Late Scientific and Sporting Party with the Full Descriptions of the Indian As He Is, the Habits of the Buffalo, Wolf, and Wild Horse.* 1872.
(— And I thought I was the first to discover the wild hoof! - J.J.)

BOOKS BY JAIME JACKSON

The Natural Horse – Lessons from the Wild (1992, 1997 rev.)

Horse Owners Guide to Natural Hoof Care (1999, 2002 rev.)

Founder – Prevention and Cure the Natural Way (2000)

Boot Your Horse! (2001)

What Every Horse Owner Should Know About Natural Trims (2002)

COMPANION VIDEOS BY JAIME JACKSON

Creating the Perfect Hoof – Learn to do a Natural Trim with Jaime Jackson (2000)

Boot Your Horse! (2001)

ARTICLES BY JAIME JACKSON — AMERICAN FARRIERS JOURNAL

"Spirit of the Natural Horse," Jan/Feb, 1992.

"Forging the Naturally Shaped Hoof," Dec, 1992.

"The Naturally Shaped Hoof," Sep/Oct, 1992.

"The Natural Draft Horse Hoof," Sep/Oct, 1993.

"Mule Hooves In The Outback," Jul/Aug, 1993.

"Naturally Colored Hooves – White Hooves In the Wild," May/Jun, 1993.

"Going Barefooted," Dec, 1997.

"Hoof Balance . . . Getting In Step With Nature's Way," Jan/Feb, 1994.

CONTENTS

RESOURCES

ACKNOWLEDGEMENTS

A work like this is never the labor or product of one person. For nearly two decades my wife Nancy has steadfastly taken her position as a key steward in the holistic path culminating in whatever value this work accords the world. Contrapuntal to her prodigious efforts and countenance are the anti-contributions of what can only be called the "blasphemers" of the natural path — de-bunkers, self-proclaimed arbiters not qualified to enter the debate or contribute to an intelligible discussion, experts who have never spent a day among wild horses, experts at received information, charlatans, and a fantastic endless stream of "expert" carpet knights who cannot hold a horse competently at halter let alone trim his feet properly — all of whom I must nevertheless thank as heartily as Nancy, sans any sense of love or respect of course. Without distinguishing them by name or deed, they have strengthened my raw determination to hold and advance my ground as an advocate of the horse's natural world in spite of their sheer babble, stupidity and arrogance.

I wish to thank the corps of natural hoof care practitioners cited in Chapter 17, who rushed to get their images and bios to me at the last moment, and who have helped greatly to render this work more interesting, and I trust, inspiring to readers. Some of these persons have also provided me with a palpable and needed connection to the field, where many of the theories and methods presented in this *Guide* have been tested by others than myself. A special note of appreciation is extended to Ms. Cindy Sullivan who has worked closely with me in defending the wild horse model where it has come under attack by the noodle brains, and advancing it forward in the new frontier of the American Association of Natural Hoof Care Practitioners. Cindy's colorful photographic images have also added sparkle to the *Guide*. Michael LaGrone is also honored, for he is the first clinician-at-large attempting to present the basics of the model to the general horse using community. Hubert and Ruth Rohner have given us the Swiss Horse Boot, our most effective weapon in the battle of "transition" from shod to high performance barefootedness, and deserve recognition. Robin Duxbury of Project Equus, long a supporter of my works, particularly *The Natural Horse*, has defended and championed our cause of "natural is best." Karen Sussman of the International Society for the Preservation of Mustangs and Burros has aided me through the years in understanding the insidious politics of wild horse country. Of course, there are legions of hidden persons who I worked with in publishing this book per se, and if they are reading this, they know who they are and that they are much appreciated.

Now, having acknowledged the indispensable support and contributions of the above precious souls, may I go a step further to suggest that this *Guide* is not solely the creative inspiration borne of simple observation or mathematical computation alone. Much of what is said forming the core of the Philosophy and Methods have been "thought across" from the still shadowy world of the wild horse. Large segments of what I've "thought" in the transmutation of wild to domestic have even startled me. From whence does it come? Perhaps the paraphrased words (—after composing the Hallelujah chorus) of the great composer George Frederick Handel provide hidden clues, "Whether I was in my body as I wrote it, I know not. *God* knows."

The vast majesty of wild horse country. *U.S. Department of the Interior (USDOI)*

Preface to the new 2002 Edition

Four years have now passed since I first published this book — a *method* of natural hoof care based on the sound, healthy hooves of the wild horse. Thousands of horse owners and professionals have in that time tested its merit at the hoof. Most have sought out the method because their instincts and common sense told them it was "right" for their horses. Many others were motivated out of a justified fear of the adverse effects of horseshoeing, and of these, not a few have had horrifying experiences with more than ample reason to come. Then, I suppose, there have been a few sightseers, bargain hunters, and debunkers, who simply have time on their hands and are oblivious to why all of this is happening.

The latter aside, most who have come and worked the method learn quickly to appreciate its merit and applicability. Discovering that the trim is not hard to do, and healthy strong hooves are the reward. For this reason, it's worth mentioning, few have retreated back into the haunts of black-smithing. If you are new to the natural hoof care movement, then you can at least take confidence in the success of those who have come before you.

Now, I'd like to offer some advice for using this *Guide* effectively and safely. First, if you're going to attempt to trim your own horse, and you're a novice, do so under the guidance of a professional natural hoof care practitioner. Let this person check out your work to make sure you're on the right track.

Second, learn to observe how the hoof *responds* to your trimming. If the response isn't good, meaning the finished hoof has deviated substantially from the wild hoof model, you need to go back and review your understanding of the basic trimming principles and recommendations discussed in this *Guide*, and make adjustments accordingly. In this respect, the sage advice of the ancient Roman poet, Juvenal, is worth contemplating, "Never does Nature say one thing, and wisdom another." Good luck!

Jaime Jackson

This good-looking naturally shaped hoof is the result of natural trimming and boarding. The horse wearing it can go for miles barefooted in one of the wettest climates in the U.S. He can also travel over rock-hard ground. Your horse can do it too! Follow the instructions faithfully in this *Guide* and you will reap success. You won't have to shoe your horse again. (Pete Ramey/Star Ridge files.)

INTRODUCTION

"All too little attention has been paid to that 'natural' foot. That's the way he was made; that's the way he should go."
J.R. Rooney, DVM (*The Lame Horse*)

This concise comprehensive *Guide to Natural Hoof Care* was written to help interested horse owners like yourself bridge the gap between conventional horseshoeing practices and high performance barefootedness. According to the American Farriers Journal (May, 1998), over 17 percent of all U.S. horses go without shoes. Some of these horses are simply "at pasture" and are not ridden. Others are fitted with modern, state-of-the-art hoof boots and are routinely ridden in many horse sport activities. Still others are ridden barefoot all the time—they are neither shod nor do they wear hoof boots.

Why do people shoe their horses? The answer is invariably the same: horse owners and their service providers assume that their horses' hooves are too weak and too sensitive to go unshod. Further, they believe that high performance horsemanship is only possible if the hooves are given the type of support that only horseshoes can provide.

A new generation of natural hoof care practitioners has arisen to challenge this assumption. They neither shoe horses nor coddle their feet once they are set free of the horseshoe. To the contrary, unshod horses in their care are trimmed and expected to out-perform their shod brethren.

How is this possible? The answer is *natural hoof care.*

PRINCIPLES OF NATURAL HOOF CARE

This new realm of hoof care is founded on the following beliefs:

◊ Nature created a hoof that can do the job without our nailing horseshoes to it.
◊ The natural, unshod hoof is a hoof that is vastly superior to the same hoof shod. This belief is bolstered by research and practical experience, described in this *Guide*.
◊ Conventional horseshoeing, along with unnatural boarding practices, is directly or indirectly responsible for most lamenesses suffered by horses. The natural hoof is a sound one.
◊ Horseshoes preclude the hoof from functioning normally as nature intended. Horseshoeing causes hoof pain, eventually cuts off feeling in the feet, unbalances the horse, and tragically sends many horses to

an early grave. Tens of thousands of riders also suffer serious trauma injuries as a result. All unnecessarily.

◊ Horseshoeing, unbeknownst to its practitioners and most horse owners, is often the pernicious culprit at the bottom of mediocre and poor equestrian performance. Most equestrians, trainers, vets, and others often assume that faulty riding methods, poor conformation, overly temperamental horses, and pathological disorders in the horse's body above the hooves, are responsible for performance problems. Proponents of natural hoof care argue that these problems, in many cases, can be traced instead directly to the egregious and insidious side-effects of horseshoeing, in addition to unnatural lifestyles and riding/training methods in conflict with horse's natural capabilities.

◊ Natural hoof care is equally concerned with providing horses with more natural living conditions. Natural living conditions are crucial to the success of any natural hoof care program. What are natural living conditions, and, are such conditions feasible in these modern times? The answer is that the essential natural living conditions requisite for high performance barefootedness are easily provided today. This *Guide* addresses these, and many other concerns.

ILL EFFECTS OF HORSESHOEING: AN HISTORICAL PERSPECTIVE

Until more recent centuries, the historical record shows that most horses have been ridden unshod since their domestication 8,000 or more years ago.* They lived relatively pastoral lives, in fact, under conditions which favored strong, healthy, and naturally shaped hooves. The ancient Greeks and Romans, Scythians, Mesopotamians, Huns, Mongolians, Turks, Arabs, Bedouins, Berbers, for example, all rode unshod horses — domesticated horses that lived the better part of their lives

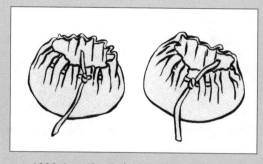

ca. 1800 Arapaho Indian hoof booties
— not the first nor the last.

on the rugged mountain ranges, deserts, and semi-arid regions of the world. The barefoot cavalries of Hannibal and Xenophon have left vivid records of their systems of natural hoof care and military triumphs using unshod horses.

Eventually, and coinciding with the rise of modern civilization, the riding stock of these early horsed peoples found their way into the hands of Northern Europeans. Significantly, these horses were also passed into an alien habitat whose moist, lush grasses and cold winters contrasted sharply with the sparse bunch grasses and dry browse of the arid high desert biome of their ancient homeland. There is credible evidence that this change in natural habitat may very well explain the epidemic numbers of horses that have succumbed to founder ever since. But another event soon occurred which, in the stream of creating the modern horse breeds, obscured this issue — and nearly buried forever our knowledge of the true natural hoof of the ancient homeland.

By 700 A.D., increasing numbers of European horses found themselves living in close confinement. This was a by-product of the new feudalism, an era ushered in by the conquest of the Western Roman Empire by "barbarian" Germanic tribes. Castles, complemented with armies and cavalries, were built by the victorious German tribal chiefs to give their subjects security from rival kingdoms. Horses were stabled in paddocks and stalls, where the hooves were subjected to the ani-

*The "Red Earth Peoples" of upper Mesopotamia are thought to be the first horsed society, ca. 5,000 BC. (See Francis Haines, Horses In America.) Other authorities place the peoples of ancient Susa in Southwest Asia as the first domesticators, ca 3,000 BC. Conceivably, however, North American tribes may have adapted horses to their cultures 10,000 years ago or earlier.

"The same care which is given to the horse's food and exercise, to make his body grow strong, should also be devoted to keeping his feet in condition. Even naturally sound hoofs get spoiled in stalls with moist smooth floors. [A] place outside of the stall would be best suited to the purpose of strengthening the horse's feet if you threw down loosely four or five cartloads of round stones, each big enough to fill your hand and about a pound and a half in weight, surrounding the whole with an iron border to keep them from getting scattered. Standing on these would be as good for him as traveling a stony road for some part of every day."

— Xenophon, Greek General, *The Art of Horsemanship* (ca. 400 BC)

XENOPHON

ANCIENT
ART OF
HORSEMANSHIP

mal's own wastes, day in and day out. Moreover, constantly confined, the hooves could neither function naturally nor optimally. The result was that hooves began to deteriorate systematically across feudal Europe during this period.

It was thought that horseshoeing, a technology with obscure roots that may have originated with the pagan priests of ancient Gaul (France), and as yet not widely practiced during the Middle Ages, could provide a remedy. Horseshoeing, or blacksmithing, henceforth, would evolve inexorably as a commonplace practice, its lampblack roots at last wedged firmly in medieval Europe for the reasons given here.

Feudalism, however, soon declined, undermined by prosperous new economic conditions, and, very important, the invention of gunpowder and the long bow, the latter rendering castles with knighted horsemen ineffectual against cannons, harquebuses, long distance archery, and other "modern" inventions of war. Kingdoms were then replaced by thriving cities.

But the practice of close confinement of horses and horseshoeing in particular, held its ground into the Renaissance. Horses were put to more uses than war, and the conveniences of stalling horses was never questioned as a means of boarding them. Guilds were formed to advance the position of the blacksmith,

now needed more than ever to meet the growing needs of a horse dependent civilization.

With the advent of the Industrial Revolution, the late 18th century, most European, and later, American horses, were routinely shod. This was in keeping with the continuing custom of close confinement, augmented, as it were, by the old and entrenched feudal shoeing protocols few ever bothered to question.

Interestingly, some did. As early as 1800, the ill-effects of horseshoeing were beginning to be recognized and documented by veterinary authorities; wrote Bracey Clark, F.L.S., a British equine surgeon:

For a period of more than a thousand years has the present mode of shoeing been in use, without the public being aware that there was anything wrong or injurious about it.

For a period of more than a thousand years has the present mode of shoeing been in use, without the public being aware that there was anything wrong or injurious about it, if it was but properly executed; and though accidents, and unequivocal expressions of suffering accompanied it continually, and were visible to the eye of every one, yet no one ventured to think upon a subject that appeared so abstruse; or if he did, was it likely to be received but with rebuff and insolence: and the mischief's arising from it were constantly evaded or denied, and were attempted to be overcome in every way but the proper and natural one—that of removing the cause—which cause also was, to the simple as to the more knowing ones, alike unperceived.*

*Clark, Bracey. Podophthora: Demonstration of a Pernicious Defect in the Principle of the Common shoe. Royal Veterinary College Library, London, 1829, p. 2. [Farriers reading this will be interested to know that Dr. Doug Butler—an icon of modern farriery science, should others wonder—noted, in his landmark work, Principles of Horseshoeing, that Dr. Clark was one of history's most knowledgeable hoof care authorities. Coming from Butler, no small praise.]

Blacksmiths, as they were then called, were not unversed themselves in the early protestations, and some went so far as to manufacture the first modern hoof boots. Still, by 1900, most horse owners had no memory of the pre-horseshoeing days.

After World War II, automobiles and tractors replaced horses for transportation, drayage, and farm work. Most horses would become "pleasure" animals, used recreationally for competition, trail, and companionship. Although many of these horses would be returned to the country or suburbs, some even living in pastures most of the time rather than in stalls, most owners by and large continued to keep their horses in close confinement and shod. After all, this had always been customary — who could remember back to a time otherwise?

ABOUT THIS GUIDE

This *Guide* reunites the horse owner with the horse's forgotten past and natural world— and to the prospects of a superior hoof with a happier horse attached to them. It has been slow in coming. A few words in this regard are worth sharing.

The *Guide* actually evolved from my earlier work, *The Natural Horse: Lessons From The Wild For Domestic Horse Care* (1992) — the subtitle later changed to *Foundations For Natural Horsemanship* with the second edition (1997). This work provided a model for barefootedness, the result of my extensive personal observations of numerous wild horses in the Great Basin of the U.S., and a thorough and systematic study of their hooves from 1982 to 1986.

The Natural Horse provides the specific trimming protocols for the current *Guide*. As of this writing (2002), I have been a professional hoof care provider — a traditional farrier until a decade ago — for over 25 years.

The prospect of a high performance barefooted horse as an alternative to a conventionally shod one is something I have thought closely about ever since I left wild horse country. At the time I wrote *The Natural Horse*, I confess that I was under a certain amount of "political" pressure from various parties to leave out any discussion of riding barefooted horses. The matter was simply too controversial (— not that it still isn't!), and the process too little understood at the time (1980s) to even consider asking horse owners to "de-shoe" their horses.

As a result, the hoof care guidelines provided in *The Natural Horse* emphasize shoeing. Nevertheless, the specific trimming guidelines for barefootedness are given, and I use them unaltered to this day. This current *Guide* goes one step further, however, and adapts the hoof care process entirely to barefootedness, including riding barefooted horses.

The "jump" to barefootedness did not occur overnight. It began rather slowly, and privately, with certain of my professional shoeing clients who seemed open-minded to the possibilities. I also began to take note of the now and then horses crossing my path in various barns that went unshod. This, coupled with my many returns to wild horse country to see the natural hoof in action, gave me the confidence, and inspiration, to continue my experiments.

Eventually, I was contracted to trim all the horses at a Peruvian Paso breeding ranch, whose owners — as well as the breed registry itself — did not want the horses shod. Until the ranch closed four years later, I had at my disposal a true experimental station to test my method. And that I did, keeping data records for each horse, and there were over 300 horses at the ranch.

I compared my data with the measurements I collected for the wild horses. Every effort was made to bring each hoof into the natural form, and as I was the only professional working the horses, it was simply "me working with nature" and there was no "outside" interference. It was a great learning experience, and without going into the mass of detail, the experiment was a great success.

By 1990, I had de-shod many other horses outside the Paso operation. I was now satisfied that barefootedness was not only possible, and beneficial, but that horseshoeing wasn't the "necessary evil" history and convention proclaimed it to be. I had by then also finished writing *The Natural Horse*, and pretty much decided that my career as a farrier was over. The future lay ahead, but I didn't know what it had exactly in store for me at the time.*

TRIMMING THE NATURAL WAY

The actual process of trimming the horse's hooves naturally as described in this *Guide* is fairly technical and, to steer you away from getting into trouble, I recommend that you learn with a competent natural hoof care practitioner. At least have such a person monitor your work until you are confident.

Naturally trimmed hooves are worked quite differently than with conventional farriery methods — until now, the only hoof care standard horse owners like yourself would probably be aware of. Indeed, there is very little in common between blacksmithing and natural hoof care, except the horse and its hooves awaiting care. The reader is urged to forget about horseshoeing standards and methods altogether. It should be obvious that they don't apply.

How are things done differently?

◊   Most important, natural hoof care practitioners don't put shoes on the horse's feet. Shoes prevent natural wear and naturally shaped hooves.

◊   The bare hoof is trimmed to optimize what we call the "hoof mechanism" — the natural "flexing" and "contracting" of the hoof as it loads (bears weight) and unloads (is in flight) during the normal course of movement. The mechanism is very important for optimal blood circulation and shock dissipation — in short, for a healthy hoof. Horseshoeing, as I'll explain later, seriously impedes the hoof mechanism. For this reason, too, horseshoeing and natural hoof care are incompatible.

◊   The hooves are trimmed at a minimum of four week intervals. But if the hooves are worn and don't need trimming, they aren't trimmed until they need it.

◊   Hoof boots for riding are fitted for horses that are going barefooted for the first time, or that are being ridden in terrain their hooves are unaccustomed to.

*Readers interested in the whole story here are invited to go to my website — www.jaime-jackson. com — for a complete biography and discussion of my role in the natural hoof care and barefoot movement.

(left) Lexus, an 18 year old registered Missouri Fox Trotter, and a tremendous mover — and barefooted — prepares under light rein to canter up a rocky hillside here in Ozark country with her owner and excellent rider, Angel.

Me and "Lexus"; a close-up of one of her tough, white hooves, fresh from a rugged 15 mile bare-foot ride in the Ozark mountains. The hooves must be conditioned to do this.

◊ Horse owners are encouraged to understand how the horse's lifeway can impact his feet — both good and bad. Much attention is given to ways that we can provide horses with more natural living conditions. Surprisingly, these changes are not difficult to make; they are more a matter of using many resources already available in new ways. As a rule, "naturalizing" the horse's life means "simplifying" the way he lives.

◊ Natural hoof care practitioners encourage horse owners to understand the biomechanics of the horse's natural gaits and how movement, both natural and unnatural, can impact his feet. The hooves are repositories for the many locomotive forces in the horse's life, and each force contributes to the shaping, and mis-shaping of the foot.

◊ Riders are encouraged to learn what it means precisely to have a properly fitted saddle. An unnaturally fit saddle can obstruct the full rotation of the shoulder joint, and, as a result of muscle/tendon reciprocities connecting the joint with the front hoof, impede the natural support/flight phases of the foot. This can lead to ligament strain, and if left unchecked, cause life-threatening lamenesses such as navicular.

ORGANIZATION OF GUIDE

Finally, let me lay out the learning sequences of this *Guide*. I suggest reading it like a novel, that is, by starting at the front and working to the back. Use the companion video, *Creating the Perfect Hoof* (see Resources) to flesh out the concepts, and have your work checked by a professional. The video includes wild horse footage and close up views of their hooves to help you visualize the kind of hoof nature has provided us with and to strive toward. *This is the model.* It is not something to ignore. Aspire to it and you will reap success.

In learning to trim, you will inevitably ask around to learn more, and in so doing, become aware of what is practically an epidemic of ersatz "natural" trim methods out there. The rise of these methods has paralleled the growing popularity of the natural hoof care movement, largely spawned by this book's first printing in 1999. I always tell people to stay focused on Nature's *truth* and you'll never get lost in the jungle of conflicting trimming advice. Remember, too, that a barefoot trim method does not necessarily mean a natural trim. Trimming methods not based on the wild horse hoof are problematic. Your main defense against unnatural, harmful trimming practices is to know what constitutes a true, naturally shaped hoof. This Guide's **Appendix** (discussed shortly) will also help you identify some of the more blatant, if not tragic, trimming violations of the natural trim conjured and practiced by misguided practitioners hawking their wares among the uninformed.

Chapter 1, "Going Barefoot," discusses the meaning of natural barefootedness and its implications so far as riding goes. The term "high performance barefootedness" is a new term (you won't find it in horse books five years ago) coined in recent years by those of us who have been trying to redefine hoof care standards.

Many horse owners, as well as virtually all farriers and vets, believe that barefoot horses are at risk of causing injury to their feet if they go without shoes for any reason. Riding a horse barefoot is assailed by some as being inhumane. But natural hoof care advocates have always pointed to the wild horse model as incontrovertible evidence that barefoot horses are fully capable of "high performance" movement. It wasn't until practitioners like myself began to "de-shoe" horses, as I explained earlier, and trim and condition hooves to the model that we learned that domestic horses

are capable of the same high standard. Thousands of horses around the world are now going barefoot, and none have required horseshoes to do what they've always done.

So, in **Chapter 2**, "The Perfectly Natural Hoof", I'll review the meaning of the "natural hoof" that I described in *The Natural Horse*, but in light of this *Guide's* holistic focus on natural hoof care, natural boarding, and high performance barefootedness.

I'll also discuss "hoof balance". Let's define this term right now. It means, simply, *a hoof naturally shaped and able to support the natural movements of the horse.* But make no bones about it, when you're dealing with barefooted horses, hoof balance is nothing to approach capriciously or without much thought. It's very serious business. An unbalanced (that is, an unnaturally trimmed) hoof will tend to unravel on you sooner or later. Happily, the natural trim is easy to do and nature only requires that we get it reasonably into the ballpark of what's truly natural to keep us out of trouble.

E.V. Wolfwalker/Star Ridge Files

"SHORTY"

LAMENESS TO SOUNDNESS

"In early 2001 'Shorty,' a spotted Draft cross, was diagnosed with ringbone. At that time he was very lame and given 'no chance of recover.' After 6th trimming, he is sound again — packed out an elk this hunting season over really rough terrain in Kenosha Pass (CO) for his owner who is a local outfitter. Since Shorty has done so well, this former shoe 'die hard' has now had all shoes removed from the rest of his part-Draft string of working horses and is a barefoot advocate."

Eryn Wolfwalker
(see bio in Chapter 17)

I'll address other concerns and "myths" of the modern horse world too. For example, the issue of *hoof color*. I am practically in despair that so many vets, shoers, and horse owners still persist in the untenable belief that white hooves are inferior, and, therefore, horses so endowed are precluded from going unshod. In case you are one of those espousing or cowering under such notions, let me say here that it is nonsense. The white (i.e., un-pigmented) hoof goes barefooted no differently than the black one; Chapter 1 explains why.

Chapter 3 explains the "hoof mechanism," mentioned earlier. Briefly, when the horseshoe is removed, and the hoof is trimmed according to the specifications of this *Guide* (based on the wild horse hoof), and the horse is provided with sufficient natural living conditions, then the hoof goes through an extraordinary — by industry standards — transformation in terms of shape, hardness (which I call callusing) and capacity to function without artificial protection (e.g., horseshoes). The mechanism plays a vital role in this metamorphosis from a shod, weak caricature of what nature intended to a tough structure fully capable of serving the horse without anything artificially attached to it. Chapter 3 explains why and how it happens.

Chapter 4 provides you with an overview of natural trimming — a bird's eye view of the process to help prepare you for all the technical details that will come in the ensuing chapters. The natural trim is defined here and I also describe the essential characteristics of naturally trimmed hooves.

With the natural trimming pathway laid out conceptually before us, it's time to take the first step. **Chapter 5** helps you identify the specific tools and equipment you will need to get the job done right. Since these can be very difficult to locate, the Resource section at the back of the *Guide* will connect you to my suppliers.

In **Chapter 6**, I provide tips on how to handle your horse during the hoof care proc-

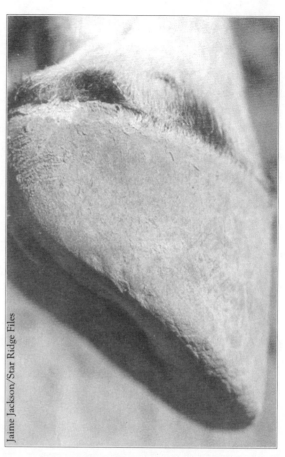

Jaime Jackson/Star Ridge Files

White Hoof — tough, sound, wild!

ess. These are the things that I've done for many years, and they incorporate the "best" of what I've learned from others — humans and horses. As an advocate of cooperative horsemanship, I oppose the use of violence against horses. The alternative is to take a few moments to get to know them and show them what you want and that you mean no harm. I don't say this capriciously, but with the utmost sincerity. Horses are very intelligent, observant, and capable of cooperating. However, if you rush them into something they don't understand, they will tend towards resistance. Personally, I simply enjoy working with horses; and the horses sense this and will go out of their way to cooperate rather than fight me.

It has been my observation, though, that many people fear horses. So, instinctively they act aggressively towards them with an eye to dominance rather than true partnership.

(Continued on page 22)

Cindy Sullivan, diligent natural hoof care practitioner from Georgia, trims her own horses as well as a professional clientele which include rescue operations for abused horses in the Southeastern United States.

Sooner or later, however, this will lead to trouble. 70,000 horse owners enter U.S. hospital emergency rooms each year from horse-related injuries. A fair number are hoof care practitioners. Since this has never happened to me in 25 years of hoof work, and I have been under thousands of horses, I hope you will take my recommendations seriously in this chapter.

Study the methods thoughtfully and allow yourself time to practice on a willing horse. Soon you will discover that virtually all horses will yield to your approaches. Those that won't are probably abused animals, and if this is the case, my advice here is to refer these to rehab trainers and experienced hoof care professionals.

Now armed with the right tools, and your horse calmed and balanced for his foot work, **Chapters 7, 8 and 9**, will take you through the de-shoeing and trimming process. We go through it together, step by step, as though I were there with you trimming your horse, or giving you advice on how to do it. The companion video, *Creating the Perfect Hoof*, includes several trimming sessions on various horses and will aid you in this learning experience too. And don't forget to consult a professional natural hoof care practitioner — one can be located in just about any area of the U.S. today.

This is how I do things personally. And it is only that — my way. There are many roads to Rome, and readers will pave their own paths based on their own experiences and many talents. My goal is simply to give you the vision of a sound, naturally shaped hoof, and the confidence to pursue a program of natural hoof care for your horse, and hopefully to convey at least one useful piece of information to help you make the transition.

"RED"

IT'S NO BIG DEAL!

Richard Drewry of Arkansas is a U.S. Soil Conservation District Manager who also happens to own horses. He once shod them, but now rides them barefoot or with boots. "Whether I shod my own, or hired someone to do it, it was always chance that all the shoes would still be on when it came time to ride. I also dreaded our horses throwing their shoes out on the trail. Natural trimming and booting has changed all that. The worst that might happen now is that a boot might snag on a branch. But it's only happened twice in two years. And it's no big deal, you just put it back on!" [Richard's bio is in Chapter 17]

Richard Drewry/Star Ridge Files

The truth is that the hoof, within reasonable limits, is very forgiving of our mistakes. So don't tarry, but push on, experiment, do the best you can and observe the hoof's short and long terms responses to your trimming and management efforts.

Chapter 10 is very important. Everyone wants to know when they're done if they did a good job. What we really need to know, though, is whether or not we've done a "good" natural trim. That's the purpose of this chapter — to help you assess your work.

Donkeys, mules, ponies, miniature horses, and draft horses, are also part of the domestic horse world, and I don't want to overlook them in this *Guide*. The principles and methods of natural hoof care apply equally to them. So **Chapter 11** recruits our natural hoof care talents and brings them to bear for these animals' needs as well.

Everyone also wants to know how often they should trim their horses' feet. In response, I've written **Chapter 12** ("Trim Schedule") to answer this and related questions. Planning your horse's long term hoof care is just as important as planning and conducting his first natural trim. You want to schedule his trim sessions at regular intervals, just as though you were the professional coming regularly to do it.

But regular trims aren't enough to sustain sound, healthy natural hooves. There is also the issue of "holistic" care to make sure they stay natural. By holistic I mean all management practices that affect the horse's life and which you have control over and can influence. Exactly what this means is spelled out in practical ways that you can help your horse's feet in **Chapter 13**, "Natural Boarding."

Now that your horse has naturally trimmed hooves which are being properly cared for holistically, the time has come to address the issue of riding your barefoot horse. This *Guide* is sprinkled with horse owners riding their barefoot horses. I did that intentionally to inspire you to go with the program. **Chapter 14** is included to help you and your horse to transition safely and responsibly to high performance barefootedness. This is the real "testing ground" in which you — and others watching you — will evaluate the merits and success of your trim program.

Chapter 15 presents an overview of booting horses. These are not medicinal boots, but riding boots. Horse boots are an important facet of natural hoof care. They are indispensable during *transition* — that period of adjustment the hooves go through following deshoeing before they are tough enough to go without artificial protection.

Horse owners will be surprised and delighted to learn that hoof lamenesses that they believed were incurable, are, in fact, completely healable through natural hoof care. Hence, **Chapter 16**, "Natural Healing and Prevention of Lameness," will be very important for readers with lame horses or who are prevention-minded.

Many hoof-based lamenesses have a biomechanical derivative in hoof imbalance — which, as I explained earlier, stems from unnaturally shaped feet. Thus, by restoring the hoof to its natural shape, hoof balance is also restored. And, if indeed that was the cause, the hoof will proceed to heal itself. "Natural healing" means letting the hoof heal itself.

But beyond misshapen hooves, the "hoof" per se, is normally not the main issue. The harmful effects of unnatural living conditions and diet on the horse's feet are. For example, lush green pastures, contrary to popular opinion, are unnatural habitats for horses and they are also the source of a harmful diet. As a result, tens of thousands of U.S. horses succumb to laminitis each year because they are turned out to live on grass and legume fields. The grass pasture not only fails to provide the dry, abrasive surface the hoof needs to wear naturally, the grass itself at certain times of the year is toxic to the horse's natural digestive system. Digestive disorders stimulate the proliferation of harmful bacteria which cause catastrophic enzymatic changes within the hoof. I'll take a look at laminitis and other lamenesses that express themselves at the hoof in Chapter 16.

Chapter 17, "Natural Hoof Care Practitioners," of course, could not have been included in the first edition of this *Guide*. But in recent years, many hoof care professionals, including farriers, and countless amateur horse owner trimmers, have since "gone natural" and now distinguish themselves as natural hoof care practitioners. I've included a few profiles of those who have consented to go public.

I'm hoping these mini-bios will inspire others to follow in their footsteps. Indeed, the rise of natural trimming and booting promises to be an exciting new hoof care profession — one unthinkable 25 years ago when I nailed on my first horseshoe, oblivious to the unprecedented changes that would alter my own career and others' forever. Also discussed briefly is the formation of a new organization dedicated to raising the natural model as an industry standard. Myself and others have been working conceptually on this project for some time, and we agree the time has come to make it reality.

After considerable thought, I elected not to include the content of **Chapter 18** in the first edition. But with the ranks of natural hoof care practitioners swelling with each passing year, it seems justified now. Chapter 18, "The Natural Model: What We Don't Know," explores various aspects of the natural paradigm and raises questions about causality, adaptation, the ramifications of domestic forces, and the implications for new research. I consider the suggested investigations to be of paramount importance, not only for an improved understanding of the natural hoof model, but as an indirect means of improving our natural hoof care standard.

An **Epilogue** concludes the main body of text. Briefly I offer my assessment of the natural hoof care movement, past, present, and my hopes for the future.

There is one **Appendix** in this *Guide*: "Troubleshooting." The intent of this appendix is not to address de-shoeing issues, pathology, or the indiscretions of the naïve newcomer at the hoof, for these are discussed amply in the chapters which precede it. Instead, it represents an assessment of several problematic barefoot trimming methods now in vogue. I've selected those which in my professional opinion conflict seriously with natural hoof care based on the wild horse hoof model presented in this text. I believe they are harmful and could cause irreparable damage. While common sense promises that most people would never think of engaging in a method that harms the horse, there are those regrettably who have deluded themselves and others into believing that bringing harm to hoof is prerequisite to healing it of whatever ailment, real or putative, it possesses. If you find yourself contemplating or executing any of the procedures described in this appendix, my advice is to desist and rethink what you are doing, including consulting others for their objective opinions. *No genuine natural trim should harm the hoof, give pain to the horse, cause abscessing, or leave him lame for any reason.*

The **Resources** section immediately follows the troubleshooter. Its purpose is to bring you further into the fold of the natural hoof care movement by introducing you to quality tools and equipment, apparel, and related learning materials, that you will need to get started. This is an interesting and inviting section of the *Guide*, particularly for those of you with "hands on" propensities and a sincere desire to become more self-sufficient in the realm of hoof care.

The *Guide* reaches its terminus in a new **Glossary** which offers concise definitions for natural hoof care terms. I've focused especially on those words which enjoy precise meaning among natural hoof care practitioners. Avoided are definitions specific to the veterinary and farriery lexicons, as these may be found in the numerous books and technical manuals of those disciplines.

Matt Worley (Georgia) sets to work with his hoof knife on a string of rental riding horses. Working horses like these can truly benefit greatly from a program of natural trimming and barefootedness. Ridden daily by the public, the horses' feet are adapted to the environment and ready for action.

D. Dutra/Star Ridge Files

Debbie Dutra trims her own horses and her clients. She also gives natural hoof care clinics in her home state of California. [See bio in Chapter 16]

The **Index** is a badly needed expansion of the original from the first edition. My apologies to those returning readers who, like myself, enjoy a good index that leads comprehensively into the inner life of a complex work, but were justifiably disappointed at the skeletal parody haunting the first edition. In future editions I will take the liberty to improve it still further. *Voilà!*

ANGEL HOPE

Arkansas

On the Buffalo River, where I do most of my trail riding, hills, mud, river crossings, river rock, stumps, boulders, sand, and sharp rocks are everyday obstacles. All of my horses handle them with ease. I was met with teasing and skepticism, when I first started riding barefooted, but I am continuing on, as I know my horses' hooves are healthier, and I have even had some interest from those skeptics! The more I learn about my horses, the more I observe and try to get in tune with my horses' moods and body language. They have always been able to let me know what works and doesn't work for them, but I was not always aware or observant enough. I'm still learning, but thanks to Jaime Jackson and his example, I feel I'm on the right path.

CHAPTER ONE

GOING BAREFOOT

"The handsome little Horses of Sweden and Norway travel often at the rate of ten, twelve, and even fourteen miles an hour, in their usual work, with a gaiety and vivacity never seen in our Post Horses . . . The Horses of the West Indies travel delightfully over the rocky ground of those regions, and nearly all the Horses of North and South America, go equally well, and are admired by all strangers for their sound pacing, yet to all these Horses are the blessings of shoeing happily unknown, and they are used entirely without shoes." Bracey Clark (DVM), Guide to the Shoeing-Forge (1830)

Quite the quote, yes? Twenty five years ago, I would have called Dr. Clark crazy — as many of his colleagues did two hundred years earlier. Indeed, the idea of "high performance barefootedness" loomed more as a haunting specter of sore-footedness than a wonderful new prospect of hoof soundness with relief for the animal.

But twenty five years ago, I had never heard of Clark nor ever contemplated the possibilities of horses going barefooted. I had not seen my first wild horse foot either. Personally, I was still locked rigidly into the limited awareness of "blacksmith logic" like everyone else.

In this *Guide's* Introduction I explained briefly why horseshoeing came about. And why barefootedness is rejected out of hand by virtually all horse owners, farriers, and vets — although there are now definite signs that this wall of resistance is beginning to crack. As I think about it, one could try to build a "conspiracy" theory against horseshoers and vets, that "they" are trying to "protect" their economic special interests, and the horse be damned.*

But this is nonsense. There is no conspir-acy! Or, as a professional farrier myself, I would have been a part of it and known. Shoers, vets, and horse owners, all, are as ignorant as I was before the wild horse awakened me.

The status quo, the shoeing of horses without question, is systematically reinforced daily by the common horseshoeing experience. Typically, when the shoes are removed, let's say between shoeings, the hoof is normally very moist, relatively soft, and generally pretty sensitive. Now, if you took the average horse following this pre-shoeing trim, and tried to lead him (or worse, ride him) down a gravel road, you will have the perfect picture of a miserable, stumbling, tender-footed animal. Certainly not the picture of "high performance barefootedness."

Probably fewer than 2 percent of all horses could have their shoes pulled and be expected to walk — at the outset — without discomfort. Most shoers, understandably, would dread to find out what would happen next if the horse owner kept it up. The shoeing experience logically leads them both (shoer and horse owner) but to one conclusion: the horse's hooves will be ruined. At least if the owner persists in rid-

*Here's why: U.S. horse owners spend over 2 billion dollars annually on hoof care; Texas horse owners — notorious for under- paying their farriers for a shoe job — alone spend over a quarter of a billion dollars, more than any other state (American Farriers Journal, November, 1993).

ing the horse barefooted over rough ground.

But few shoers today would offer that the horse's state of tenderness *is the result of shoeing.* That refraining from shoeing would allow nature to reconstruct a tough hoof without need of the shoe for ancillary protection — if only the horse were afforded the opportunity to go barefooted.

Yet unbeknownst to most rank-and-file farriers, some of their most respected leaders and industry spokesmen have actually argued in recent years that shoeing does harm the hoof. According to Emile Carré, a certified journeyman farrier and the current president of the American Farriers Association:

> The foot was designed to be unshod. Anything that you add to the foot, like a horseshoe that is nailed on, is going to interfere with the foot's natural process. Most horseshoes have six to eight nails, possibly one to three clips, all of which constrict the foot's ability to expand and contract. Add pads, packing, any number of alternatives to the shoe, and you create a gait alteration. It all interferes with the natural process of the mechanism. Ideally, for the foot to work the way it has been designed through evolution to work, you would rather do less than more to the foot.*

And, according to one of the AFA's certification examiners, Deborah Ash—

> The greatest advantage is to hoof health. By leaving a horse barefoot, one allows the hoof's natural functions of shock absorption, traction, and biomechanics to perform at their optimum. Shoes inhibit natural function and the horse's natural way of going, and limb interference with shoes can cause injury.*

Of course, there are hints lurking about that suggest other possible outcomes of the interim shoeing hiatus: young horses running about barefooted which have not yet been shod, the occasional horse that loses a shoe on a ride but doesn't come up sore or lame after several hours, and the all too common scenario where the horse is not seen for six months by the shoer until all the shoes have been thrown. More than one shoer has confided in me half-bemoaningly: "You know, the toughest hooves seem to be the ones that have lost their shoes while the horse was at pasture and I've not trimmed for months."

Then, too, there are those uncustomary equine "freaks" in a few stables whose owners never have them shod. To be honest, as a pro-

(Continued on page 33)

*"STEP BY STEP: The Barefoot Horse: Romance vs. Reality." By Marcia King. (The Horse Magazine, Internet Interactive, Nov./2000)

(Above, facing page) Local horseman and friend, Fred, astride his 1100-lb. registered Quarter Horse, peers across 100 years to *circa* 1890 Metis (French-Indian mixed-blood) buffalo hunter astride Indian pony on the Canadian Great Plains. Besides their hunting rifles, both men have another thing in common: they are riding barefooted horses. Flip the page and we'll take a closer look at the hooves of Fred's horse.

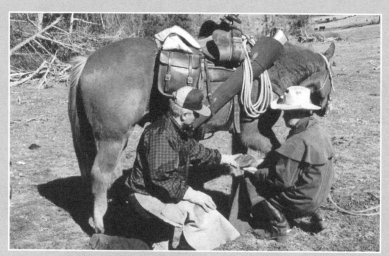

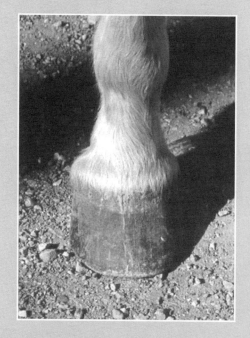

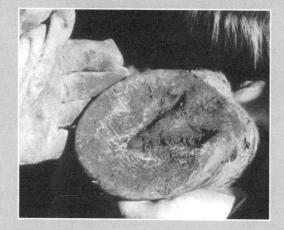

The author with a brave heart pioneer of the natural way. *Top*, the tough Metis is too much for Fred, who dispatches his rifle to scabbard and heads on down the rocky stream, where he runs into me. That's convenient, because I want you to see his horse's hooves up close. This is the kind of hoof that not only Quarter Horses should be wearing, it's the rugged, healthy hoof that belongs on all horses.

fessional farrier, I personally didn't always make a point of being alert to these barefooted anomalies among my clients or other shoer's clients. I'm thinking now of one gelding I trimmed for several years — never shod him once — in the Contra Costa hills near Oakland, California.

The horse's owner, a quiet, unassuming fellow, never gave a reason, other than he didn't feel it was necessary. I always thought the guy a little peculiar anyway, so I just forgot about him and his horse as quick as I left the barn. I never stopped to think that this horse was trail ridden nearly every day for miles, that it was never lame, and that there was seldom anything to trim. I just blocked it all out, so powerful was the influence of blacksmith logic within me at the time.

There is another dimension to this reluctance of shoers to "not shoe" horses. I call it the "feel of steel" addiction. When I first began to de-shoe horses and trim them for barefootedness, I found myself "missing" the final step of "working" the shoe over the anvil and nailing it to the hoof. When the day came that I wasn't shoeing any horses, that missing step had actually turned into a crave of sorts. I would liken it to someone trying to kick a cigarette habit. It was like a part of me was missing, I really "needed" to "feel" that shoe in my hands, shape it over the anvil, sink those nails through the soft flesh of the hoof wall to set it. I was addicted and I was dying to shoe a horse, any horse—and part of me thinks I might have done it for nothing just to satisfy my "habit" had someone offered me the opportunity. To this day, I still get that feeling, that crave, if I go near my old anvil or pick up a horseshoe somewhere. I have no doubt that there are shoers who just can't kick the habit, just like there are people who can't quit smoking. They're going to shoe horses no matter what.

Anyway, it was about this time, the early 1980s, that another client of mine had just purchased a "mustang" mare from the Bureau of Land Management (BLM). I was asked to inspect her hooves to see what they needed. The mare, which hadn't been in captivity long

enough to cause too much damage to her naturally shaped hooves, didn't need much so far as I could surmise. In fact, her hooves were so thick and tough, I didn't know what to think of them. The truth is, I was flabbergasted by what I saw. They were beautiful! And this was the event that originally inspired me to venture into wild horse country, and later to write *The Natural Horse*.

So I headed into the mountains east of Reno, Nevada. There were, then, many wild horses in the area (since removed by BLM gathers). While I didn't understand natural horse behavior at first, which prevented me from immediately mingling and bonding with the various bands so that I could study their hooves in action at arm's length, I saw enough that the sooty darkness of blacksmith logic within me felt its first piercing ray of light. I was awakened for the first time to the *reality* of high performance barefootedness.

Okay, what exactly is "high performance barefootedness"? Simply, and I would like you to commit this definition to memory: *It is the horse moving naturally on his unshod feet with optimal efficiency.*

Said another way, high performance barefootedness is "competence in performance." On the grounds of our wild horses alone, it is nothing to speculate about or to bother debating. It is real, and, in my estimation, there isn't a horse, wild or domestic, on the face of the earth that nature hasn't fully prepared for it. Only that horseshoe and all that craving to put it on threatens to stand in the way.

But, you may be wondering, and rightfully so, how is it possible that the de-shod horse now before us, perhaps your horse, suffering with excruciating discomfort as it stumbles over the rocky path between its shoeings, is capable of anything but the soft hay-packed floor of its stall? Perhaps you are thinking too, "My horse is the exception. He needs his shoes as bad as I need mine. Just look at the poor thing. And just listen to what my vet and farrier are saying." In the words of Emile Carre, "Man entered the picture with his breeding

(Continued on page 36)

THE NATURAL HOOF ACCORDING TO CHARLES HALL

BAREFOOT HORSES IN TENNESSEE

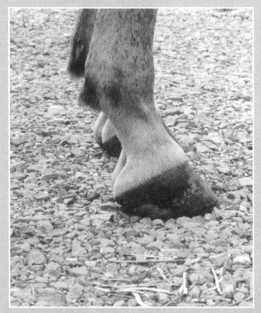

Charles has formed a 100 horse strong barefoot riding club in three contiguous states. The hooves on these pages are typical of what is possible when your horse is given true natural trimming and his feet are allowed to work without protection. Just like Bracey Clark states in the quote at the beginning of this chapter. — JJ

"This horse just finished a 17 mile ride over rocky ground . . ."

". . . and there's only a small amount of horn to trim."

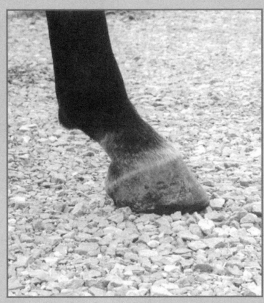

Charles Hall
Tennessee
(See bio, Chapter 17)

"(*Above*) This horse also just finished a 17 mile ride over rocky ground . . . and (*left*) there's only a small amount of horn to trim."

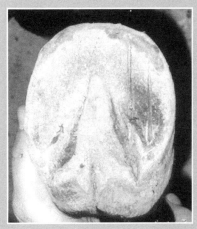

"This left front (Arab) hoof just finished a 100 mile barefoot ride. No shoes and no boots!"

Barefoot and up for the chase!

(Continued from page 33)
fancies, and we see horses today that are incapable of walking a gravel parking lot without shoes on their feet. They've had the feet bred right out of them!"

Nothing could be further from the truth! [See, as an example, "The Natural Hoof According to Charles Hall," in *Overleaf*.] And that's why this *Guide* was written. So you and your horse can avoid all that awful stumbling, the unfriendly stares, snooty gossip, sooty blacksmith logic, and your own self-doubt. Indeed, nearly every horse owner cherishes his or her horse, and the specter of tenderfootedness or lameness naturally elicits fear, ambivalence, and even paralysis. *Blacksmithery forges fear of the horse's natural capacity for high performance barefootedness.*

But there is nothing to fear but soot! The horse's weak hooves are not congenital (or wild horse country would be full of lame horses), they are the *products* of blacksmithery

and, depending on your boarding arrangement, close confinement and other unnatural management practices.

This *Guide*, however, will lead you right out of the soot to hoof care independence.

First, you need to "exorcise" those fears by educating yourself with some important facts about "why" barefootedness is nothing to fear. You need to know exactly why it works — and why horseshoeing and unnatural trimming methods prevent it from working. Once you know *why*, then the *how* comes easily. Okay?

Second, you'll have to shore up against the intimidations of the blacksmithing and veterinary communities, as well as the exhortations of horse owners who will be equally intimidated when you order your horse's shoes removed.

So, to start, let's begin with a solid discussion of the very hoof care model that will make riding your horse barefoot possible: *the wild horse hoof.*

(Overleaf) "The Natural Hoof According to Charles Hall"

(*Above*) There they go! — the wild ones rumbling barefooted across America's rocky back country. White hooves, black hooves (*right*), striped hooves. And not a horseshoe in sight! What do they "feel" with those tough hooves? Pain, discomfort, anxiety? No, not at all. Haven't you ever gone barefooted as a child? Maybe you should ask the next barefooted child that comes along — ask them what they "feel." They'll tell you it feels good. Real good! We adults, we've just forgotten. Civilization has made us forget.

CHAPTER TWO

THE PERFECTLY

NATURAL HOOF

"Nature is the art of God." Dante

The *Horse Owner's Guide To Natural Hoof Care* has as its model the hooves of America's wild, free-roaming horses. *The wild horse hoof defines the natural state of the hoof.* Why this model? And, what exactly is a "natural state"?

At first thought, there is a tendency among many horse enthusiasts and professionals to reject the wild horse hoof as a model worthy of emulation. This is understandable. What business does a "wild" hoof have being on a "domestic" horse? More often I hear, "What applies to wild horses doesn't apply to domestic horses, because domestic horses aren't wild and they don't live naturally." Or, just as common, "I don't want anything 'wild' on my horse!"

This type of logic, on closer inspection, is fraught with misunderstandings. First, there is no physiological or genetic difference between wild horse hooves and domestic horse hooves. That's because there's no physiological difference between wild and domestic horses. Both are members of the same species, or if we are talking about near relatives, such as the ass, or mule, they are members of the same genus or are interspecies hybrids.

So, when we say that a horse is "wild" all

we're really saying is that it isn't "domesticated." But it's the same animal, either way. As I described in *The Natural Horse*, the domestic horse originally came from the wild, thousands of years ago. So rejecting the value of "wildness" in the horse, in a sense, is foolish because it means rejecting the horse's biological roots. It blinds us to the essence of what it means to be a horse.

Our wild horses of the American West are sometimes said to be "feral", which simply means they have returned to their natural wildness, having been previously tamed or domesticated (*Overleaf*, "Once Domestic, Now Feral, and Very Wild"). The term "feral" means *wild beast* (in Latin) and refers to any animal that makes the transition from being tamed to living naturally in the wild. So feral horses, wild horses, and domestic horses, biologically speaking, are the same animal. Just like camels, llamas, and elephants, all of which have known feral, wild, and domestic lifestyles too.

So, if there is an issue here in applying what is "wild" among feral horses to horses in captivity, such as their hooves being worthy as models, it is a question of the effects of lifestyle, rather than inherited biology.

(Continued on page 42)

Overleaf, "Once Domestic, Now Feral, and Very Wild"

DOMESTIC, NOW FERAL, AND VERY WILD

THERE IS NO DIFFERENCE

Few horse owners or hoof care professionals today have a clear understanding of the complexity of wild horse country, including where the horses came from. This ignorance has played into the hands of de-bunkers who would have everyone believe that wild horses have no relationship what-soever to domestic horses and therefore are irrelevant as models for study. In fact, as the BLM tract below explains, the colorful, sound, and tractable wild horses seen on the facing page, are essentially nothing more than former domestic stock that are now running free and barefoot on lands so harsh that the uninformed can only conclude someone must be up there shoeing them.

DIVIDE BASIN HERD MANAGEMENT AREA

The Divide Basin HMA encompasses a total of 778,915 acres; 562,702 of these acres are managed by BLM. The range can support between 415 and 600 head of wild horses. Currently there are an estimated 660 wild horses, and with the 2001 post-foaling population, the number is predicted to be approximately 763 wild horses.

The climate within the area is typical of a cold desert. Summers are generally hot and dry with long, cold winters. Temperatures can range from well below zero to the upper 90s. Annual precipitation ranges from a low of 7 inches up to 15 inches at higher elevations. Some wind is seemingly inevitable. Direction of prevailing winds is variable but is generally westerly.

Topography within the area is highly variable, ranging from mostly flat to slightly rolling foothills carved by drainages, and desert mountains featuring steep slopes, cliffs, and canyons. Preferred habitat for wild horses in the Divide Basin HMA is the rolling hills and flats found at lower elevations.

Wild horses in the Divide Basin HMA have many domestic bloodlines in their background including American Quarter Horse, Thoroughbred, Standardbred, Arabian, and smaller draft breeds such as Percheron. Nearly every coat color can be found within the herds. The animals tend to be of moderate to large size for wild horses. Habitat conditions are such that the horses are in very good condition. The combinations of size, conformation, coat colors and patterns, and excellent physical condition have become a draw for potential adopters.

The normal breeding period runs from March through September each year but peaks around mid to late June. The peak of foaling season for wild horses in the Divide Basin HMA has been documented to be on or around June 1. The horses social structure, combined with their size, strength, and adaptability allows them to compete favorably with wildlife and domestic livestock. Horses traveling up to 10 miles to water have been noted, although 2 to 5 mile distances are more common. An adult horse normally consumes 10 to 12 gallons of water per day. Horses usually have adequate water from winter snows and spring runoff which fill reservoirs and intermittent streams.

During late summer and early fall, horses depend on the fewer perennial sources of water (i.e., reservoirs, streams, springs, and flowing wells), and on water wells pumped for domestic livestock and wildlife. No predation of wild horses has been documented in the Rock Springs Field Office area and is considered to have little or no effect on wild horse populations.

Wildlife are an integral part of the environment. The Great Divide Basin HMA provides habitat for a variety of wildlife species, including big game species (elk, mule deer, and pronghorn antelope). There is potential for competition between wild horses and antelope, deer, and elk; however, this potential is generally minimal during all four seasons.

#0986: Three yr old pinto gelding, captured Feb 14, 2001, in the Cyclone Rim HMA, in Wyoming. He is fully halter trained and has worn a saddle. Good natured and good looking, could be a great saddle horse someday.

These and many other wild horses may be purchased from the government for $125 at:

http://www.adoptahorse.blm.gov/bid-t.htm

[The preceding information was excerpted from the BLM website cited above.]

#1632: Three yr old palomino gelding, captured July 23, 2001, in the Salt Wells Creek HMA, in Wyoming. He is fully halter trained and has worn a saddle. He is gentle and quiet, and easy to get along with.

#0178: Five yr old sorrel mare, captured July 27, 2000, in the White Mountain HMA, in Wyoming. She is fully halter trained and has worn a saddle. She is gentle, quiet, stout, and has good bone.

#0809: Four yr old gray mare, captured Oct 30, 2000, in the Divide Basin HMA, in Wyoming. She is fully halter trained and has worn a saddle. She has good growth, and is ready to start saddle training.

#0467: Four yr old black mare, captured Sept 20, 2000, in the Divide Basin HMA, in Wyoming. She is fully halter trained and has worn a saddle. She is gentle and quiet, and has good growth and color.

(Continued from page 39)

The difference then between wild horses and domestic horses is not in the species, but in the wilderness and domestic *experiences*. The domestic experience is inseparable from the human influence. Wildness, on the other hand, bears the hand of *nature*.

Going one step further — at issue, really, is not wildness, but "naturalness." What does that mean? It means living in accordance with a living thing's nature. The word "nature" comes from the Latin derivative, *natal*, meaning belonging to one's birth—hence, "natural order."

Aristotle, the Greek philosopher, further defined nature in terms of *telos* — or teleology, meaning inner "design" or "purpose." This is the mysterious "force" that makes something "be" what it is. The physical and psychological design of horses, for example, is unique, and horses—notwithstanding human influences to the contrary—will behave according to their own telos given the opportunity. In wildness, the horse's telos is brought to fruition— meaning, horses behave freely and naturally according to their natality.

Because "wild" horses live according to their species' telos — again, they live naturally and are not subject to the domestic influences of humans — they provide us with a truer picture of what nature's grand design for horses really is. In a very real sense, only they can teach us what it means to be a natural horse.

Accepting that horses have their own way

(i.e., telos), we are compelled to examine what that means in terms of their hooves. When I first went among the wild ones, this was my perspective. I simply raised the question: what is a *natural hoof?* Not what is a natural hoof according to human wishful thinking, conjecture, or extrapolations based on confined or pastured domestic horses — but according to the laws of Nature in wild horse country. This outlook enabled me to appreciate and learn from our wild horses many things, including the precise meaning of a natural hoof.

Now anyone, like myself, who has studied "wild" animals very closely sooner or later comes to appreciate another dimension to the term natural. This is *efficiency*. In the wild, horses live efficiently in order to survive. Efficiency means "competence in performance."

In the wild, incompetence leads to extinction. Les Emery, author of the great work, *Horseshoeing Theory and Hoof Care,** once defined "natural" as "efficiency". I agree. So, when we talk about natural hooves, we're really talking about efficient hooves. Hooves that serve one purpose: *competence in performance*.

Naturally, this makes sense. In the wild, horses are foremost concerned with their survival. Any facet of their being that does not serve this purpose, logically is removed through natural selection. This makes the natural hoof all the more important as a model. Whatever problems it may have inherently possessed at one time, have been rooted

(Continued on page 44)

*I consider this book to be the first modern work on natural hoof care. Unfortunately, it is out of print. While the authors recommended shoeing, the premise of the book is a genuine "natural hoof." Lacking the wild hoof model, however, they could not visualize the possibilities of high performance barefootedness; hence, they availed themselves of the only model they knew: shoeing.

"Thus it appears advisable to me to look back from the perfect animal and to inquire by what process it has arisen and grown to maturity, to retrace our steps as it were, from the goal to the starting place, so at last when we can retreat no further, we shall feel assured that we have attained to the principles." *William Harvey, M.D. Essays On The Generation of Animals (1651)*

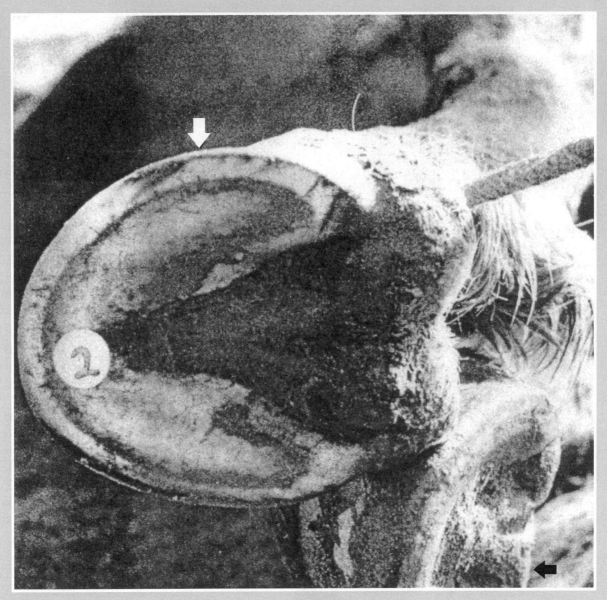

The first time I saw a wild horse hoof — the most natural hoof in the world — up close, like this hind one, which I photographed at some personal risk, was from the end of a BLM wrangler's rope 20 years ago. Even experienced as I was being a professional hoof care provider, the natural hoof you see here challenged me to reassess my most basic assumptions and understandings of the equine hoof's size, shape, proportion, and function. Just look at that thick outer wall (*white arrow*), massive frog, and concave sole (*black arrow*). The number "2" is literally pasted on the hoof, one of several hundred photographs I catalogued. — JJ

ANCIENT ROME
HORSEMEN OF THE ROMAN REPUBLIC

"The hoof horn will be hard, high, concave, round and topped by a lightly protruding coronary band." Columelle

"When the hoof strikes the earth it must resonate deeply underneath a solid hoof horn." Virgil

"The limbs must be straight, of equal length and turned inwards, with rounded and straight knees and a hard hoof horn." Varon

"A solid, dry foot which is very high and a concave hoof horn . . . with a round, firm and well attached hoof." Palladius

out by Nature.

Weak problematic hooves do not survive in the wild, because their disadvantaged owners are immediately weeded out by selection. Only that which is efficient will survive the rigors of wildness. Nature will not tolerate incompetence.

Hand in glove with efficiency, therefore, is *adaptability*. For something to survive in the wild, it must be able to adapt. But this is not exactly the same as efficiency. For what is efficient in one environment may be cumbersome and inefficient in another.

As I've described in *The Natural Horse*, wild horse country is extremely diverse, yet the consummate natural hoof found there (as a result of natural selection) represents an *adaptation*. Meaning, the natural hoof has undergone changes in form in order to be efficient. In order to adapt, so that its owner of the high desert biome can survive. The wild horse hooves of the Camargue wetlands, sandy Assateague Island, and elsewhere, have made their own unique adaptations. In order to be efficient — in order to survive. So, efficiency depends upon adaptability.

This was another reason for my many sojourns into wild horse country. To study the adaptations made by the efficient hooves of our wild horses. One of the great pitfalls in blacksmith logic is that it fails to appreciate that the domestic horse's hooves are unable to "adapt" to any environment through the abiotic barrier of the fixed shoe. The horse's foot must be "bare."

This is extremely important from the standpoint of our natural hoof care program. Because we are able to stimulate the bare hoof's adaptive mechanisms through natural lifestyle changes and natural hoof care so that they become stronger, tougher, healthier — in short, more efficient. The same exemplary qualities that wild horses profit from are thus transferred to their domestic brethren.

Make no bones about it, the incredibly powerful forces of adaptation will be there to help us. In every domestic horse, the hooves have a unique "will" (i.e., telos) to adapt to

their native efficient form. Interestingly, every "breed" of horse makes the transition slightly different than the next. Most horse owners and professionals, for example, recognize that Arabian horses have a different "kind" of hoof than a Thoroughbred, or mule, or burro, or pony, or draft horse. The relative size of the hoof, the density of the horn, and even differences in proportion, testify to this. Yet all their hooves — given the opportunity through natural lifestyle and natural hoof care — will adapt to their fundamental natural form if stimulated to do so.

As a professional hoof care provider, being at the "cutting edge" of this transformation process, has been exciting and rewarding. I remember the first time, fifteen years ago, when I applied the principles espoused in this *Guide* to a string of 300 barefoot Peruvian Pasos in my care over a three year period. The ranch's attending vet let the owner's staff know that he had never seen so many "sound" horses with perfect hooves in one place. These horses were also ridden barefooted by their Peruvian trainer, "Jorge."

It is interesting to hear many horse enthusiasts declare or speculate that we have "bred out" good hooves through domestication. This is not the case at all, in my opinion.

Instead, we have merely failed to recognize and stimulate the hoof's natural adaptive mechanisms — through lifestyle and natural hoof care — that render a tough, efficient hoof like we see in the wild. It's not something that is either bred in or bred out, any more than you can breed in or out "eyes" and "ears" or equine consciousness. They are teleologically imbued in the animal. The tough natural hoof lies dormant in every horse — only the timeless gatekeeper of natural selection can rule otherwise.

I have now seen the natural model cut through breed differences and turn the very worst of hooves among them — some diagnosed with incurable lamenesses such as navicular, laminitis, and contraction — into sound, functioning, and efficient hooves that would

(Continued on page 46)

The characteristics of naturally shaped hooves, like the principles of natural hoof care, apply equally to horses, donkeys and mules. I'll have more to say about these close cousins of Equus caballus in Chapter 11.

DONKEYS & MULES

NOT FORGOTTEN

survive in the rigors of wild horse country. Rest assured that your equine, whatever its breed, species (horse, ass, or hybrid mule), sex, temperament, state of soundness or lameness, is a good candidate for natural hoof care.

But, we must learn to crawl before we walk, and until we can identify a naturally configured hoof from an ersatz or unnatural one, we will get nowhere. This is the first step. Everyone must take it to break the first link in the shackles of blacksmith logic. What, then, is a natural hoof?

UNDERSTANDING
the NATURAL HOOF

When professional hoof care providers like myself assess hooves we generally do so in terms of *size* (e.g. toe length), *proportion* (e.g., toe angle), and *balance* — that is, how the horse wears its hooves so that optimal locomotive efficiency is sustained. *Texture* (e.g., quality of horn), *contour* and *color* provide other elements of nuance to consider. Let's look at some of these characteristics as we try to understand the basic form of the naturally shaped hoof seen among wild horses.

Please refer to the companion video, *Creating the Perfect Hoof*, for visual assistance. You will see the actual wild horse hoof biospecimens described here. Every person who has seen or held these unique hooves at my various speaking engagements — including some of the most distinguished horse industry professionals in the world — has been profoundly influenced by them, and has come away with a deep appreciation for the natural model and an intensified interest in how it can by applied to our domestic horses.

Now it is your turn! Let's flip the page and get down to business . . . . study hard, do it for your horse, who counts on you for the best hoof care possible, and for your own edification — so you can say that you've left "no hoof unturned."

GRULLA: (Grew-ya) Body coat slate colored (bluish gray as the blue heron) from light blue gray to a brownish shade. Points and dun factor markings are black. Dorsal stripe required. The color Grulla is the rarest of all horse body coat colors. The word Grulla is Spanish and translated into English is "crane".

HOOF SIZE

Hoof size refers to several growth dimensions: *toe length* (abbreviated "TL"), refers to the length of the toe wall from the hairline down to the ground; *hoof width* (HW), the width of the hoof across the quarters — in other words, the widest expanse of the hoof; and *hoof length* (HL), the length of the hoof from the tip of the toe to the rearmost protrusion of the heel-buttresses.

I always measure for these dimensions because the data helps me to understand growth changes as the hooves adapt to the natural hoof care program. The data is also necessary for properly fitting hoof boots, which I'll discuss in Chapter 15.

The naturally shaped hoof has a relatively short toe by common domestic horse standards (Figure 2-1). Typically among wild horses, toe lengths ranged from just over 2½ inches to less than 3½ inches. Most hooves measure around 3 inches. This is not surprising. Nature opts for a short hoof (i.e., minimal toe length) to ease "breakover" and optimize locomotive efficiency. Figure 2-2 provides a data chart in case you want to pull out a ruler to measure your horse's toes for the sake of comparison with our wild horses.

Figure 2-2 also lists hoof widths (HW) for wild horses. I was really amazed by the range of hoof widths among the wild ones. One Oregon stallion comes to mind: a 1400 lb. big guy, he had really short toes, about 2½ in. — so short I asked the BLM's Wild Horse Management Specialist helping me to check my measurements in case I was imagining things. But while the toes were so short (by industry standards), the widths (HW) were massive — probably over seven inches, without the mustang roll (which I'll define shortly). This monarch was also a great mover, besides being a real beauty and awesome soldier — tall, muscular, perfectly sound, bold, yet soft inquisitive eyes, a great flowing mane, a regal tail that touched the ground, a confident and fearless demeanor, and a spar-pocked grulla coat that emitted a faint blue tint in the high desert sun.*

I've purposely omitted data in Figure 2-2 for

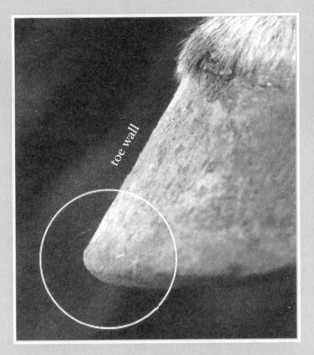
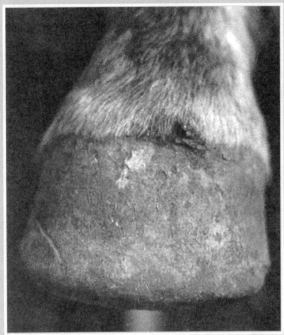

Figure 2-1 ON TOE LENGTHS

Naturally shaped hooves have relatively short toes; most wild horse hooves measured less that 3¼ inches. The circle marks the "mustang roll" or turn of the wall — an engineering marvel. The walls grow in straight lines, neither concave nor convex. Note the "roughened" outer wall, reflecting the abrasive effects of a rugged environment typical of wild horse country; we'll use the farrier's rasp in Chapter 9 to simulate this natural wear.

	MEAN (AVERAGE)		RANGE	
	Front	Hind	Front	Hind
TOE LENGTH	3 in.	3 in.	2½ - 3¾ in.	2½ - 3¾ in.
TOE ANGLE	54°	58°	48° - 62°	51° - 65°
HOOF WIDTH	5 in.	4¾ in.	3¾ - 6¼ in.	3½ - 5¾ in.

Figure 2-2 Wild Hoof Data

The table above is a condensed summary of measurement data I collected from wild horses I sampled in the 1980's. A complete compilation can be found in my book, *The Natural Horse* (1992).

hoof length (HL) because it's a tricky measurement to take and to explain without further groundwork. But I will discuss it in Chapter 10 (see also Figure 10-3), where it has specific "hands on" application and will be more meaningful. HL is also important in fitting horse boots (Chapter 15) and I explain it in great detail in my companion book for professional booters, *Guide To Booting Horses For Natural Hoof Care Practitioners*.

ANGLE-OF-GROWTH

The outer wall of the naturally shaped hoof normally grows down in a relatively straight plane; that is, it is neither concave (dished in) nor convex (bulging out). This can be seen in the hoof profiles in Figure 2-1.

The organization of horn is such that growth is directed forward and downward from the hairline at specific angles, all the way around the coronary band. As illustrated in Figure 2-3, the hoof's angle-of-growth is con-

siderably lower at the heels than at the quarters (i.e., the widest expanse of the hoof from side to side), and still lower yet than at the toe. We can interpret this to mean the toe wall is designed to absorb most of the horse's weight during the hoof's support phase. This is based, in part, on the shape and position of the coffin bone inside the hoof capsule. And also on how the coffin bone bonds to the hoof wall by means of a vast array of interlocking, leaf-like structures called *lamina* (Figure 2-4). Let's discuss this further.

Briefly, body weight is transferred — via a complex interplay between muscle, tendon, and bone — across these lamina from the coffin bone to the hoof wall. The toe wall is favored in this loading of weight because of its great number of laminar attachments; because of its higher angle, which enables the vertical grain of the wall to withstand impact with less stress and unnatural deformation; and because of forward momentum and breakover. I'll have more to say about these concerns in Chapter

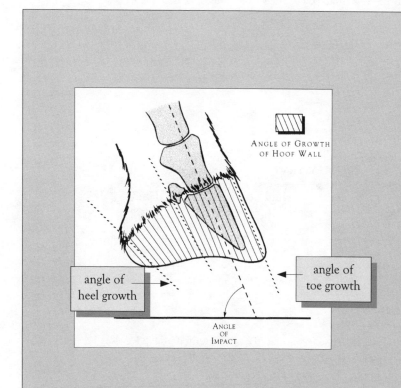

FIGURE 2-3

ANGLE-OF-GROWTH

The hoof's angle-of-growth is extremely complex. At the toe, densely packed horn grows down from the hairline at a higher angle than at the heel. This, and other factors, such as the size and alignment of the coffin bone inside the hoof capsule, suggest that the toe wall is a main weight bearing pillar. The message: keep toes short to ease breakover and minimize hoof wall stress.

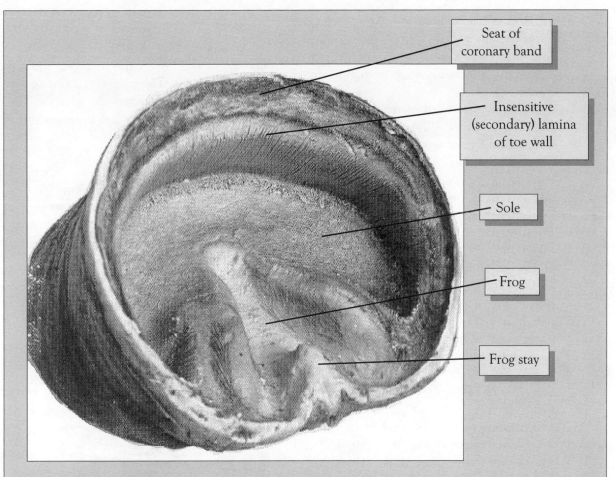

Seat of
coronary band

Insensitive
(secondary) lamina
of toe wall

Sole

Frog

Frog stay

FIGURE 2-4 UNCANNY VIEW OF INTERIOR OF HOOF

An incredible array of intermeshing leaf-like structures, called lamina, bond the hoof wall to the bone (here removed). The "pedal" or *coffin bone*, as it is called, is literally "slung" inside the hoof capsule by means of these laminar attachments. A naturally short toe minimizes stress on these sensitive structures. Excessively long toes and imbalanced hooves may cause a levered biomechanical disadvantage that weakens them, possibly predisposing some horses to laminitis, navicular, and a host of other hoof lamenesses. Connected as they are directly to the horse's limbs, imbalanced hooves influence the horse's entire musculoskelature—putting the horse at risk of breakdown. Nature's warning: keep your horse's hooves trimmed short.

3.

I realize that these are pretty technical concepts to fathom at this point — but please try not to feel daunted if you're a little confused or overwhelmed! For now, what's important to understand is that these hoof characteristics conspire to produce a very efficient hoof form based on a relatively short toe, by industry standards anyway. Long hooves, in other words, are not efficient because they weaken the laminar attachments and because they impede breakover — forcing the horse to work harder in order to move his feet inefficiently.

Some horse owners are concerned that such a short toe puts the horse's soles at risk of injury. They feel that a longer hoof with a lot more toe horn is necessary to protect the sensitive and vascular structures within the sole. But this perception is based on the characteristics of a weak hoof freshly liberated from a horseshoe.

In a naturally worn or trimmed hoof, the situation is entirely different. Nature — by means of the hoof mechanism — protects the hoof by hardening, or callusing, the sole and embedding the vascular and nerve endings well within. This is not unlike the horse's thermoregulatory system, which protects the horse from freezing to death from the cold by making changes in the skin, coat, blood vessels, and sweat glands.

Continuing, "angle-of-growth" at the toe is called "toe angle" among natural hoof care practitioners. This is measured using a hoof gauge or protractor, which many horse owners have probably watched their farriers use, such as the one in Figure 2-5. I have invented an inexpensive one for horse owners not wanting to invest in the high cost professional ones, which, for reasons I will explain in Chapter 10, are not reliable for naturally trimmed and worn hooves (see Resources, "Hoof Meter Reader").

Toe angle (T°), like toe length (TL), can help you to assess how natural and healthy your horse's hooves are growing. Use the gauge often to check the hooves just like you use a dip stick to check your car's oil or an air gauge to check tire pressure.

Figure 2-2 also provides typical angle ranges for wild horses. Note that toe angles for left and right hooves are the same. However, hind hooves, on average, measured nearly 3 to 4 degrees *higher* than fronts. This is significant. I believe that higher hind angles relate directly to the increased carrying of body weight during collection by the horse's hindquarters. If your horse's hind hoof angles are less than the front hoof angles, your horse may be at risk of locomotory inefficiency because the hooves are probably unbalanced.

I'll discuss how to identify and correct unbalanced hooves in the following chapters on trimming and assessing hoof balance.

MUSTANG ROLL

Among domestic horses we commonly see hooves shod with sharply beveled, squared, and dubbed toes. This is not seen among wild horses. Instead, nature provides what I call the "mustang roll" — a sobriquet in honor of the wild horse: a unique turn, or radius, of the outer wall's bearing surface.

The mustang roll can be seen in Figure 2-1. The roll is an interesting engineering feat, and one that a qualified hoof care provider can simulate readily with a quality trimmer's rasp. (The "correct" application of the mustang roll is illustrated in Figure 9-6, Chapter 9.)

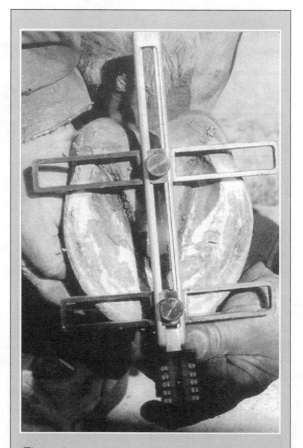

Figure 2-5

GAUGING THE HOOF FOR TOE ANGLE

Farrier's hoof gauge applied to heel-buttresses and toe wall will enable you to get an accurate toe angle measurement. Use a ruler to measure toe length.

In the wild, the mustang roll is very smooth, as though sanded, and, like the rest of the outer wall and sole, is nearly rock hard. The video footage in *Creating the Perfect Hoof,* focuses closely on the mustang roll so you can see exactly what I am describing here.

The mustang roll, of course, is a standard feature of the natural hoof care program. It is an extremely crucial part of the trimming process since it prevents ravel, facilitates breakover, aids the mechanism, is integral to hoof balance, and helps immensely in the healing of wall cracks. I would add that the mustang roll also contributes aesthetically to the naturally shaped hoof's appearance. In this regard, my clients always marvel at the neatly finished hoof with its striking roll, and this can be seen in any of the many trim jobs seen throughout this *Guide.*

THICKNESS OF HOOF WALL

Most farriery and veterinary textbooks today describe the bearing surface of the outer wall being thickest at the toe, thinner at the quarters, and depending on which book you read, thicker or thinner at the heel buttresses. I have not found any of these descriptions to be the case — either in wild horse populations or with domestic horses trimmed according to the natural model espoused by this *Guide.*

For example, of the 1,000 or so hooves I sampled at the BLM's Litchfield wild horse processing center, the degree of turn of the mustang roll and the thickness of the outer wall was essentially the same all the way around the hoof wall. Whether this is due to heavier wear at the toe (likely), differences in rates of horn growth (likely too), or variations in horn density (I am dubious), only further research can elucidate the truth. As I've described in *The Natural Horse,** the consistent radius of the roll from toe to heel certainly facilitates the hoof's natural locomotive habit of breaking over both forwards and from the sides.

FRONT AND HIND SHAPES

The basic shape of front hooves is signifi-cantly different than hind hooves when viewed from beneath. Many horse owners, I've observed, are unaware of this.

Look at the bottom of your horse's hooves to compare them front to hind. Here's what to look for and measure: the expanse of the front hoof across the toe will tend to be wider than in hind hooves. This will often be the case across the quarters too. On average, however, the expanse across the heels is the same for front and hind hooves.

These are averages, of course, and typically we'll find exceptions to the rule. These figures generally mean that front hooves are somewhat larger and rounder than hinds, hinds being slightly smaller and more pointed across the toe. Figure 2-2 also gives ranges for hoof size in this profile.

These distinctive front and hind shapes are based on biomechanical differences between front and hind limbs. By that, I mean the action of the front limb is principally of a supportive nature, favoring a broader hoof. The hind limb, in contrast, is more adapted for propulsion and lateral thrust, so a narrower hoof is logical. Natural hoof care practitioners are aware of this difference and will shape your horse's hooves accordingly.

These front-to-hind differences are illustrated in Figure 2-6 for your familiarization. It is very important to be cognizant of them before commencing with trimming.

HOOF COLOR

This should come as good news for concerned owners of horses with white-colored hooves: white hooves are as durable as black ones in wild horse country. But as I mentioned in the introduction to this *Guide,* the myth of white hoof inferiority persists among horse owners and professionals alike. The fact is, however, no less than a third of wild horse hooves are either completely white or white-streaked. Further, my data shows that white colored hooves do not differ from dark hooves in size, shape, or proportion.

Actually, white hooves are not really white

*Please refer to the related discussion in The Natural Horse, page. 92, Figures 4-23 A-B, and pages 74-75.

colored at all. Rather, they lack pigmentation. This can be seen in the cross-section of a black pigmented wild horse hoof in Figure 2-7. According to Dr. Doug Leach, a Canadian veterinary researcher who has studied hoof structure extensively, this difference in pigmentation has no significant impact on hoof durability one way or the other. Summarizing his findings in the *Journal* of the American Farriers Association, Leach stated:

> Hoof color has traditionally been implicated as an important factor in the durability and strength of horse hooves. However, it has been shown that black and white hooves do not differ in water content, chemical composition, hardness, or compressive strength.*

*Leach, Doug, "The Structure and Function of the Equine Hoof," American Farriers Journal (5) (1) (1981) p. 179.

Leach also pointed out that only the outer two thirds of the hoof wall contains pigment, "The inner third of the hoof wall," wrote Leach, "is unpigmented." He also contends that if white hooves were inherently weaker, then a "vertical shear force" would erupt along the junctures between pigmented and unpigmented horn, causing breakdown in Paint Horses and Appaloosas that he studied. "Such breakdowns are not seen," he added.

Given the foregoing, I'd like to assume that the issue is over with once and for all. But wherever I go, it seems, I continue to be lectured to the contrary by horse owners who have nothing but the best of intentions and concerns for white-hoofed horses: "They must be shod because they are white."

FROG

The frog serves several very important functions. Foremost, it serves as a "hinge," enabling the hoof to spread apart, thus contributing significantly to the "hoof mechanism" — and, therefore, contributes indirectly to blood

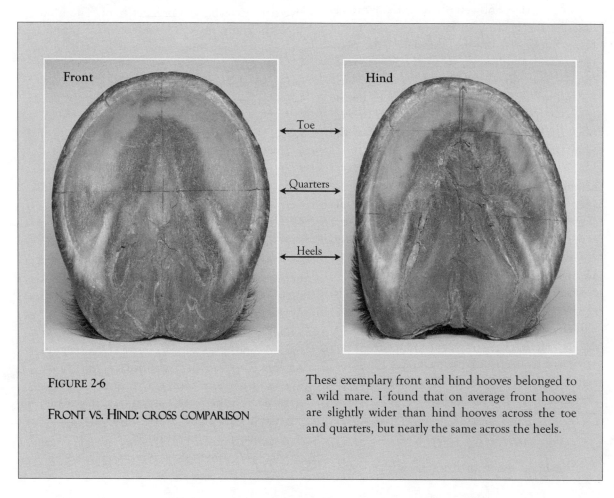

FIGURE 2-6

FRONT VS. HIND: CROSS COMPARISON

These exemplary front and hind hooves belonged to a wild mare. I found that on average front hooves are slightly wider than hind hooves across the toe and quarters, but nearly the same across the heels.

circulation and the dissipation of heat energy. The frog also provides traction, and thus dynamic balance for the horse during movement. And, due to its relative flexibility, the frog provides resilience to the entire *hoof capsule* (all the hard, horny structures composing the outer hoof) while absorbing both *compressional* and *concussional shock* — two biomechanical processes which cushion and protect the entire limb above it.

Many horse owners and professionals wonder about the frog. Should — or shouldn't — it press directly against the ground to promote a healthy hoof and simulate natural wear? Our wild horses are very clear on this: yes, although it should press "passively" against the ground. Let's discuss what this means exactly.

First, note that the naturally worn frog, as can be seen in Figure 2-8, is typically flat, dry and leathery. Furthermore, it is tucked away into a unique concave recession in the hoof's solar "dome," or sole. This horny, wedged shaped niche matches the triangular shaped frog.

In contrast, the frog seen commonly among domestic horses is frequently thick, rubbery, and relatively moist. This can result from unnatural boarding conditions, insufficient wear, the presence of a

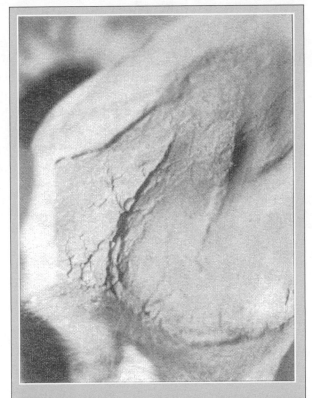

Figure 2-8

NATURALLY WORN FROG

The naturally worn frog is typically flat, dry and leathery, as can be seen in this rare close-up of a wild horse hoof. The frog is protected by the sole, bars, and the hoof's natural concavity.

horseshoe, or the lack of frequent trimming. An unworn, that is overgrown, frog can predispose the *sensitive frog* (the inner dermis from which the frog is produced) to fungal and bacterial attack — specifically, thrush — an issue I'll discuss further in Chapter 16.

Figure 2-9 (facing page) illustrates how these differences between "natural" and "unnatural" frogs can arise as a result of shoeing. As can be seen, the shod hoof prevents the frog from ever touching the ground. For all practical purposes, there is no wear at all. It is ironic that blacksmith logic traditionally argues the importance of "frog pressure" — the frog being pressed against the ground, or vice versa — to blood circulation in the hoof, yet deprives the frog of all such possibility by raising it up off the ground with the shoe where virtually no contact at all is possible!

In contrast, the naturally worn frog is constantly in contact with the ground, albeit passively. As is illustrated in Figure 2-10 (facing page), the heel-buttresses, bars and sole, which completely surround the frog, in effect, contain it in a kind of niche, preventing the frog from wearing actively, and, thus, excessively.

"Stones strewn about [the stall] in this way also strengthen the frog."
Xenophon

The solar dome's natural concavity also prevents excessive frog wear. Clearly, the frog can only be worn to the extent that these protective structures are themselves worn down or deformed. These structures take the brunt of the wear, especially wear resulting from body weight pressing downward through the hooves. For this reason, the frog is said to endure *passive wear.*

The naturally worn frog also provides the hoof with traction. As body weight descends upon the hoof during its support phase, the hoof spreads out — largely due to the flexibility of the frog (and another structure above it called the *digital cushion,* discussed below) which puts the frog closer still to the ground. As such outwardly and naturally deformed, the surface area of the bottom of the foot is greater, thereby increasing the degree of friction, and, hence, traction, with the ground.

The frog's flexibility is enhanced in this process by two hemispherical protuberances called the *heel-bulbs.* The bulbs, in fact, are posterior salients of the digital cushion, a sensitive, fibro-fatty structure situated roughly

(Continued on page 57)

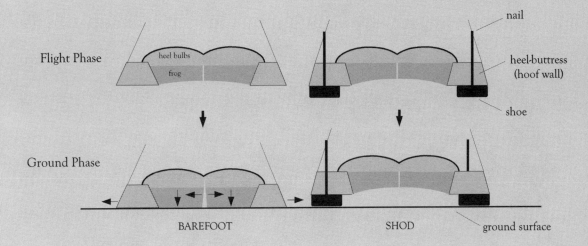

Flight Phase — heel bulbs — frog

nail — heel-buttress (hoof wall) — shoe

Ground Phase

BAREFOOT   SHOD   ground surface

Figure 2-9   FROG PRESSURE

Although the frog is situated "passively" within a niche in the bottom of the hoof (*above, top/left*), it is still designed by nature to endure contact with the ground (*above, bottom/left*). The frog, under the descending weight of the horse, is designed to press down against the ground while spreading outward. This "compressional force" facilitates the hoof mechanism and initi-

ates frog wear. An opposing concussive force (shock wave) arising from the ground complements the downward compressional force and also contributes to wear. Horseshoes (including clips and nails) prevent natural frog wear and they impede frog expansion (*above, bottom/right*). Many "systemic" problems can then beset the hoof — what are these and why do they happen?

Figure 2-10

THE FROG

INSIDE THE SOLAR DOME

Concavity and frog pressure: the bottom or sole of the naturally shaped hoof is concaved, that is, dished like a bowl, or the arch of your foot. The frog is wedged deep within a triangular mass of tough horn formed by the sole, bars, heel-buttresses, as well as by the very arch of the solar dome itself. Active frog pressure is thus rendered impossible — a very important lesson for natural hoof care practitioners.

"Mustang roll"

Sole

The deepest point in the "solar dome" lies near the center of the frog.

Bar

Heel-buttress

Frog cleft

Heel bulb

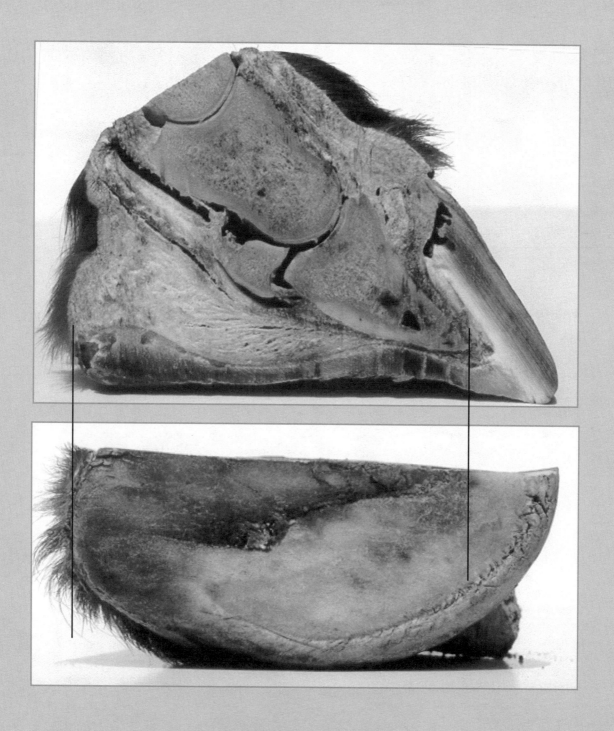

Figure 2-11   THE FROG AND DIGITAL CUSHION NATURALLY

This is an interesting view of a wild hoof, which shows clearly how extensively the frog and digital cushion pass through the solar dome.

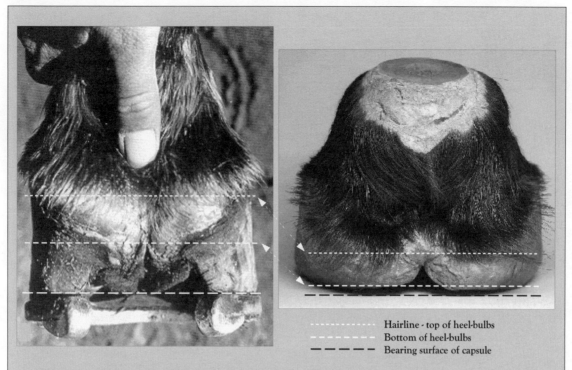

Hairline · top of heel-bulbs
Bottom of heel-bulbs
Bearing surface of capsule

Figure 2-12 THE FROG: NATURAL VS. UNNATURAL

Unnaturally worn hooves, due to shoeing, with the frog off the ground and completely dysfunctional; heels are excessively — and dangerously — long too. To be natural, the frog should have passive ground contact as seen in the wild hoof at right. Note also how compressed the heel bulbs are in the wild hoof. The upper and lower white lines mark the hairlines and ground-bearing surfaces of the hooves respectively.

above and to each side of the frog. This can be seen in the sagittal section of a wild hoof in Figure 2-11; note in the lower image of the same hoof that the digital cushion spans almost two thirds of the length (HL) of the volar profile.

Figure 2-12 contrasts the typical orientation of the frog in a shod hoof versus its position relative to the ground in a naturally trimmed hoof. The "natural" position is the one you want to keep in mind as you work to transform your own horse's feet. And I will add here that this "flattened" heel-bulb-frog conformation is only attainable through natural trimming and natural wear.

OUTER WALL:
ACTIVE AND PASSIVE WEAR

In the wild, the bearing surface of the hoof wall, including the toe, quarters, heel-buttresses, and bars, are not naturally worn into a flat, or level, single plane — like a horse-shoe. There are convolutions, "rises" and "shallows", around the hoof wall, corresponding to apparent areas of "active" and "passive" wear. Unquestionably, these can be attributed to the weight-loading idiosyncrasies of the hoof wall.

My studies of wild horse hooves show that there is considerable variation in the relative positions of these active and passive convolutions of the outer wall. Let's look at several examples of this.

Take a look at the hoof in Figure 2-13 (you can see the same hoof from different angles in my book, *The Natural Horse*, or better yet, in the companion video to this *Guide*). This is a front hoof removed from a wild horse that died following a BLM "gather."

The starbursts indicate the hoof's "active" wear points, or *support pillars* as they are called by some natural hoof care practitioners. These are the segments of the hoof wall that would support the hoof if the horse were standing on a flat, firm. Just like the heel and ball of your own foot. The passive wear points lie in between these active points; on firm ground, we would expect that they bear less weight than the active points. Just like the arch of your foot bears less weight than the heel and ball.

The heel-buttresses without exception always formed the rear pillars in wild hooves I examined with press-boards. But the location and size of the forward pillar, or pillars as the case may be, varied widely from hoof to hoof depending on the individual wild horse. I was struck, however, by the consistency of the wear patterns from left to right (not front to hind!)

for each horse. They were very much mirror images of each other, reflecting a unique dimension of symmetry based on locomotive balance.

In this particular horse (Figure 2-13), the "toe pillar" (there is just one) exists right at the hoof's median line. The pillar is no more than half an inch wide along the circumference of the outer wall at the center of the toe. What is interesting is that from this toe pillar back to each heel-buttress, the hoof wall endures no active contact with the ground (or, more accurately, with a perfectly level bearing surface). In effect, the outer wall is worn or "hollowed" out. These "hollows" or shallows represent areas of "passive wear". In the companion video, I actually press the hoof in Figure 2-13 against a flat board, and you can see exactly what I'm writing about here.

In some hooves, two pillars emerged along the toe wall near each quarter — forming a "four pillar" hoof. A few that I examined, however, were almost as level as horseshoe from toe to heel, except for a slight shallow at the toe. Hind hooves, it is worth noting, most commonly formed three pillars, with one toe pillar emerging to one side or the other of the

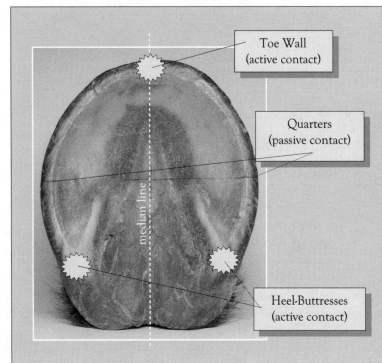

Toe Wall
(active contact)

Quarters
(passive contact)

median line

Heel-Buttresses
(active contact)

FIGURE 2-13

ACTIVE AND PASSIVE WEAR

In naturally shaped hooves, areas of greatest wear are those bearing surfaces of the hoof that endure most of the horse's body weight during the hoof's support phase. These "active" support surfaces are analogous to the calluses on the bottom of your own feet, if you go barefooted often. They are also mirrored on the hoof-side of well worn horseshoes, where the hoof, transmitting body weight — a compressional force — from "bone to outer wall to horseshoe to ground" quite literally gouges a depression into the horseshoe. Check this out the next time your horse's shoes are removed.

BALANCE

BALANCED LIVES · BALANCED HOOVES

Without balance, wild horses like these could not survive. Balanced lives translate to balanced hooves. Balanced hooves in turn draw us into the true meaning of balanced life ways. What are these? And what are balanced hooves?

median line, supported by two posterior pillars at the heel-buttresses.

The emergence of active and passive wear pillars can give the impression to those unfamiliar with true naturally shaped hooves, that the bottom of the hoof capsule is deformed or "unbalanced." This perception is due to the contours of the hoof wall, which can become extremely exaggerated — particularly among the most senior wild horses I examined.

For those readers now wondering how these active/passive pillars and hollows are worked into the hoof during the trimming process, the answer is in my opinion that they are not worked in at all. Rather, they emerge quite naturally as the horse wears his own hooves. Like calluses building on the active support surfaces of your own foot, horn concentrates along the support pillars of the hoof wall. There is less wear and tear on the passive points, hence they remain passive.

Active and passive wear is an important dimension of hoof balance. Yet, owing to its complexity, it is poorly understood in my estimation by both natural hoof care practitioners and hoof care providers in the veterinary and farriery sectors. For this reason, I've included it in Chapter 18 as a potentially invaluable area of research that ought to be conducted by our research sector.

HOOF BALANCE

Our final focus in this chapter concerns *natural hoof balance*. It is interesting to note that some authorities (although very few) believe that there is no such thing as hoof "balance" and defy others to even define such a thing. In my opinion, hoof balance is not only real, it has extraordinary implications not only for the health and integrity of the hoof, but for the overall health of the horse.

I suppose if one were to arbitrarily separate the hoof from the horse's limb, it would be difficult to justify a definition of hoof balance. But the hoof is attached and it provides a fixed foundation — albeit one that is capable of changing dynamically through adaptation — for the horse to stand upon and propel himself from. If that foundation is unbalanced —as is par for the course for shod horses and unnaturally trimmed hooves generally — the horse himself will be unbalanced.

Because the hoof can be artificially unbalanced through unnatural trimming methods, as well as through excessive growth (one of the many deleterious side effects of shoeing), the issue of hoof balance is a real and serious one. Natural hoof care practitioners should be on the alert for the tell-tale signs of hoof imbalance. What are these, in fact?

Balanced Hoof. What constitutes a balanced hoof is easier to understand when we visualize how the natural hoof supports itself on a firm and level surface. This is what I did with the wild horse hooves I studied: I pressed them against a flat board ("press-board") and analyzed how the horn, hairline, and other hoof structures aligned with this level supporting surface.

Figure 2-14 (facing page) illustrates some of what I discovered. First, note the hoof's *median line* (also called *midline*). This is an imaginary line that roughly bisects or divides the hoof right down its center. This line also bisects the hoof down the center of the frog (Figure 2-13). Viewed from the front, the "grain" of a balanced hoof aligns roughly parallel with the midline. How the hoof is worn with respect to active/passive wear does not seem to affect this alignment of horn. So, this is an important signature of a balanced hoof and I recommend committing it to memory.

I have already described what constitutes hoof balance in the side (lateral) view (see Figure 2-3); again: the angle-of-growth is steeper at the toe than anywhere else in the hoof wall, the heels being the lowest. Now, commit that to memory too! But why, you may be asking yourself, is this the case? I think there are several "connected" reasons.

First, the ends of the horn tubules comprising the toe wall, which are "cemented" together by tough keritinized intertubular horn, are more in line with the hoof's angle-of-impact than the horn comprising the heels. This means superior strength and resistance to ravel.

Second, recent research by Swedish scientists (discussed further in Chapter 3) shows unequivocally that the heel-buttresses, which lack direct laminar attachments to the coffin bone (they are supported by the collateral cartilages beyond the palmer processes — discussed in the next chapter also), provide only momentary support as the hoof loads. The toe wall almost immediately takes over.

Third, the coffin bone has greater mass at the toe wall than anywhere else. The palmer processes (wing-like extensions) at the back of the bone are connected to cartilage and con-tribute very little mass for support. Hence the great "dorsal wall" of the coffin bone is anatomically suited for the task of loading weight, while its more vertically oriented horn tubules fused across its laminar horn are better organized to resist compressional forces and abrasion.

What this all boils down to in terms of hoof balance is that the higher angled toe wall is designed to endure the brunt of the weight bearing force during support, and long heels are going to get in the way. Thus, long-heeled hooves that are artificially set at a high angle (easy to achieve with padded horseshoes or unnatural trimming) is, therefore, not only unnatural, it's a sign of hoof imbalance and to be avoided at all costs. In short, it conflicts with nature.

Practically speaking, we "balance" the hoof by making sure the toes are kept within their natural ranges for length and angle; by keeping the heels short and with passive frog pressure; and by adjusting the side-to-side tilt of the hoof capsule with respect to its median line. All of this is discussed in detail in Chapter 8, but go ahead and commit these points to memory now.

Balanced Body. A natural corollary of balanced hooves is a balanced horse attached to them. This is the ultimate test of hoof balance and the reason for taking the trouble to balance the hooves to begin with. Always ask yourself: is your horse comfortable and moving in a balanced way upon his bare feet?

A balanced horse, moving upon balanced hooves, will be sound and fully capable of traveling (without you on his back) a minimum of 10 to 25 miles daily over varied terrain without discomfort, just like horses in the wild do every day. This is a standard which I think all horse owners should hold up as a goal to aspire to. How quickly you will be able to attain it with your horse will depend on a range of factors, including the extant effects of shoeing, your horse's boarding conditions, his diet, your natural hoof care program, whether or not you use hoof boots, his conditioning pro-

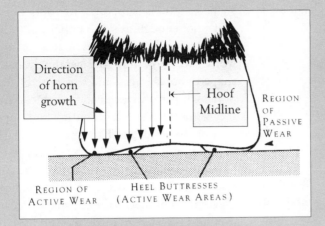

Direction of horn growth

Hoof Midline

REGION OF PASSIVE WEAR

REGION OF ACTIVE WEAR

HEEL BUTTRESSES (ACTIVE WEAR AREAS)

FIGURE 2-14

ALIGNMENT-OF-GROWTH

The hoof's angle-of-horn growth is an important feature of hoof balance.

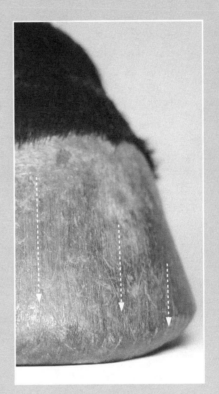

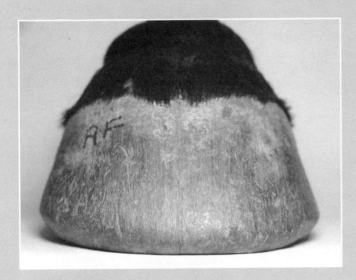

gram, where you ride and how often you ride, and even how he is fit with his saddle. I discuss these concerns in considerable detail over the next two chapters.

SUMMARY

In learning to recognize and identify the true characteristics of a genuine naturally shaped hoof, you will know instantly whether your horse has "got 'em" or not. Why bother?

Naturally shaped, naturally balanced hooves favor your horse in two important ways: *First*, they enable him to move unencumbered as nature intended. *Second*, in facilitating natural movement, they optimize his chances for soundness and health. Surely, this is reason enough for any conscientious horse owner to make it his or her business to know the difference.

Okay, you now have a sense that barefoot-

edness is not only good for your horse's feet (it's natural!), you also know what a naturally shaped hoof is supposed to look like. But that's not enough. It's also important to have a good grasp of what makes it tick — in other words, to know how the genuinely naturally shaped hoof is forged and why it is able to support high performance barefootedness. Believe me, without this understanding and appreciation of the inner mechanisms of natural hoof function, it is much easier to fall prey to a host of faulty trimming methods that can undermine your work and your horse's chances for powerful, genuinely naturally shaped feet.

Our first step towards this understanding brings us directly to the discussion of the "hoof mechanism," one of the most controversial and least understood facets of hoof science plaguing the hoof care industry. This is really the science of "natural hoof function" and the vital key to successful high performance barefootedness.

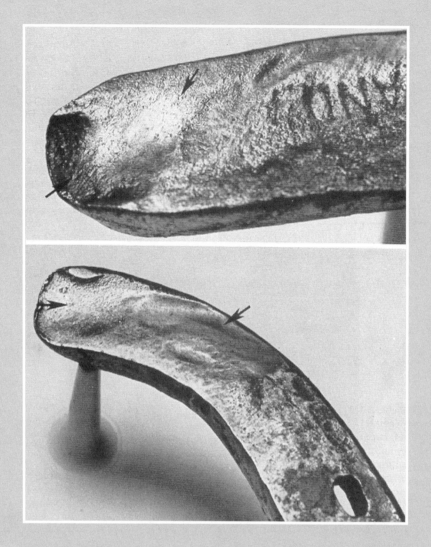

HOOF MECHANISM

THE KEY TO NATURAL HOOF HEALTH

Figure 3-1. Even when shod, the hoof "tries" to expand and contract as best it can, witness the "grooves" worn into the heel branches of these horseshoes. For many horses, though, it isn't enough — contraction, navicular, and other debilitating deformities and lamenesses ensue. Shoeing impairs the vital hoof mechanism — the key to natural hoof health — and predisposes the hoof to pathology. At best, it becomes a weak caricature of what Nature intended.

CHAPTER THREE

THE HOOF MECHANISM

"Human subtlety will never devise an invention more beautiful,
more simple, or more direct than does Nature." Leonard da Vinci

The term "hoof mechanism" was first coined by European veterinary anatomists many years ago. I want you to commit its definition to memory too. It may be defined as the natural expanding or spreading of the hoof as it undergoes weight bearing (called "loading") during the hoof's support phase, *and*, the reciprocal contracting of the hoof as it unloads during its flight phase.

When the horse is standing, his hooves "deform" or expand outward under his body weight. When the horse lifts a foot off the ground, the hoof is freed from the descending weight and it once more contracts, or "un-deforms"; that is, it returns to its normal and natural "contracted" size. When weight is again brought to bear, the hoof once more expands. And so forth, repeating itself with each footfall. We recall from the last chapter that the hoof capsule is rendered deformable due to the flexible frog and digital cushion, which together act like a hinge to enable the otherwise rigid capsule to "expand" and "contract."

So, the hoof mechanism is all about the hoof expanding and contracting, deforming and un-deforming, as the horse moves along. And there's probably not a vet or farrier any-

where today who isn't aware of this. And the more astute observers among them will point readily to the heel branches of the pulled shoe, whose grooved wear testifies to the hoof's mutable nature (facing page, Figure 3-1).

Given that the hoof expands and contracts as the horse moves along, how does it happen exactly? How do the various parts of the hoof capsule (everything below the hairline) contribute to the hoof mechanism? And, very important, what other vital hoof functions are facilitated by the mechanism?

Figure 3-2 illustrates some of the major changes — structural deformities, really — that the hoof capsule undergoes during the hoof mechanism. These changes are normal, natural, and essential for optimally healthy hooves. Let's discuss them now, and please bear with me as I repeat some of the information we've already covered.

As the hoof presses against the ground, the hoof begins to deform under the weight of the horse. The outer wall spreads and the bottom of the hoof — the sole — flattens out. We recall from Chapter 1 (Figure 1-10) that the sole is naturally a concaved or arched structure. It is also anatomically designed to descend like a

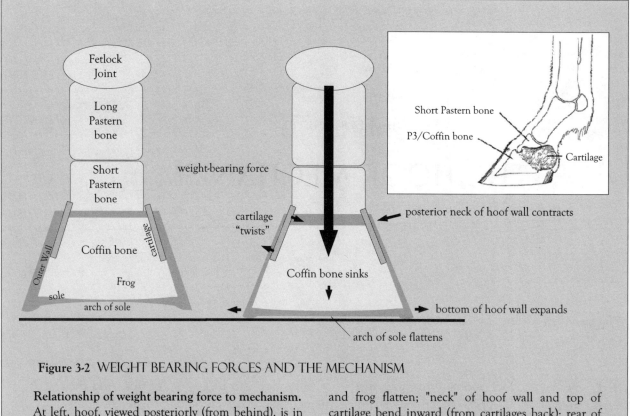

Figure 3-2 WEIGHT BEARING FORCES AND THE MECHANISM

Relationship of weight bearing force to mechanism. At left, hoof, viewed posteriorly (from behind), is in flight and there is no force applied to the hoof. At right, force has entered hoof and deformed it: sole and frog flatten; "neck" of hoof wall and top of cartilage bend inward (from cartilages back); rear of coffin bone sinks (slightly!); and bearing surface of outer wall and bottom of cartilage spread outward.

trampoline when compressed from above, and, as I've said, flatten out.

It is aided in this flattening, first, by the flexible frog, which is wedged into the solar dome; second, by the elastic heel-bulbs ("posterior salients of the digital cushion"), which intermesh with the frog, both of which together compress and stretch apart; and third, by the (medial and lateral) cartilages, which "bend" with the deforming capsule (Figure 3-2).

Figure 3-3 illustrates how the outer wall expands everywhere from the toe to the heel. Recent studies conducted by the Institute of Anatomy and Physiology at the Swedish Agricultural University suggest also that the mechanism of hoof expansion is still more specific.* During support, the heels expand first, but quickly contract as the forward portions of the hoof load and expand, not unlike a wave

moving through the hoof, which then culminates in breakover.

You can squeeze together the heel-bulbs of your own horse's hoof to gain a sense of its compressibility and capacity to expand. Just bear in mind that the compressional weight bearing force exerted on the hoof by the horse's body is extraordinary — enough to cause those wear grooves in the shoe branches seen in Figure 3-1 — but does not "split" open the back of the hoof along the central frog sulcus. Why?

Not surprising, some have argued that the digital cushion prevents this occurrence by acting as a major compression "brake" in conjunction with the expanding frog (and hoof capsule) during loading. The cushion is thought to absorb weight pressing down from the "digit bones" below the fetlock joint, while pushing the cartilages apart (Figure 3-2).

*Anderson, Ingrid. "Rubber Horseshoe In A Large Study." European Farriers Journal. Dec. 1998 (75) 35-45.

Logical as this sounds, however, I disagree with this interpretation. Here's why:

During the frog's expansion phase, the nexus of major semi-flexural joints (shoulder, hip, stifle, and hock) accounting for propulsion in the upper limbs are in an expanding (opening) mode. Hence, the digital cushion is from the moment of impact being actively unloaded — the support tendons above it are pulling upward — while the frog is spreading and the hoof capsule is deforming.

This can only mean one thing: the cushion is meant principally to impart elasticity to the capsule during early support. If its purpose was simply to resist descending body weight, I have no doubt that it and the frog would split wide open along the frog's central sulcus. The answer then, consistent with the Swedish research, is that load forces dissipate quickly from the posterior half of the hoof following early support, and accumulate immediately over the relatively unyielding coffin bone. And apparently well before the rear of the hoof has "maxed out" its expansion threshold.

Continuing, note too in Figure 3-2 that the "neck" of the hoof capsule, below the coronary band, and principally in the back half of the hoof (from the cartilages back) bends slightly inward. This contraction, albeit minor, is necessary if the hoof wall below is to expand outward at its bearing surface at the same time the sole flattens. Once more, it is able to deform inwardly due to the elasticity of the frog and heel bulbs (i.e., the digital cushion), which expand during weight bearing as described above.

If you look closely, you will see also that the coffin bone, squeezed by the outer wall, responding to the spreading heel-buttress, tilts backward and sinks very slightly towards the ground. It must do this since it is structurally incapable of compressing and because the "neck" of the outer wall is contracting around it.

To resolve this "conflict," the coffin bone simply occupies a slightly lower position within the outer wall during the hoof's support phase. The flexible, specialized leaf

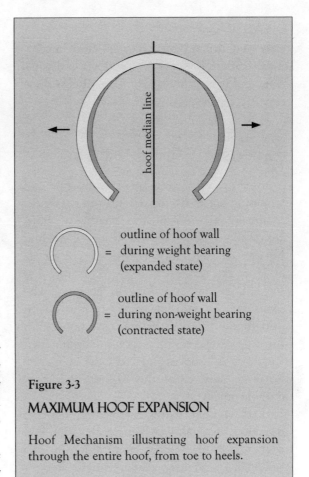

outline of hoof wall
= during weight bearing
(expanded state)

outline of hoof wall
= during non-weight bearing
(contracted state)

Figure 3-3

MAXIMUM HOOF EXPANSION

Hoof Mechanism illustrating hoof expansion through the entire hoof, from toe to heels.

(laminar) attachments that connect the bone to the outer wall (see Figure 1-4) facilitate this downward shift. But the "shift" is minimal, and the true expansion of the hoof occurs between the buttresses and is attributed to the flexible hinge between them — the frog and digital cushion.

So, there you have it, a roughed out model of the "hoof mechanism" in action as seen from the outside. Of course, there's another realm of physiological activity going on inside the hoof that corresponds directly with these visible deformations occurring throughout the hoof capsule. We need a simplified model of these inner workings too, not only to flesh out our understanding of the mechanism, but because it will help us to understand how our trimming method can affect — either favorably or adversely — the hoof's internal physiology and, therefore, its health.

There are three main areas of hoof func-

(Continued from page 67)

tion that depend on a normal hoof mechanism: callusing, shock absorption or dissipation, and blood circulation. Let's discuss these now.

CALLUSING

Anyone who has spent a lifetime of trimming horses like myself, realizes that there is much variation in the quality of horn composing their hooves. Especially shod horses. Typically, shod hooves can be brittle and weak, moist and soft, hard and unyielding, and everything in between. The same can be said of barefoot horses with unnaturally trimmed or managed hooves. In the wild, however, there is virtually no such variation. All hooves are, and must be for the horse to survive, of the highest and most durable quality.

Part of what makes the natural hoof so durable is its quality of being both tough and resilient. Many things contribute to its resiliency, particularly diet, the right amount of moisture in the environment, natural movement, and the type of environment wild horses have adapted to. But the characteristic tough hoof capsule results from one thing only — rigorous wear. The generally poor quality horn and excessive growth we see commonly among domestic horses results from insufficient wear.

The hoof *must* endure direct contact with the ground if it is to toughen up, called "callusing." What kind of ground? *Any kind of ground*. Within reason, the kind of ground doesn't really matter, although abrasive surfaces (rock, sand) will produce a tougher hoof easier than a pasture of grass or dirt. All that matters is that the hoof make barefoot contact with whatever it is, rigorously and with much natural movement. Hooves are not meant to be coddled. They are intended by nature to work, and work hard. Harder than most of us can even imagine.

Physical movement, we've seen, produces

compressional (loading) forces inside the hoof. The growth coriums are genetically encoded to produce the right amount of horn — approximately 1 cm of wall growth per month — to offset normal amounts of horn lost to natural wear. To give you an idea of what "natural" means exactly, horses living in the wild typically move 15 to 30 miles per day! Vigorously so, and over a range of abrasive terrain. No wonder they don't need professionals out there to trim their hooves! At any rate, this balance between horn produced and horn lost represents "adaptation."

Callusing occurs when normal growth is subjected to loading and abrasion in a principally dry environment. Epidermis produced by the growth coriums is keritinous (made of scleroproteins — proteins that are fibrous and water-resistant). As the epidermal horn grows out, it is compressed and tamped against the ground, subjected to heat and moisture, and hardened off. I have dissected wild horse hooves with soles as thick and hard as a horseshoe (Figure 8-5). This enables the horse to move rigorously according to his survival needs without foot pain. An abundance of natural movement ensues that, in turn, wears away the hardened capsule. In the wild, there is wonderful equilibrium between the genetically driven rate of hoof growth, the rate of horn lost to abrasion from natural wear, and the survival requirements of the species.

If we look a little closer at this callusing process, I am inclined to believe that a kind of specialized "hide tanning" mechanism is also at work. By way of analogy, consider how rawhide is produced by a tanner. The raw skin is subjected to heat from friction (scraping, pounding, rubbing), soakings, and fire, to dry it out and to harden it. The skin's epidermis, tantamount to the hoof capsule, is normally left intact to add strength, as well as to provide for scrimshawed, "base-relief" type decorations. During the firing, organic chemicals called *aldehydes* are introduced to the epidermis from the smoke. Their effect is to "tan" the proteins within the epidermis, that is, to give them strength and make them less vulnerable to the deleterious effects of moisture. Sometimes urea is added to enhance this effect.

Conceivably, similar processes, in addition to keritinization, occur in the hoof capsule as the wild horse roams through his environment. Holistically, in other words, many forces are at work to "tan" the naturally worn hoof. For example, there is the friction and heat from moving over hard rock and through hot sand, and from pawing as bands instinctively "mine" mineral deposits for nutritional purposes. Wild horses inevitably stand in their own urine, if not at stud piles, during group resting behavior and "camp sites". Then, of course, there are the many trips to watering holes where they regularly soak their hooves. All of these behaviors contribute to the natural hardening and texturizing of the hooves — a kind of "equine tanning operation" as I think of it.

I think it's also important to point out that a tough, calloused hoof isn't a desensitized one. To the contrary, the horse is meant to feel the ground through its feet—like us if we were to wear a moccasin. Riders who have made the switch to barefootedness immediately sense this difference in the horse. Horses tend to become more "surefooted" after they make the transition because they are able to feel where they're going and are paying closer attention to how they're moving. In the wild, horses really do watch where they put their feet. A twisted ankle from careless movement is a misstep that could cost a life.

SHOCK ABSORPTION

The vast majority of shock absorption within the hoof occurs through the flexions of the hoof mechanism. The hoof's natural "give" softens the impact of all that weight loading into the hoof. The remaining shock is absorbed within the bones and joints of the limb, by the horny "leaves" which connect the hoof capsule to the coffin bone (Figure 4), by

the spring-like tubular horn composing the outer wall, and according to recent research, through the vascular system leaving the hoof in the form of converted heat energy.

A highly detailed discussion of the above is very technical and goes beyond the scope of this *Guide*.* I'll simply say here that when the hoof is unnaturally shaped, these shock absorbing structures are rendered inefficient — setting the stage for a host of problems that can, and do, beset many horses with hoof, ligament, and joint breakdowns. I'll address some of these in Chapters 4 and 16.

BLOOD CIRCULATION

The other area of interest regarding the hoof mechanism is how it impacts blood circulation within the hoof and, some readers may be surprised to learn, throughout the horse's body. The adverse effects of unnatural hoof care, especially shoeing, on blood circulation is also an important focus of this discussion.

Blood, essential for healthy horn growth (as well as shock energy dissipation), ceases to flow optimally through the hoof when the mechanism is impeded either through unnatural trimming or shoeing (also close confinement!). The consequence of abnormal diminished blood flow — anything less than what nature intended for the horse — thus carries with it the potential to impact the hooves in various harmful ways.

For example, we've seen that blood is important to the dissipation of shock energy, and that healthy lamina (inner hoof wall) are essential for supporting the coffin bone during loading; thus, obstructing the mechanism can directly affect the blood's capacity to mitigate shock and nourish the lamina. The long term effects of this have not been studied to the best of my knowledge, but my experience as a 25 year hoof care professional has been that barefoot hooves are clearly stronger and healthier than shod ones and it isn't hard to appreciate how an impaired mechanism with

(Continued on page 72)

*For an accessible discussion of the hoof's inner wall (lamina), see Chris Pollit's "The Anatomy and Physiology of the Hoof Wall," European Farriers Journal, no. 84, 6/2000. Regarding heat energy dissipation, see Bowker, R M, Kimberly K, Van Wulfen, K, Springer, S E, and Linder, K E (1998). Functional anatomy of the cartilage of the distal phalanx and digital cushion in the equine foot and a hemodynamic flow hypothesis of energy dissipation. American Journal of Veterinary Research. 59: 961-968.

FIGURE 3-5

THE HOOF MECHANISM

HOW BLOOD MOVES THROUGH THE HOOF

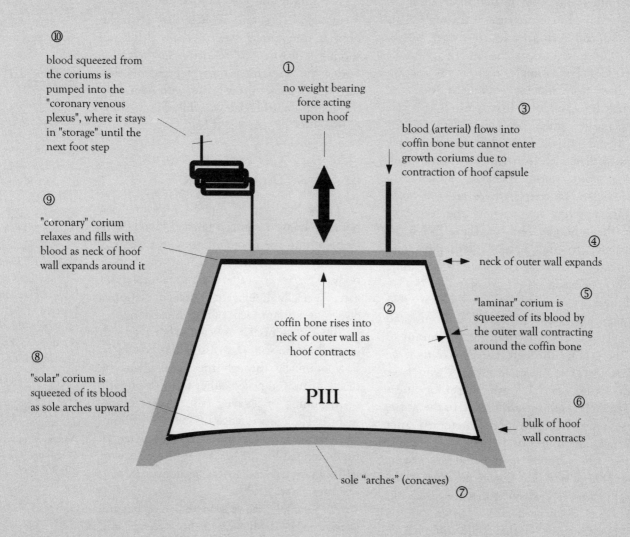

⑩ blood squeezed from the coriums is pumped into the "coronary venous plexus", where it stays in "storage" until the next foot step

① no weight bearing force acting upon hoof

③ blood (arterial) flows into coffin bone but cannot enter growth coriums due to contraction of hoof capsule

⑨ "coronary" corium relaxes and fills with blood as neck of hoof wall expands around it

④ neck of outer wall expands

② coffin bone rises into neck of outer wall as hoof contracts

⑤ "laminar" corium is squeezed of its blood by the outer wall contracting around the coffin bone

PIII

⑧ "solar" corium is squeezed of its blood as sole arches upward

⑥ bulk of hoof wall contracts

sole "arches" (concaves) ⑦

ground surface

HOOF IN FLIGHT

Impact of hoof mechanism on blood circulation within hoof

With hoof in flight, the outer wall contracts around coffin bone, squeezing blood from coriums and out of hoof.

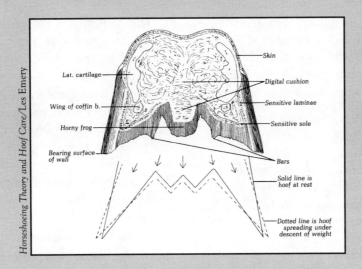

Horseshoeing Theory and Hoof Care/Les Emery

Skin

Lat. cartilage

Digital cushion

Wing of coffin b.

Sensitive laminae

Horny frog

Sensitive sole

Bearing surface
of wall

Bars

Solid line is
hoof at rest

Dotted line is hoof
spreading under
descent of weight

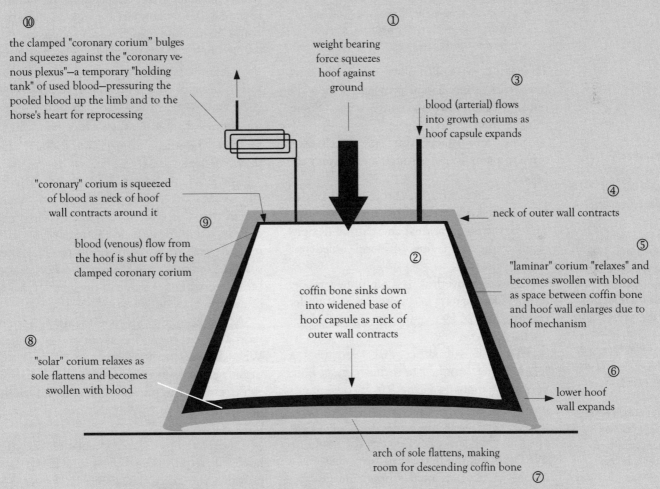

⑩ the clamped "coronary corium" bulges and squeezes against the "coronary venous plexus"—a temporary "holding tank" of used blood—pressuring the pooled blood up the limb and to the horse's heart for reprocessing

① weight bearing force squeezes hoof against ground

③ blood (arterial) flows into growth coriums as hoof capsule expands

"coronary" corium is squeezed of blood as neck of hoof wall contracts around it

④ neck of outer wall contracts

⑨ blood (venous) flow from the hoof is shut off by the clamped coronary corium

② coffin bone sinks down into widened base of hoof capsule as neck of outer wall contracts

⑤ "laminar" corium "relaxes" and becomes swollen with blood as space between coffin bone and hoof wall enlarges due to hoof mechanism

⑧ "solar" corium relaxes as sole flattens and becomes swollen with blood

⑥ lower hoof wall expands

arch of sole flattens, making room for descending coffin bone ⑦

HOOF IN SUPPORT

Impact of hoof mechanism on blood circulation within hoof

Hoof wall expands under pressure from body weight; the hoof coriums, no longer squeezed between hoof wall and coffin bone, relax and fill with blood.

(Continued from page 69)

less than optimal blood circulation isn't at least partly responsible for this difference. Moreover, we cannot overlook the potential ramifications of what this means above the hoof:

- Pathological disfigurement of the hoof capsule, causing
- locomotive imbalance, and stumbling or less than athletic performance, and
- Joint and ligament damage (e.g., lower leg swelling, ringbone, and navicular syndrome); and
- less than optimal circulation of blood to the horse's heart, resulting in
- muscle fatigue and psychological distress (e.g., resistance, neurotic stall behaviors, and listlessness).

The *total* horse, holistically speaking, is hence put at risk as circulation problems within the hoof manifest into his entire being. Something to think about.

Now, how exactly does the mechanism serve to pump blood through and beyond the hoof?

Blood circulation in, through and out of the hoof follows directly from the mechanism. That is, the hoof's normal and natural flexions facilitate the actual flow of blood, aided passively by the heart.

Figure 3-5 (overleaf) is a simplified model of how blood enters and exits the hoof under pressure exerted by the hoof mechanism. Let's discuss it briefly.

First, you will notice that I've added a "black" region around the coffin bone in both hoof illustrations in Figure 3-5. It corresponds to what is called the "hoof corium." This is a thin layer of tissue that, like a sock between one's foot and shoe, lies between the hoof capsule (again, all the horny structures that make up the visible part of the hoof) and all the "internal" sensitive and vascular structures within the hoof that we can't see.

*Incidentally, according to Professor Robert Bowker's "Hemodynamic Flow Theory" (American Farriers Journal, Dec./1998), heat energy created at impact is absorbed into and dissipated by the micro-vascular tracts passing below the coffin bone to the back of the hoof and out through the cartilages. This transmission results from a "suction" force caused by a vacuum in the cartilages when they are pressed outward during support.

The corium is a rather spongy, blood engorged structure not much more than an eighth of an inch thick. It is a unique manufacturing plant of sorts — it literally "produces" the entire hoof capsule. In other words, the hoof capsule grows right out of the corium.

Actually, the corium is a "super corium" composed of a series of five connected "subcoriums". Each of these growth "matrices" produces a different kind of horn, corresponding to different parts of the hoof. Briefly, let's discuss these:

There is the *coronary corium*, which produces the outer wall; the *laminar corium*, which produces the inner wall, or lamina (Figure 1-4), that connect the outer wall to the coffin bone (and which you can see as the "white line" in the bottom of the hoof around the sole); the *perioplic corium*, which produces a thin layer of soft horn called periople that coats and protects the upper part of the outer wall from dehydration; the *solar corium*, which produces the sole; and *frog corium*, which produces the frog.

The hoof mechanism is designed to literally squeeze or "pump" blood into and then out of this vast corium "carpet." In this way, each sub-corium will have enough cellular material derived from the blood to produce and sustain optimal hoof growth. The hoof "circulatory pump" is one of the great miracles of nature. How does it work?

As the horse lifts his foot, the hoof capsule narrows and squeezes blood out of the corium. When he puts his foot down again, the hoof capsule expands to its larger shape, and the corium resumes its normal form and fills with blood once more.* With the next step, the process is repeated.

Understanding blood circulation in the hoof will require some effort and study. I've provided a numerical sequence in Figure 3-5 to help make sense of it. The illustration on

(Overleaf: Figure 3-5) Whew! — the complex hoof mechanism described. Follow the numbers like a road map and you won't get lost.

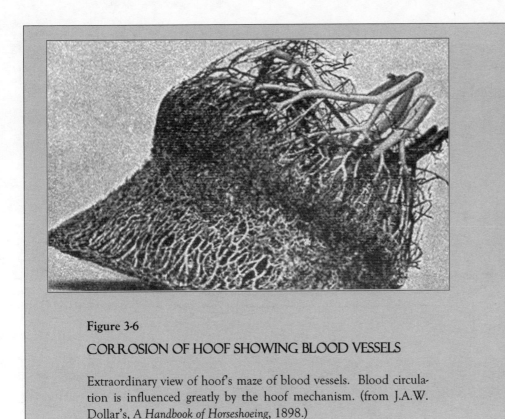

Figure 3-6

CORROSION OF HOOF SHOWING BLOOD VESSELS

Extraordinary view of hoof's maze of blood vessels. Blood circulation is influenced greatly by the hoof mechanism. (from J.A.W. Dollar's, *A Handbook of Horseshoeing*, 1898.)

the left traces the deformations of the hoof capsule and corresponding flow of blood before the hoof strikes the ground, called the "flight phase". On the right, the converse relationships of circulation and deformity are shown as the hoof enters its "support phase" on the ground.

This is a very simplified version of what is an extremely complex process. To give you an idea of just how complex, take a look at the cobweb of blood vessels that are involved in Figure 3-6! Nevertheless, Figure 3-5 provides a reasonable schematic based on the European version of the hoof mechanism that will serve our purposes in this *Guide*.

Take your time and read through it, bearing in mind that every time the horse steps on the ground, blood is driven a little further through the hoof. But that for the blood to flow optimally, the hoof mechanism must not be impeded. I'll refer back to these diagrams again and again as we engage the natural trim-

ming process ahead in Chapters 8 and 9, and especially when we treat hoof lamenesses in Chapter 16.

Now let's consider the effects that horseshoeing has on the hoof mechanism, including callusing, shock absorption, and blood circulation.

EFFECTS OF HORSESHOEING ON THE HOOF MECHANISM

The deleterious effects of shoeing on the hoof and the mechanism is primarily of a "mechanical" nature — the natural flexibility of the capsule is impeded, natural wear is prevented, shock waves are exacerbated, blood circulation is rendered less than optimal, and the shoe itself damages the hoof.* The secondary effects of shoeing—joint disorders, ligament strain, obstruction of the natural gaits, lameness, poor horn quality, and so forth —result

*In addition to the Swedish study which details the impeding nature of metal shoes on the mechanism, see – P. Dyhre-Poulsen, H.H. Smedegaard, J. Roed, and E. Korsgaard in the Equine Veterinary Journal 1994 26(5) 362-366 – for study showing ill-effects of shoe on shock absorbency. For impact of shoes on circulation, see "Horse Foot Studies Video" by Chris Pollitt – available Hoofcare & Lameness Magazine, PO Box 6600, Gloucester, MA 01930 USA Tel 978/281-3222 E-mail: hoofcare@earthlink.net

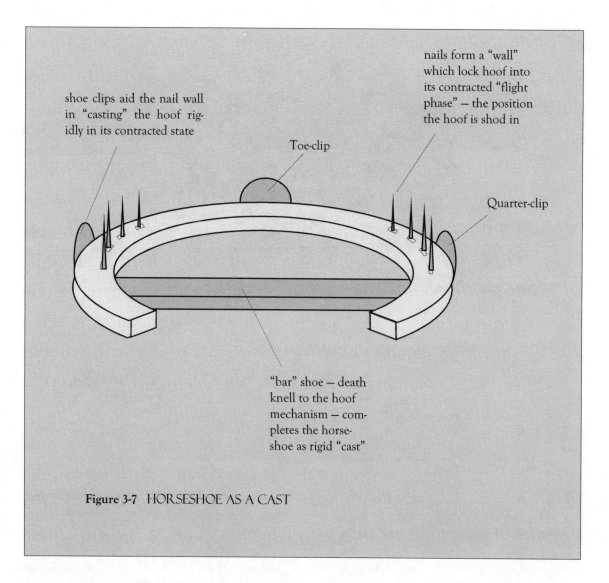

shoe clips aid the nail wall in "casting" the hoof rigidly in its contracted state

nails form a "wall" which lock hoof into its contracted "flight phase" — the position the hoof is shod in

Toe-clip

Quarter-clip

"bar" shoe — death knell to the hoof mechanism — completes the horseshoe as rigid "cast"

Figure 3-7 HORSESHOE AS A CAST

from the mechanism having been rendered dysfunctional. The question to be answered here is how does horseshoeing per se impede the mechanism and damage the hoof outright?

NAILING

Recall that the horseshoe is nailed to the hoof while it is off the ground, that is, while the hoof is in its "contracted" phase (Figure 3-5, "Hoof in flight"). When the last nail is set, generally near the widest expanse of the hoof (i.e. the quarters), and sometimes further back, the hoof wall in some measure becomes "locked" into its contracted state by the nails binding it to the shoe.

Immediately, however, the hoof will begin to expand and contract upon the upper (i.e., weight bearing) surface of the horseshoe, since the rigid shoe is not made of sprung metal (i. e., it lacks memory) and will not move inward and outward in concert with the hoof. But it is greatly hindered by the "brick wall" barrier of the nails embedded firmly in the outer wall (Figure 3-7). The nails, which also lack memory, prevent free expansion of the hoof capsule, at least at first.

Eventually, the sheer force of the mechanism will begin to deform the nails embedded in the wall. Commonly the nails tear the middle wall (*stratum medium*) press outward, ripping through the wall, causing the shoe to come loose or fall off. The same set of nails might also tear into the white line above the

(Continued from page 74)

sole, in effect opening a passage for opportunistic pathogens to enter the laminar corium from the environment (e.g., White Line Disease — Figure 3-8). Ironically, the "better" the shoeing job — meaning the "tighter" and "closer in" the nails are set in the wall — the more devastating is it on the mechanism and on the structural integrity of the hoof itself.

Eventually, the mechanism prevails and this is evidenced by the wear seen on the branches of the horseshoe (Figure 3-1). In some instances, the mechanism (aided by rapid heel growth) is so pronounced that the hoof spreads over the branches of the shoes, and the latter become "stuck" in the seats-of-corn of the heel-buttresses. This may cause "corns" — an inflammation, or pressure necrosis, of the sole — at the turn of the bars.

CLIPS

Clips are rigid vertical extensions of the fixed shoe (Figure 3-7). Since the shoe is fitted to the hoof in its contracted phase, so are the clips — even if the shoer hammers them against the hoof wall while the hoof is set on the ground. Clips, therefore, aid the nails in casting the hoof in its contracted phase. In fact, this is the reason that clips are added to horseshoes — to "stabilize" the hoof upon the shoe during support. Stabilization, of course, means impeding the mechanism.

BARS

Bars are rigid extensions that connect and stabilize the branches of the shoe (Figure 3-7). Bars prevent the branches from spreading outward or compressing inward. There are many types of bar shoes, and farriers and vets employ them for as many different reasons. But without exception, all impede the mechanism. Particularly so when they are forged in conjunction with clips. Together bars and clips completely obstruct the mechanism.

Figure 3-9 illustrates how a clipped bar

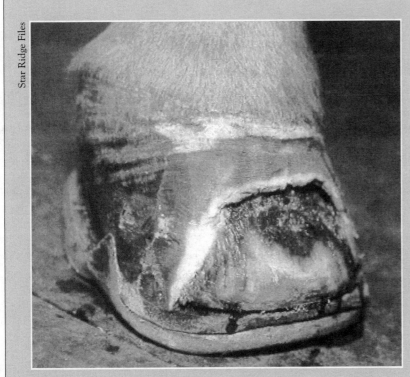

Star Ridge Files

FIGURE 3-8

A CAST HOOF

This hoof suffers the effects of laminitis and White Line Disease, and has been surgically resected. The shoe, which impedes the mechanism — casting the hoof in its contracted state — includes quarter clips, wedge pads, and heart bar.

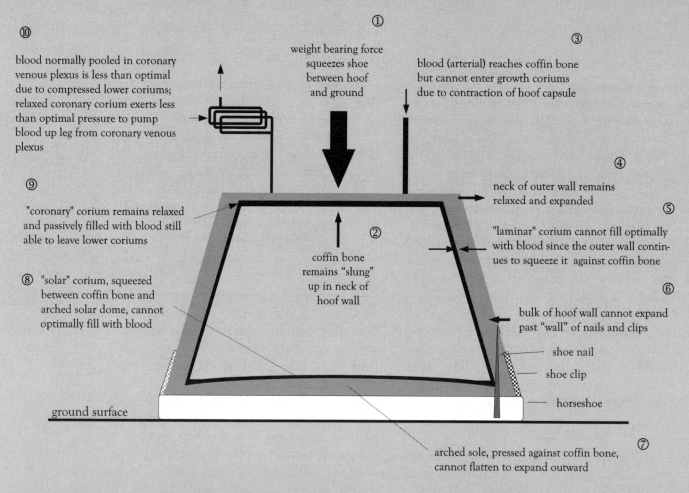

① weight bearing force squeezes shoe between hoof and ground

③ blood (arterial) reaches coffin bone but cannot enter growth coriums due to contraction of hoof capsule

⑩ blood normally pooled in coronary venous plexus is less than optimal due to compressed lower coriums; relaxed coronary corium exerts less than optimal pressure to pump blood up leg from coronary venous plexus

④ neck of outer wall remains relaxed and expanded

⑨ "coronary" corium remains relaxed and passively filled with blood still able to leave lower coriums

② coffin bone remains "slung" up in neck of hoof wall

⑤ "laminar" corium cannot fill optimally with blood since the outer wall continues to squeeze it against coffin bone

⑧ "solar" corium, squeezed between coffin bone and arched solar dome, cannot optimally fill with blood

⑥ bulk of hoof wall cannot expand past "wall" of nails and clips

shoe nail

shoe clip

horseshoe

ground surface

⑦ arched sole, pressed against coffin bone, cannot flatten to expand outward

FIGURE 3-9   EFFECT OF FIXED SHOEING ON THE HOOF MECHANISM

How does the presence of the horseshoe restrict blood flow in the hoof?

Recognizing that the hoof is shod while the limb is off the ground, it has no weightbearing force acting upon it, and, thus, it has assumed its "contracted" or undeformed shape when the shoe is nailed on. Figure 3-9, across, illustrates this; I've added quarter clips to accentuate the clamping effect of the horseshoe. Again, as in Figure 3-5, study the diagram to get a sense of where blood is in the hoof and at what phase the hoof mechanism is at.

Note that the growth coriums of the outer wall and sole (and also of the frog and heel bulbs, although they are not shown) are compressed and evacuated of blood. This is because the hoof, restricted by the shoe (clips, bar, and nails), cannot expand except marginally. So, the coriums are blood deficient. Further, because the coronary corium is

relaxed, blood pooled in the coronary venous plexus fails to pump optimally up the limb during the hoof's support phase.

The **sole**, also deprived of blood within its corium, is cast as a rigid dome. It cannot flex but marginally. No longer under the influence of the hoof mechanism, and no longer conditioned through contact with the ground, the sole and frog begin to weaken. The sole becomes pressure hypersensitive, abundantly clear when the shoe is removed and the horse is asked to go barefooted. Moreover, the solar coriums of most domestic horses, denied full flexion, remain pressed up against the bottom of the coffin bone. This sets the stage for solar injuries and abscesses. I'm thinking now back to dressage horses I have seen with "soft" soles with pockets of pus. You could push them in with your thumb—providing the shoers didn't have them padded over. Shoeing caused

this — not genetically impoverished hooves or faulty riding. Remove those shoes, and the soles —every one of them without exception — will toughen and become flexible again. I can speak from years of personal experience, the ease with which the farrier's hoof knife can scrape away the cruddy remnants of wasted sole horn — what would take a jack hammer to penetrate in the average wild horse hoof.

The **frog** becomes excessively moist — bloated — and prone to infection and atrophy. Ultimately the loss of frog mass and function renders the capsule pathologically contracted. Gait obstruction then ensues, and many horses are put on a direct path to life-threatening lamenesses.

Without normal blood flow, the **hoof wall** itself loses its native resiliance. White line infections, wall splits, and outer wall flares become common.

shoe obstructs the mechanism (see also Figure 3-8). As a professional booter of horses, I am keenly aware of just how much shoeing "compresses" the hoof's natural size. Following removal of the shoes, the hooves in most instances began to enlarge over several months. We call this period of change "transition." Attempts to fit horses with boots before transition has run its full course will usually require that the horse be re-fitted again once the hooves have fully restored to their natural size.

PADS

There are many types of pads used in conjunction with horseshoes. Pads are sandwiched between the horseshoe and the hoof and are secured with the nails. Pads prevent the sole from "breathing" and having contact directly with the ground; hence, they trap moisture from the perspiring sole and keep the sole from hardening off. Commonly, pad-ding causes "mushy" soles and renders the bottom of the horse's foot tender.

SUMMARY

The horseshoe weakens the hoof's natural structure and impedes the mechanism. It prevents natural callusing. It prevents natural shock absorbency. And it imperils every growth corium and every facet of blood circulation known in the hoof. The adverse effects may be immediate, or accumulative and long range.

Fortunately, the metallic cast of the modern horseshoe and the co-dependent blacksmith logic behind it, are not invincible. And the way out is easy. It's called high performance barefootedness. The first step, however, is to pull out those horseshoe nails and de-shoe the horse.

Let's do that now.

Going barefoot on an arid plain in New Mexico.

CHAPTER FOUR

ABOUT NATURAL

TRIMMING

natural (nach´er al) *existing in nature; in accordance with the principles of nature; as formed by nature without human intervention; wild condition*

What is a *natural trim*? It is a trim based precisely on the hooves of wild horses — healthy barefoot horses with a long, proven history of soundness and lameness-free lives. It is the only model known today that can claim this distinction.

Skilled natural hoof care practitioners recognize the adaptability of domestic horse hooves to the wild model. They use the natural trim based on this model to enable high performance barefootedness in their clients' horses. The domestic horse is expected to move as freely on his own bare hooves as his wild cousin.

GOALS OF NATURAL TRIMMING

Natural trimming encompasses two main objectives: the hoof is to be shaped according to its unique size, shape, and proportion; and, at the same time, the shaping is done so as to simulate natural wear.

In the wild, we learned in Chapter 2, there is a broad and distinctive range of hoof sizes, shapes, and colors. In nature, every hoof reflects the individual influences, or conformation, of the "whole horse". This explains the range, or variation, of hoof shape characteristics seen in wild horse populations. No two horses are identical. And no two hooves are exactly alike either.

Yet all naturally shaped hooves share common traits — for example, specific limits in toe length and angle, shortness in heel length, the "mustang roll," and concavity of sole. These characteristics are influenced by movement and environment.

Natural hoof care practitioners trim each hoof according to the limits of its individual conformation while simulating the type of natural wear seen in wild horse country. They are able to do this by closely studying wild horse hooves, by observing how horses move naturally, and by learning as much as they can about the horse's natural habitat.

Natural hoof care practitioners also study the effects of unnatural horse management practices on the hooves. This might include diet, pasture turnout, veterinary care, saddling practices, and riding methods. They counsel horse owners on how to effect changes in these practices in order to improve their horses' feet.

CHARACTERISTICS OF A NATURAL TRIM

A genuine natural trim leaves a hoof in better condition than it was before it was trimmed. Natural trims do not hurt the hoof

or leave the horse sore-footed. A naturally trimmed hoof is a beautiful sight to behold, just like its "wild" counterpart, which serves as our model.

In accordance with the two objectives of natural trimming, the finished hoof corresponds in size, shape, and proportion to its unique and natural conformation; and, the outward appearance resembles a naturally worn hoof as we see in the wild. Natural trimming applies equally to all saddle and draft horse breeds, ponies and miniatures, donkeys (asses), and the mule.

OUTER WALL

A naturally trimmed hoof will have a smooth, straight *outer wall* that angles down from the hairline to the ground. The natural hoof care practitioner uses the rasp to remove any unnatural bulges or "flares" in the wall. Most rasping occurs below the perioplic horn,

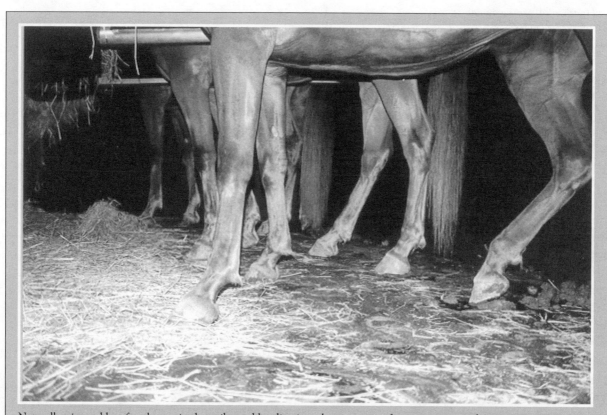

Naturally trimmed barefoot horses in the trailer and heading into the mountains for some serious riding.

from the toe to the heels. This rasping simulates natural wear, for in the wild, hooves are heavily worn by sand, gravel, mud, and other abrasive surfaces.

TOE ANGLES

Toe angles will vary from 50 to 60 degrees for most horses; very few will measured higher or lower. The toe (*toe length*) itself will measure from 2½ to 3½ inches long from the hairline to the ground. Both toe angle and toe length are important indicators of natural hoof size and proportion, hence natural hoof care practitioners record this information following each trim and use this data to monitor changes in hoof growth.

MUSTANG ROLL

At the hoof wall's ground bearing surface, the outer wall will turn in a distinct, smooth radius of approximately one half inch; this is the "*mustang roll*" and it is an important signature of both natural wear and natural trimming. The roll is produced with the rasp, and is reinforced by normal wear; an experienced practitioner can render a beautiful finish in minutes, and the finished hoof is a wonderful sight to behold!

CONFORMATION OF HAIRLINE

The *hairline* will descend gradually from the midline of the toe wall to each quarter, at which point it will tend to descend sharply in a distinct curve to the heels and heel bulbs. At the heels, which are very short by industry standards, the hairline nearly merges with the frog at ground bearing level.

There is much variation in the actual *angle of the hairline* from horse to horse, as its slope is much influenced by the size and shape of the cartilages of the coffin bone, the size and shape of the coffin bone itself, the amount of soft tissue mass associated with the lower pastern, and even old injuries of the hairline. Natural hoof care practitioners respect this variation in the contour of the hairline, and make no attempt to "modify" its natural position through manipulative trimming techniques.

FROG

Looking under the hoof, we see that the back of the *frog* is trimmed or worn level with the ground and the surrounding heel buttresses. The naturally trimmed frog enjoys direct, but passive, contact with the ground. At its sides (commissures), the *bars* form a niche, or recession, into which the frog is passively trimmed and worn. Natural hoof care practitioners carefully and skillfully contour the bars, frog, and heel-buttresses with their hoof knives, following the natural convolutions of the individual hoof.

HEEL-BUTTRESSES

It is worth noting, that the *heel-buttresses* are trimmed and worn like one never sees in conventional shoeing. Most farriers, vets, and horse owners would call naturally trimmed heels "run under" or "sheared". But this is their natural conformation; indeed, in the wild, horses commonly walk on the "back" of their heels! Natural hoof care practitioners simulate this wear characteristic by applying the mustang roll to the entire heel buttress.

SOLE

The *sole* of the naturally trimmed hoof is concaved everywhere from the white line of the outer wall inward to the frog. The deepest, or lowest, point of solar concavity is roughly over the forward half of the frog, behind its apex (called the point-of-frog).

Natural hoof care practitioners trim the sole with the hoof knife, carefully excising old, flaky or compacted horn. The sole is never "thinned" so much as to leave it soft, spongy, or hypersensitive; to the contrary, the hoof is encouraged to develop a thick, tough and pain-free sole, just like its wild counterpart.

handwritten on photo: ARABIAN HORSE'S 3-18-2000 ON ROCKS NO STALL'S

handwritten on photo: I TRIM ABOUT ONE TIME A YEAR

TESTIMONY

AGAINST THE GRAIN

CHARLES HALL, TN

I decided to include Tennessee natural hoof care practitioner and farrier Charles Hall's (see bio, Chapter 17) comments right on the photo of a foot he sent me. What a great hoof — it doesn't get any better. Charles is definitely going "against the grain" in trimming this horse only once a year. But that's the reality of natural hoof care. You can trim your horse when he really needs it. Lots of natural wear, as proven here, is Nature's alternative to trimming.

HOOF BALANCE

Another very important dimension of the natural trim is how the outer wall supports the whole hoof on the ground. Natural hoof care practitioners call this *"hoof balance."* A balanced hoof supports the horse on a flat surface with the outer wall enduring "active" or direct contact with the ground; the sole and frog, in contrast, endure "passive" or indirect contact, like the arch of your own foot.

ACTIVE VRS. PASSIVE WEAR

The outer wall itself also has areas of *active and passive support*. The location and size of these areas of support varies considerably from horse to horse. For example, some hooves have four points of support, while others have three points of support; still other hooves may have an entire one half of the outer wall worn passively. The heel-buttresses always endure active contact with the ground.

Natural hoof care practitioners "take their lead" from the individual conformation of the hoof, and how it tends to wear, in trimming the outer wall for balance. They never attempt to force the hoof to balance on three, four, or more support points. They do observe closely, however, how the "grain" of the hoof wall aligns with a flat supporting surface; the grain will be perpendicular (at right angles) to the ground when the hoof capsule is balanced.

There are many nuances of hoof shape that natural trimming can effect. The natural hoof care practitioner uses an experienced eye to gauge the effects of his or her work. And at all times, they reflect on the "wild model" to guide them. As one practitioner has said, the natural hoof must be carved from the domestic hoof like the "Wooden Indian" from a section of wood.

PREVENTIVE AND THERAPEUTIC VALUE OF NATURAL TRIM

The natural trim is, in an holistic sense, also a preventive or therapeutic trim for hoof lameness. This is due to the fact that naturally trimmed hooves trigger latent healing forces within the growth coria (coronary, laminar, solar, perioplic, frog/bulb). A proper natural trim is necessary for optimal healing to occur.

The natural trim, which only modifies or removes excessive epidermal horn — well outside each growth corium — is not considered an ablative (i.e., a surgical) veterinary procedure by the State Veterinary Licensing Boards in the United States. Therefore, it may be practiced by non-veterinarians without violating state veterinary statutes, which preclude all but licensed vets from conducting invasive therapies.

It is important to realize, though, that a newly barefooted horse may experience some tenderness following the removal of shoes. This is not due to the natural trim itself. Rather, it is a consequence of either lack of conditioning of the feet following de-shoeing, or, the harmful effects of shoeing per se. Either way, the hooves simply need a brief period of transition to enable them to inure and adapt to the environment.

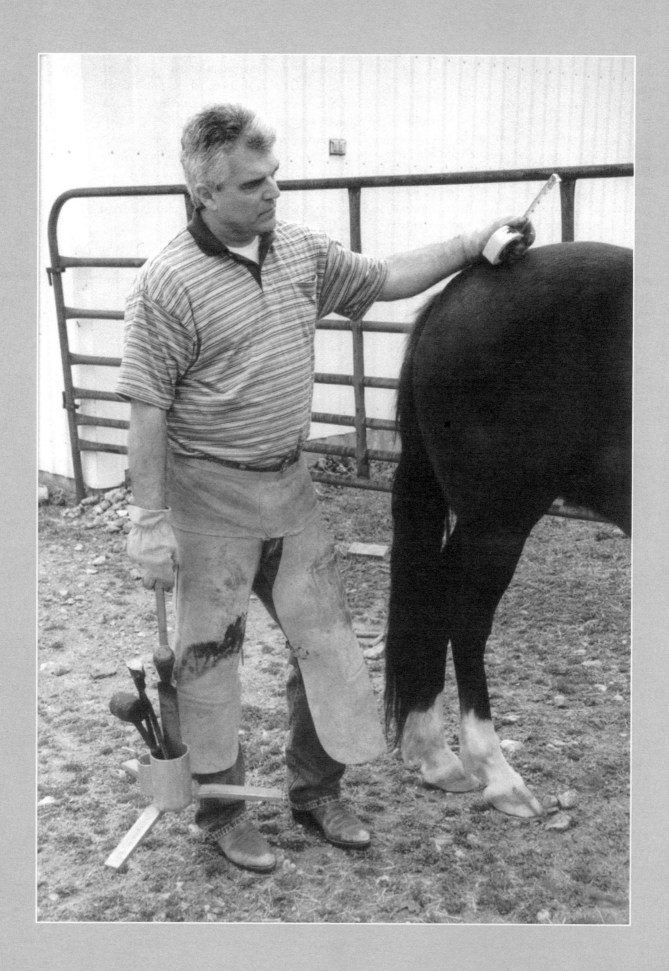

CHAPTER FIVE

TOOLS AND EQUIPMENT

Famed classical guitarist Christopher Parkening to one of his Master Class students, "Throw your guitar in the dump. Not even I can get a decent sound out of it."

If you've reached the decision that you're going to do your own trimming, then you want to purchase and use *quality* tools and equipment. Only quality tools can enable you to optimize your performance as a natural hoof care practitioner and do a quality job. Let me say here at the outset, no one, including a professional, can do a good job with lousy tools. If I can't do it, you can't.

Figure 5-1 itemizes just what you'll need — they're the tools and equipment that I use personally. Use the Resources section of this *Guide* for sources if you want to purchase what's necessary to do the work yourself.

Many of these items can be found in farrier supply houses. Unfortunately, these suppliers are not easy to locate if you are not familiar with the industry. Moreover, as a horse owner, you are entering the farrier's traditional turf, and you may get the feeling your presence is not exactly welcome.

On the other hand, some feed stores and horse equipment dealers carry shoeing supplies, but you run the risk of buying useless "beginners" tools if you don't know what you're looking for. These merchants no nothing about hoof work and probably wouldn't know what quality tools are or how to use them. They are there to take your money, and once they've got it, you're on your own to face the consequences of your ignorance. I learned this the hard way many years ago when first starting out.

You won't be needing blacksmithing equip-

(*Across*) Rigged as a professional, and seasoned by 25 years in the trenches, I'm ready to get down to it. With the proper tools and equipment I've described in this chapter, I can give a thorough natural trim to any horse hoof on the face of the earth in less than five minutes. Just let me at it! Natural trimming is that easy.

85

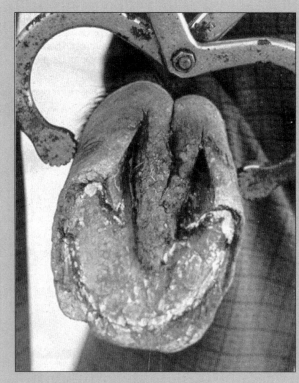

FIGURE 5-2

HOOF TESTERS

TORTURE AT THE HOOF

The notorious "hoof testers" at work. Avoid using this torture device by becoming knowledgeable about the horse's feet.

ment and tools — things specifically designed for putting horseshoes on the hooves. Forges, anvils, gas/coal, tongs, nailing hammers, and so forth, have no place in natural hoof care. So don't buy them simply because you've seen them in the back of a farrier's truck.

You'll notice one item missing from the list that you've probably seen used diagnostically by farriers and particularly vets. This is the notorious "hoof tester" (Figure 5-2). Modeled in principle after skull presses — torturing devices used by priests and their henchmen during the Spanish Inquisition—testers prove only one

thing: anybody can induce pain in a hoof, sound or unsound, if only sufficient pressure is brought to bear.

Tantamount to a "witch hunt" within the hoof, they are touted as an indispensable diagnostic tool with which to pinpoint pain. But squeeze any healthy hoof hard enough (and usually not very hard), and you can not only extract pain, you will cause tissue damage. There's simply no justification for using a hoof tester. It's been my observation that people who use them just don't know hooves. A real

(Continued on page 93)

FIGURE 5-1

ESSENTIAL EQUIPMENT

AN IMPORTANT WORK CENTER
LEG PROTECTION

HOOF STAND

PORTABLE WORK CENTER

Hoof Stand & Tool Caddy

With this handy hoof stand, you can carry all your tools right with you as you go from hoof to hoof, and horse to horse. Caddy swivels at base of this lightweight work center. In the photo at left I've got my hoof knife, rasp, nippers, and booting mallet. Hoof stand is an absolute must if you don't want to hurt your back or overwork your legs. Also, it's not easy to do a quality "mustang roll" without using the hoof stand, which has a "grip head" to secure the bottom of the horse's foot.

Star Ridge Hoof Stand and Work Center
(see Resources)

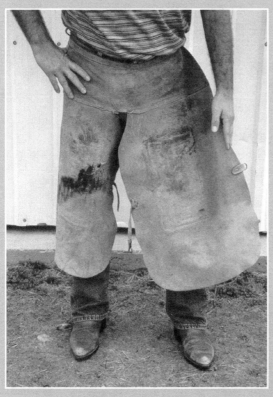

TRIMMERS APRON

PROTECT YOUR LEGS

Leather Apron

These heavily worn chaps, or trimmer's apron, as they are commonly called, have knee clips, adjustable leather belt, and padded thigh insets to protect my legs. They have lasted me 16 years and thousands of trims. Don't even try to trim a horse without them — if you look close, you can see knife slices, rasp marks, and tear holes from sharp hoof edges. So, you can see that a good apron protects more than your street clothes!

Star Ridge Trimmers Apron
(see Resources)

FIGURE 5-1 (CONT'D)

TOOLS AND EQUIPMENT

DESHOEING AND TRIMMING TOOLS

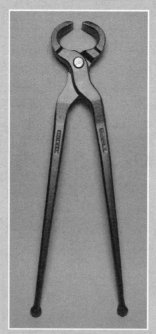

Star Ridge Shoe Pullers
(see Resources)

SHOE PULLERS

FOR DESHOEING

Pullers

These are moderately priced professional pullers, which are used for pulling shoes off. They look similar to the hoof nipper (facing page), but don't confuse the two. You can ruin your nippers if you use them to pull shoes with — and many horse owners have learned an expensive lesson the hard way! Go to Figure 7-1 or my companion video to see how I use them.

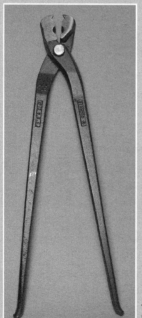

Star Ridge Crease Nail Pullers
(see Resources)

NAIL PULLER

FOR DESHOEING

Crease Nail Puller

You can see these in action in Figure 7-1 and in my companion video. I wouldn't think of deshoeing without having these in my tool box. They're for pulling stubborn horseshoe nails out of the "creases" of shoes.

TRIMMING TOOLS

Star Ridge Hoof Nippers
(see Resources)

HOOF NIPPER

ESSENTIAL TRIMMING TOOL

Nippers

Do gross horn removal with these. The nipper, like the hoof knife and rasp, is indispensable for doing quality hoof work. This is a high quality professional nipper that I personally use and recommend.

crook

blade

F. Dick Hoof Knife
(see Resources)

HOOF KNIFE

ESSENTIAL TRIMMING TOOL

Hoof Knife

Pick a quality hoof knife, like this German brand (F. Dick), as you will use this tool often. Also learn how to sharpen it; you can't slice anything with a dull blade. Hoof knives come in left and right styles.

RASP & ACCESSORIES

ESSENTIAL TRIMMING TOOL

Rasping tools and equipment

The rasp will be one of the most important tools in your work center. I use the German model at left, which has exceptional coarse (*right, bottom*) and fine (*right, top*) cutting teeth. In addition to the rasp, I recommend a quality handle, rasp brush for removing debris from the teeth, and spray lubricant to prevent rust and increase longevity of the rasp.

Star Ridge Rasps & Accesories
(see Resources)

Sharpeners, pick, measuring tape

There are several other indispensable accessories necessary for making your trimming go smoothly. You will need sharpeners for your hoof knife, a measuring tape, and a hoof pick. Without the sharpeners, your knife's sharp edge cannot be sustained. The hoof pick is a good idea for removing debris from the frog commissures and sole. The tape, which should read in Metric as well as Standard, is important for measurement data.

OTHER TOOLS

IMPORTANT ACCESSORIES

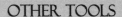

Star Ridge Trimming Accesories
(see Resources)

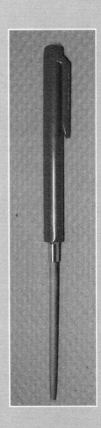

Although this young man is doing an excellent job of trimming, something is terribly wrong with what he's done here. Can you guess? That's right, his expensive tools are laying all over the ground! He needs a "work center" badly. He'll won't reach as far for his tools. He won't trip over them. He can find them! That draft horse he's trimming won't break them in two with one step. The dirt won't dull the cutting edges of his knife and nippers.

(Continued from page 86)

hoof expert has an arsenal of other ways of ascertaining what's troubling the horse's foot, and heaping more trauma upon the hoof by squeezing the heck out of it is simply voodoo medicine.

Okay, go ahead and study the recommended tools and equipment in the preceding pages. There's no tool here you can't handle effectively. As you get your feet wet, you'll do like everyone else in the trade: discover what's best for your way of doing things. Good luck!

SHAKING HANDS, NATURALLY

Before you ever pick up the horse's foot or ask him to do anything for you, "shake hands" like horses do. Offer your hand to his nose. Shaking hands means sharing scent in horse language. It's like two people offering their hands as a gesture of good faith. People always note how well I get along with horses, just like those you see me with in my companion video. The "secret" is that I take a moment to introduce myself (and my tools) to the horse — just like horses do with each other in the wild — before each trim session. I also engage in other bonding gestures such as massaging the mane. If you find yourself fighting or hassling with horses, being kicked at, or simply working in fear of them, well, you might consider this non-violent approach — a truly natural alternative to simply charging into the hooves and maybe a whole lot of management problems too.

CHAPTER SIX

BALANCING YOUR HORSE

for TRIMMING

"But there is one rule to be inviolably observed above all others; that is, never approach a horse in a passion, for anger never thinks of consequences, and forces us to do what we afterwards repent." Xenophon

Before you can pick up your horse's feet to trim them, it is necessary to first balance him so that he can give his feet without unnecessary tension and resistance. I've observed that many horses resist having their feet trimmed for no other reason than they are simply "unbalanced." The more balanced your horse is, the easier and faster you'll be able to get your job done.

But before attempting to balance your horse for his hoof work, I advise that you first take a moment to communicate good will to him. In the wild, and among domestic horses, this is done by "sharing scent" (*facing page*) and mutual grooming. These simple acts are extremely important to horses, and so I do not engage in them gratuitously but with the utmost seriousness. If you find yourself repeatedly having a difficult time managing horses in your care, please consider

All horses can bite and kick — because they have teeth and hooves.

☙

this non-violent alternative to simply forcing your actions upon the horse. Force begets resistance, and with resistance comes anger. Surely then Xenophon's wise words of admonition may come to haunt you.

We have two mains concerns in getting a horse balanced. Effecting the natural position of his head and neck for lifting his feet so you can work on them; and, conversely, positioning his feet so that his head, neck and body — and you! — are in harmony with his head.

Figure 6-1 illustrates roughly three positions of the neck and how each can help or hinder our work. Go ahead and study the diagrams and then experiment on your own horse to see how each position affects his ability to give you his feet.

Positioning your horse's feet under his body for balance is a little trickier. Figure 6-2 shows you what I do, which entails backing the horse

FIGURE 6-1

BALANCING THE HEAD AND NECK

READING THE HORSES STANCE

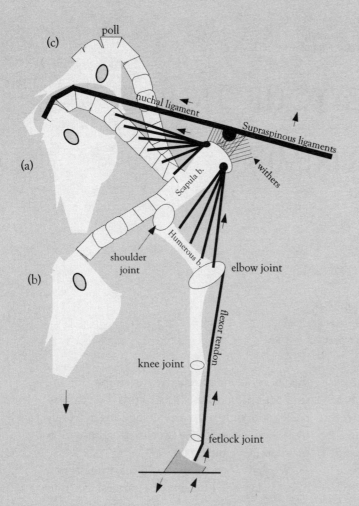

(a) **Collection stance.** Encouraging the horse to elevate head and neck while flexing at the *poll* helps balance the horse: the *nuchal* and *supraspinous* ligaments pull the withers forward and raise the horse's back; in turn, the shoulder *scapula* is pulled forward by muscles of the neck, opening the shoulder joint; this puts tension on the *deep digital flexor tendon*, which takes weight from the heels and shifts it over the toe— thereby advancing the hoof into its breakover phase, and rendering it easy to lift.

(b) **Grazing stance.** The lever effect of the neck "loads" too much weight upon the forehand for this to be a useful stance for hoof care.

(c) **Fear/flight stance.** When the head rises from tension or fear, the head is designed to look forward—as in preparation for flight. The withers and shoulder move back—which lowers the back, relaxes the flexor tendon, and presses the heels into the ground. "High-headedness" means "don't pick up my hooves."

Now, what about the horse's head? Should it be secured tightly or loosely at halter? As a rule, I tie the horse so that his stance is (bio-mechanically) optimal for the hoof care process. Which means that the horse's neck should be somewhat elevated and the head, ideally, flexed at the poll. This is illustrated in the figure above.

Asking the horse to flex at the poll will help greatly while working on the hooves. Here's why: flexion contracts the powerful nuchal ligament connecting the head to the

withers. This pulls the withers forward, raises the muscles and spine of the back, and opens the shoulder joint. This action specifically contracts the major flexor tendon (*deep digital flexor tendon*), which, further down the limb, causes the fetlock joint to hyperextend and puts the horse's hooves "on toe" — that is, ready to come off the ground lightly as during collection. (Please refer to my discussion of the "semiflexor joints" in *The Natural Horse* for a more detailed discussion of how you can use collection to your advantage.)

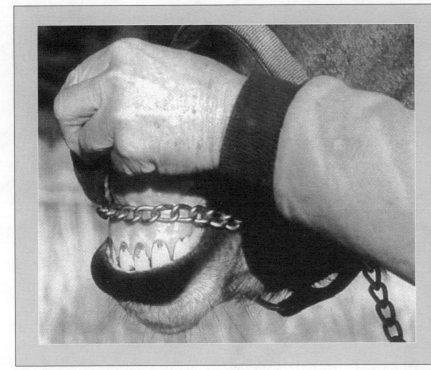

FIGURE 2-14

LIP CHAIN

MIDEVAL MADNESS

One version of the notorious "lip chain" commonly used by horseshoers and others today. Put one in your mouth and let someone yank on it — and you'll know how the horse feels. This is an example of fear training, which goes back to the days of medieval knights. Systematically develop your rapport with the horse using natural communication, and you won't have to resort to measures like this.

one-half of a footfall sequence so that he moves and supports himself alternately on diagonally paired legs. Let me tell you, this method works. It makes all the difference between having to labor to pick up the horse's feet, and enabling him to stand balanced so he can help you hold up his own foot. My companion video shows how I do this too.

Some horses can be very difficult and will resist all your efforts to balance them and trim their feet. Perhaps your horse has never had his feet handled before, particularly the hind. What do you do, especially if he offers to strike or kick at you? Well, before I suggest to you how I do things, please avoid forcing your horse, especially using such medieval torture devices as the lip chain (Figure 6-3). This is an act of violence that will only make him mad and begrudging of you; he will learn to fear you

and his trust may be sacrificed forever. Horses are fully capable of retaliating if they feel they have been wronged . . . offenders are warned.

Figure 6-4 illustrates, in sequence, how I pick up the hind feet of a kicker or any horse that's touchy about giving his feet. You'll need a soft cotton rope to secure the leg with, and a short length of metal bar rod with handle and hook for snagging the hoof. Follow the instructions carefully, allowing plenty of time for your horse to figure out what you're trying to accomplish.

Last, Figure 6-5 offers some additional suggestion for handling your horse prior to and during trimming. I realize that every competent horse handler has their own unique way of doing things; these work for me in most situations, and I have applied them successfully for over 25 years as a professional.

FIGURE 6-2

BALANCE AND PRESSURE POINTS

PICKING UP YOUR HORSE'S FEET

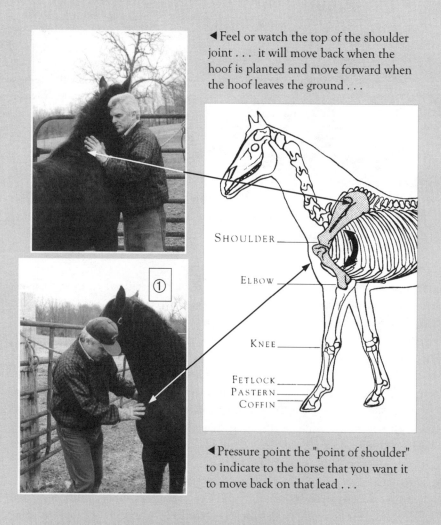

◄ Feel or watch the top of the shoulder joint . . . it will move back when the hoof is planted and move forward when the hoof leaves the ground . . .

SHOULDER

ELBOW

KNEE

FETLOCK
PASTERN
COFFIN

◄ Pressure point the "point of shoulder" to indicate to the horse that you want it to move back on that lead . . .

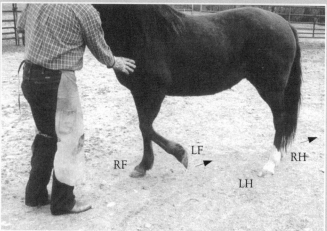

Okay, let's say you want to pick up the right front or left hind hoof. Apply pressure to left shoulder to move left front and right hind hooves back towards their respective support phases. Note that the right front and left hind are planted in support to balance horse for this move. (This would have been a good time to pick up either the left front or right hind hooves.)

Cease pressure to left shoulder once left front and right hind are in support. Now the right front or left hind are "unloaded" and ready to be picked up. This horse "knows" I'm going to pick up his left hind, so he's put his right front out to the side to balance himself. In doing so, he's formed a triangular based of support.

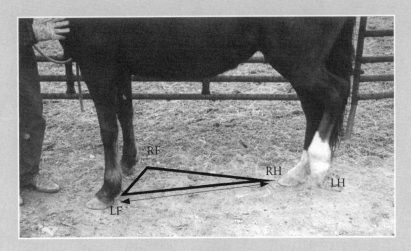

When the horse is so balanced his hoof can be held with one finger.

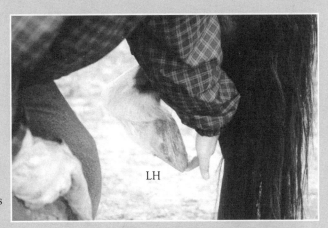

Now move to the right shoulder and apply pressure. The horse here has now followed through and his right front and left hind are in support. His left front has moved forward and to the side to form a triangular base of support so I can pick up his right hind.

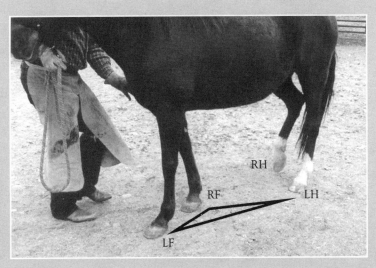

FIGURE 6-3

WORKING WITH DIFFICULT HORSES

PICKING UP YOUR HORSE'S FEET

Wear leather gloves. Use ¾ in. twist, soft white, cotton rope. Tie horse to sturdy post with panic snap and halter. Form a "loop knot" with cotton rope and bring loose end over neck as shown.

Pass short, loose end through loop knot, and tie off with "overhand knot" or "slip knot" (for quick release) — don't form a "slip noose" that will tighten when put under pressure. Keep heavy shears or knife at hand to cut rope in emergency.

Bring long end of rope wide around to haunches — touch gently. Repeat on off side of horse (repeat all lessons on off side). Keep a safe distance in case horse kicks out. If horse kicks, remain quiet or indifferent. Repeat, then end lesson for day. Reassure horse. Next day, repeat again. Once horse shows indifference or tolerance, praise lavishly and end lesson for day; move to next lesson.

After repeating lesson above once or twice more, lower rope progressively from haunch, to stifle, to hock, to fetlock, to hoof. The idea is to rub the joints, increasing the intensity incrementally. Twirl the rope if the horse will allow without going berserk. Some horses may rear, even fall over — especially the determined kickers; remain indifferent and quiet. Repeat, go slowly, day by day. Seek indifference. Some horses may respond with curiosity — that's good. Reassure horse constantly. Move to next step when you think the horse is ready.

Walk the rope behind the lower legs. Back and forth. Get the horse used to it. Work from both sides. Talk to horse constantly in an even voice. Show no alarm. Stay out of kicking range. When you think the horse is ready . . . move to next step.

(Continued on page 102)

BALANCING YOUR HORSE FOR TRIMMING

The horse may be indifferent to the rope swishing at its ankles by now; but we want to agitate enough to get the horse to raise one hoof so we can pass the rope between its legs as shown. Once you accomplish this, rub horse's inner legs with rope. The confirmed kickers will really try to let you have it now. Remain quiet and calm. Let the horse kick away. Stop, remove rope, reassure with praise, and end lesson for day. Repeat daily until you feel horse is ready to advance cooperatively—not fighting you.

Bring the rope back around to the horse's shoulder, gently taking hoof with you as shown. Drop coil on ground, so you can work rope with both hands if necessary. Play rope out against horse's kicks—don't resist, which will "lock" horse up and cause it to lose balance and possibly fall. Praise the horse in this position—turn to face the horse. Once horse relaxes, gently tug at hoof with rope as though drawing toward you. Don't forget to balance the horse on diagonal support base. Work both sides. Repeat daily until horse demonstrates acceptance.

Now secure rope with left hand and pull hoof (rope is around pastern) forward; as you pull, secure bottom of hoof with "hoof hook" (facing page). Stay at horse's shoulder to avoid being kicked. Keep others away from area — some horses will kick so hard that the hook will fling out of your hand like a bullet. Keep your fingers out of hole in hook handle. Gently move hoof back and forth. Remove hook and release hoof to rope — which is still secured to pastern. Repeat both sides daily. (See close-up detail next photo).

When applying the hoof hook, place it be-tween the turn of the rope as shown. In this way the rope can be loosened and lowered off of the hoof in the next step. Note that hook wraps around the outside quarter, its tip against the sole. Should horse kick, don't try to stop hook from leaving your grip — let it go. Before actually securing hoof with hook, merely touch hoof with it; then tap lightly; then secure as shown. Before, during, and af-ter session, introduce hook to horse. Let him smell and nuzzle it — as with all your tools and equipment.

Now release rope and secure hoof with hook. With your left side to the horse's left (on) side, reach down with left hand and touch hoof. Stay close to horse. Do this only after horse shows complete indifference to hook in previous step. Repeat on the off side if horse is ready (off side may be at a different phase of readiness — don't expect both hind legs to be foot broke at same time). Reassure mo-ment by moment, if need be. Repeat daily.

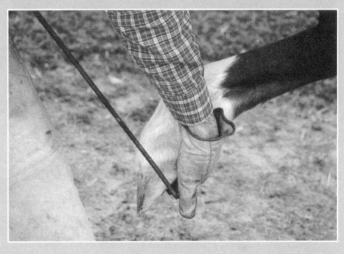

Hoof hook, ¼ inch round bar stock

24 inches

Have a "hoof hook" made, if you feel you need one, according to these specifications. [Note: This item is now available from Star Ridge — see Resources.]

Now the time has come to advance rear-ward with hook and hand only. Nor-mally, at this stage, the horse will offer his hoof. Stay with the hook, however, when securing the hoof until you are con-fident you can reach down to pick it up *after the horse has offered it*. On any new horse or kicker, I will usually bring the hoof forward onto my apron (my back to the horse) as shown in the position for the mustang roll in Figure 9-8. A profes-sional hoof care provider experienced in whole body communication can usually rope in a kicker, all the steps described, in less than an hour. Inexperienced horse owners may require several weeks or more.

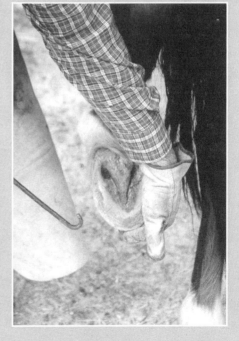

FIGURE 6-4

MORE ON HORSE AND HOOF HANDLING

DEVELOPING GOOD TECHNIQUE

Always wear supple leather gloves. Hold the halter at all times just below the chin ring where the lead snap attaches. Keep "connection" soft and passive — avoid pulling on the lead. Coil the lead so that it can slip off the ends of your fingers if the horse suddenly jerks. Keep one hand free at all times, passing coil from hand to hand. Lead horse by walking at shoulder; lean back to gesture forward movement. Rearward displaced ears indicate horse is attentive, as you can see throughout these and other photographs of horses I'm working with in this *Guide*.

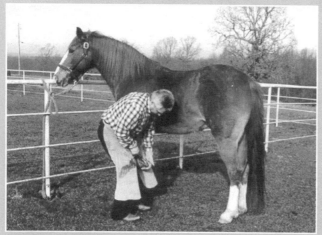

Hold front hoof between knees by pointing your toes slightly inward. To protect your back, keep your knees bent to lower your body into position to receive the hoof; this will proportionate weight distribution between your legs, lower and upper back, and shoulders. Move with the horse at all times; resisting movement creates tension and resistance — which can also hurt your back. Know why the horse is moving — does he need rest, is he out of balance, is he fearful or anxious?

Secure "busy" tail by first twisting, then (*above*, facing page) wrapping it over the hock, and finally securing under your arm. Avoid trimming horses with dangerous "clubbed" tails knotted with debris, for they can knock you unconscious and cause serious injury — owner should comb it clean first.

I've got the horse's "twisted" tail tucked under my right shoulder and out of harm's way.

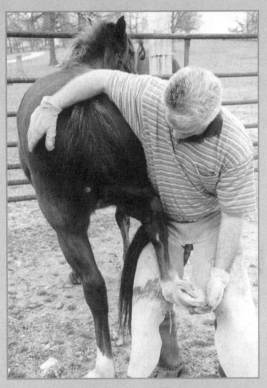

The same principles for securing the front hooves apply to the hind. Hind hoof crosses over your leg closest to the horse. You should be able to balance hoof in your lap without using your hands. Note again my pointed toes, which draw my knees and hoof together as one. Don't pick up hooves of kicker under any circumstances until they are completely foot broke as described in Figure 6-3; a horse can kick you to death or cause serious injury.

(Continued on next page)

This horse is alarmed by camera shutter — witness expression and left ear at radar. Kneel and secure hoof on knee when handling and trimming hooves of foals, miniature horses, small ponies, skittish horses being introduced to hoof handling for the first time, and other situations that preclude normal handling. For trimming, I may ask owner to hold hooves for me in these situations; in fact, this is the customary method used by many professionals in Europe. Alternatively, use a hoof cradle (see Resources — Star Ridge Hoof Stand Accessories).

Clean hoof with hoof pick — not the hoof knife; do this work with your tool box or hoof stand off to the side to keep debris out. Clean sole, frog cleft, and bar grooves; it takes no more than 30 seconds to clean out the worst. Naturally trimmed hooves are excellent "self-cleaners" — as seen in the wild. I never wash muddy hooves before trimming, but pick them out and towel dry; internal heat from hooves will dry them out very quickly for work.

I do not advise feeding horses during hoof work because it distracts them from concentrating on keeping themselves balanced while I work. But it is my practice always to chum around with them after the work is done, giving out treats, petting them, talking to them, letting them know I appreciate their help. Of course, I love horses for what they are, which helps too! — their smell, touch, unique personalities, sounds, gregariousness, curiosity, natural willingness to trust, and power. Or I would not think of doing this line of work.

CHAPTER SEVEN

REMOVING THE SHOES

"DE-SHOEING"

"Shoeing is another common fetish. Horse owners have been led to believe that all horses should be shod. Well, they shouldn't. The constant wearing of shoes is responsible for more poor feet than common neglect."
John Richard Young, author, Schooling of the Western Horse

For many horse owners, removing the horse's shoes can be an extremely harrowing experience. But it need not be. With the proper tool and reasonably good technique you can pull the shoes off of any horse. Of course, you can have a farrier or professional natural hoof care practitioner pull the shoes for you. But I recommend that you learn to do it yourself and enjoy the sense of independence and self-confidence that comes with it.

Use standard *shoe pullers* ("Trimming Tools and Equipment, Chapter 5; see also Re-

sources) to do this work. An experienced practitioner like myself can remove a tightly nailed shoe in 15 seconds; and I don't use clinch cutters, a rasp, or nail remover — just the pullers, and in a few instances a "crease nail puller." I urge you to study my companion video which shows you exactly how I do it — it is not difficult if you follow the video sequences faithfully.

Figure 7-1 provides you with some additional helpful hints. Good luck!

(Over) Figure 7-1

FIGURE 7-1

PULLING THE SHOES

DE-SHOEING YOUR HORSE

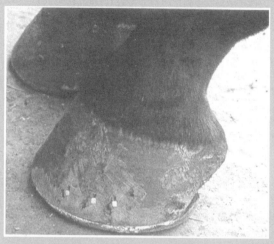

Some professionals with use the fine side of their rasps to thin down the nail clinches. There are two reasons why they do this: one, so that it will be easier to pull the nails back out through the bottom of the hoof; and two, so that the outer wall is not unnecessarily torn up by the clinches should the horn be weak and crumbly (typical with shod hooves). You can do this too, but I recommend that you use an old rasp rather than a new one; the reason is that the clinches will dull the tangs of your rasp, rendering it ineffectual for your hoof trimming work.

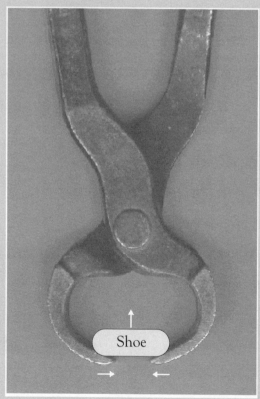

This shot and the one that follows is intended to help you understand the sequences more clearly in my companion trimming video. To begin, set the jaws of puller just under the heel of the shoe. You'll have to squeeze the handles a bit to get the jaws to work under the shoe.

If possible, squeeze the handles until the opposing jaws are nearly touching each other. Now, lift the jaws up at an angle against the shoe. Pull toward the toe in line with the branch of the shoe (see below). Listen for a slight "click" sound, which indicates that the clinches and shoe are loosening.

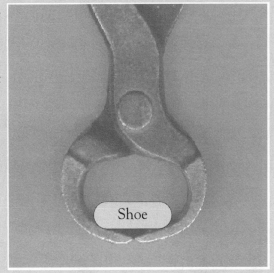

Shoe

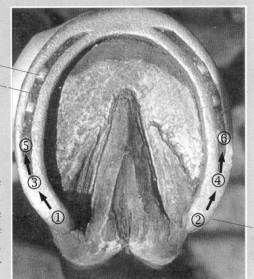

Nail

Crease (nail bed)

Heel of shoe

Beginning at the heel of the shoe (①), and alternating back and forth from one branch of the shoe to the other (①,②,③, etc.), work the shoe loose. Alternate from one branch of the shoe to the other to minimize lever forces and strain.

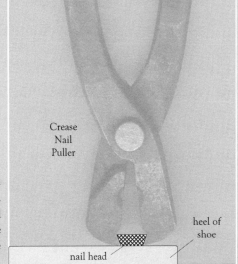

Crease
Nail
Puller

heel of shoe

nail head

If the nail clinches are just too tight for you to pull the shoe up off the hoof wall, then use the crease nail puller (*Resources*). This tool has a "bird beak" jaw which slips under the nail head. Just pull the entire nail out of the "crease" or bed of the shoe branch.

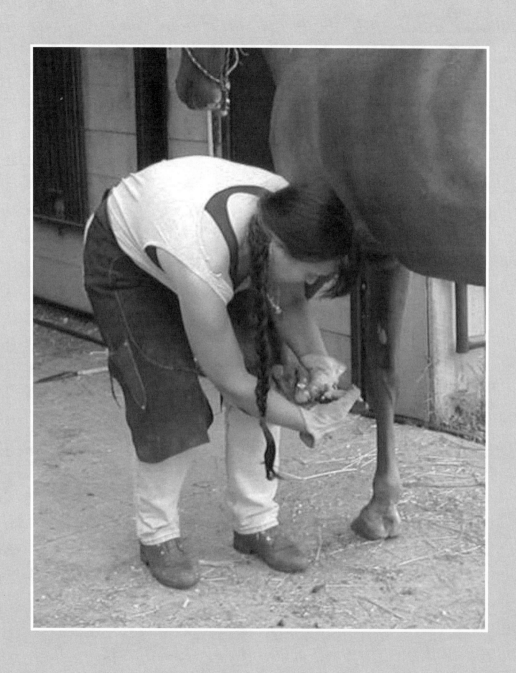

CHAPTER EIGHT

TRIMMING THE HOOF WALL

SOLE AND FROG

Trimming the horse's hooves is surprisingly simple and, with practice, requires little time to perform. Although very awkward for the average person just beginning to learn, the process is well within the reach of the typical horse, mule, or burro owner who is not suffering from back problems.

On average, it takes me about five minutes to trim each hoof. That's it! If the horse is living naturally according to the guidelines delineated later in this chapter, some hooves may not even require trimming at the scheduled session. It will depend on the degree of wear: more wear, less trimming. Either way, for a competent practitioner, trimming one horse is normally over with — start to finish — in less than 20 minutes. If you are an amateur, plan on spending 30 minutes or more, less, of course, as you gain experience.

There are two phases to the natural trim: 1) Work done in your lap to the bottom of the hoof; and 2) work done to the outer wall on the hoof stand. In this chapter, we'll begin at the bottom of the hoof, trimming the hoof wall, sole, and frog. Follow the vignette of photos in the following pages; refer also to my companion video, *Creating the Perfect Hoof*, for a visual "hands-on" demonstration.

Let's go through the steps together now, assuming the shoes are removed, and that this is your horse's first natural trim following de-shoeing.

ROUGHING OUT THE HOOF

A horse which has just been de-shod presents a hoof trimming job much different than a normal maintenance natural trim. This is because growth under the shoe is usually excessive, weak (i.e., incapable of high performance barefootedness), and lacks the high quality horn to work with that is normally seen in barefoot horses. To deal with this unnatural condition, I perform a "rough out" trim — simply put, a quick excoriation or reduction of unwanted horn. Refer now to Figure 8-1 and my companion video for specific instruction.

(Over) Figure 8-1

FIGURE 8-1

ROUGHING OUT THE HOOF

FOLLOWING DE-SHOEING

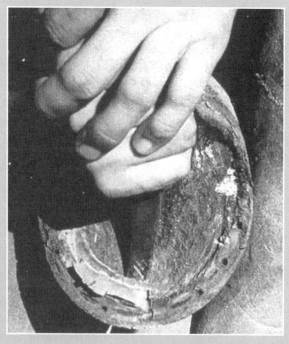

After cleaning out the de-shod hoof with your hoof pick, use the hoof knife to expose the white line. This is a potential trouble spot if you dig too close into the sole with the knife. To avoid over-trimming and quicking the sole at the white line, simply remove the flaky, dead horn that yields easily. With experience, however, this step becomes less and less problematic, and I am entirely sympathetic with beginners who must at the outset shoulder the burden of not knowing precisely how deep they can penetrate the sole with the crook of their hoof knives.

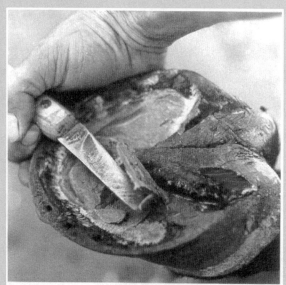

Also use the hoof knife to slice or flake away loose sole horn. This step also requires experience so watch the companion video closely to see how I do it.

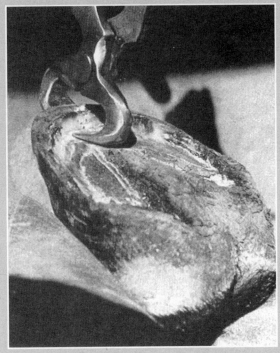

Next, take your nippers and cut off any outer wall—from the toe wall to the heel-buttresses—protruding above the white line. Using the nippers below the white line, in other words nipping into the sole, puts you at risk of entering the quick and bleeding the hoof—a no no! My companion video demonstrates where to put the nipper relative to the white line.

Here, half the toe wall has been removed and pulled back with the nips so you can see what I've done. I prefer to make my first cut with the nippers right at the center of the toe (marked by white dotted line) and then work back to each heel buttress, staying above the white line at all points around the circumference of the hoof wall.

Our objective here is to gradually work the sole, frog, and outer wall down piecemeal until all excessive and weak horn is removed. Loose, overgrown sole and frog are first pared away with the hoof knife. Then the nippers are used to cut away excess hoof wall above (i. e., distal to) the white line. It is a cardinal rule of mine never to set the blades of the nippers into the sole; I always set them above the white line in the hoof wall proper.

If the outer wall, sole, and frog are unusually dried out and resistant even to your sharp tools, consider soaking the hooves first to soften them. Standing the horse in mud for an hour before the trimming session is very effective. If you do this, dry the hooves off with a towel or rag instead of hosing them off with water. This way the pastern will dry quickly and you won't soak your trousers!

FINE TUNING THE HOOF

Personally, my clients have been very regular in having their horses' feet attended to, so I don't face the kind of excessive growth seen in Figure 8-1.* The exceptions would be new horses coming into my care that haven't yet been de-shod. Usually, I am faced with hooves that are only marginally overgrown.

In the rugged mountain country of my home, the soles and frog are worn away by the horse's lifestyle and require very little or no paring. To the extent that it is necessary, this work is done with the hoof knife. It is rare, for the same reason, that I ever have to wield the nippers to shorten the hoof wall; in lieu of the nippers, therefore, the rasp is most often relegated to this chore.

Now, let's go ahead and trim the hoof wall, sole, and frog. Figure 8-2 (*Overleaf*) provides trimming guidelines for these specific structures; and to help bring matters to life, I recommend also studying them in conjunction with my companion video.* Then practice on your own horse. Note too that the hoof in Figure 8-2 is freshly trimmed (by me), so you're looking at the aftermath of a natural trim,

rather than what needs to be done yet.

Before continuing to phase two ("working the outer wall") I have a few additional observations I want to make that will, if not impact how we trim the hoof wall, sole, and frog, at least give us further cause to think how our trimming can impact the natural functioning of the hoof.

HOOF WALL:
ACTIVE AND PASSIVE WEAR

We learned in Chapter 2 that in naturally shaped hooves the hoof wall endures most of the capsule's active contact with the ground. The sole, frog, and heel-bulbs bear the rest of the load. In Chapter 3 we learned also that the hoof wall absorbs the shock of impact (concussional force), as well as the brunt of the weight bearing force descending downward into the capsule (compressional force). The hoof wall, we know, is designed to take this "double beating," and, in fact, it must if the "mechanism" is to function normally and optimally. And really, these contraposing concussional and compressional forces form the basis for natural wear. But what do they mean in so far as our trimming goes?

Typically, as horses go barefoot and wear their hooves naturally (again the concussional and compressional forces), the capsule will begin to "remodel" or shape itself accordingly. This is natural and it is to be expected. This shaping is influenced by the horse's living quarters, how often he is ridden or exercised, his own genetic make-up, and our trimming. But if we look closer still at the remodeling hoof, we will begin to see very distinct and highly individualized wear. This variation or nuance surfaces, among other places, in the hoof wall in the form of *active* and *passive* wear.

Active wear is defined as those areas of the hoof wall having direct (hence "active") contact with the ground — or more precisely a flat bearing surface; **passive wear**, conversely, are those areas of the hoof wall having indirect (thus "passive") contact. Thus, areas of passive

*I retired as a professional trimmer last year (2001), after 25 years of trimming thousands of horses. I'm now a full time writer and charter member of the American Association of Natural Hoof Care Practitioners – a new organization dedicated to the promotion of natural hoof care based on the wild horse hoof model.

*While the guidelines given in Figure 8-2 apply equally to all the horses' hooves I trim in the video, look for the trimming sequences for "Lexus" (Missouri Fox Trotter) to see the precise hoof in Figure 8-2 being trimmed.

HORSE OWNERS GUIDE TO NATURAL HOOF CARE

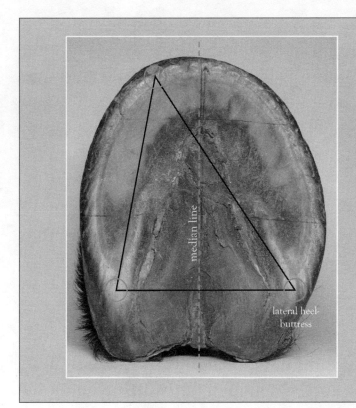

median line

lateral heel-buttress

FIGURE 8-3

ACTIVE AND PASSIVE WEAR

Active wear with this left hind wild horse hoof occurs over both heel-buttresses and a fragment (less than 1 cm) of the toe wall on the medial side. I found this wear pattern, which forms a triangular base of support as shown here, very common in most hind hooves of wild horses. Compare with the naturally worn front hoof in Figure 2-13. No credible research has been done that I'm aware of which demonstrates the relationship of active/passive wear to bone structure and limb stance.

wear are situated between areas of active wear. Said another way, when a hoof is in its weight bearing or support phase, and the horse is standing on a flat firm surface, the active points touch the supporting surface while the passive wear points do not.

Every hoof, in accordance with the horse's overall conformation, has its own unique signature of active and passive wear. Indeed, "hoof balance" is in large measure defined by the salience of the active points, in other words, how the hoof is "propped up" upon them. Horseshoeing, it is worth reflecting on, obliterates this signature by the need to level the hoof wall in order to stabilize the shoe when it is nailed on. Natural hoof care practitioners, in contrast, trim the hoof wall to facilitate the natural convolutions of the hoof wall — its signature, in other words.

Active and passive wear, we have seen, are abundantly expressed in naturally worn wild horse hooves. We recall one example in Figure 2-13 where the capsule (a front hoof) is supported actively in three spots, the center of the toe wall and upon each heel-buttress, and passively along both quarters. Figure 8-3 above illustrates a common hind hoof wear pattern. While these particular wear patterns are very common among wild horses, they are not the only ones — indeed, there is much variation.

Most hooves I sampled had "3 Points" of active support, with minor variations of those seen in Figures 2-13 and 8-3. Other hooves had "4 Points" of active support, including both heel-buttresses and two toe wall points (located generally forward of the point-of-frog and on either side of the hoof's median line).

(Continued on page 122)

(Over) Figure 8-2

FIGURE 8-2

WORKING THE HOOF IN YOUR LAP

HOOF WALL, SOLE, FROG

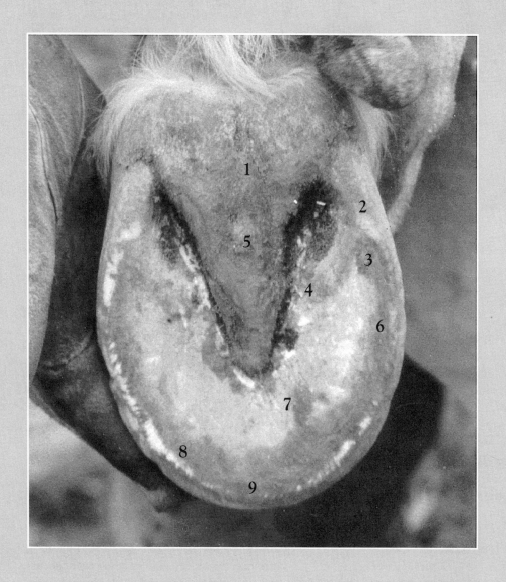

1   **Heel bulbs** — posterior projections of the frog, avoid trimming them except for minor loose flaps. Natural wear will eventually flatten them out as never seen in shod horses. This is natural, and the effect is to give the heels the appearance of being "run under." The bulbs may wear passively against the ground; which is also natural and nothing to be concerned about.

2   **Heel-Buttresses** — are an extension of the hoof wall. If they are excessively long, trim them with your nippers. Then level them down to the frog. Use rasp by drawing backwards and outward over each buttress separately. Balance them (they should be the same length) while sighting the hoof from behind, and, from the front while on a flat level surface (see Chapter 10). Round off all edges of buttresses in preparation for mustang roll. Note that the left and right buttresses may or may not be in the same position relative to the hoof's median line, nor may they be located directly across from each other left to right. In many naturally shaped hooves, the buttresses appear to be "run under" — too far under the hoof towards the toe. This is perfectly normal provided they are trimmed short.

3   **Seats-of-corn** — trim right along with bars using hoof knife. As in wild horse hooves, the "pockets" will vary in depth from horse to horse, depending on the conformation of the individual hoof.

4   **Bars** — extensions of the hoof wall, they help form the heel-buttress. The bars are very prominent in naturally shaped hooves, and should be trimmed only to the level of the sole or slightly above the sole. Some practitioners believe that the bars must be trimmed to the quick to "de-contract" hooves. Not so! The bars are part of the hoof wall proper — nature intended them to be there. Check it out for yourself in Figure 8-5. See Chapter 16, "Hoof Contraction," for additional details.

5   **Frog** — like sole, avoid trimming if at all possible; let natural wear do this work for you. Exception: the frog is excessively overgrown and/or putrid smelling. Use hoof knife, pushing down right side of frog toward toe sole, drawing back toward heel-bulb on left side. Clean out central cleft too, which is dirt packed in this photo.

6   **Quarters (mid-hoof wall)** — trim down even with toe wall and heel-buttresses. Keep quarter walls above (active to) white line, however. Quarters may "hollow" out (become passive) from wear—this is perfectly natural. Round off outer edge of quarters liberally in preparation for mustang roll.

7   **Sole** — avoid trimming if at all possible; let natural wear do this work for you. Exception: the hoof is excessively long or the sole is flat and overgrown (i.e., compacted) from lack of wear. In this case, use hoof knife, sweeping clockwise from left to right (if you are right handed) as though you were hollowing out a wooden bowl. It is important not to thin down the sole, which will leave it hypersensitive (see Figure 8-5 to compare with naturally "thick" wild hoof sole). Note that, as in the wild, the degree of solar concavity varies considerably from horse to horse, depending on the conformation of the specific hoof.

8   **White Line** — use the hoof knife in light slicing motions from left to right (if you're right-handed, reverse if left-handed) until you can see the white line. Lower the toe wall down just above the white line (Figure 8-5), but go no lower or you could quick the sole.

9   **Toe Wall** — if you trim at four week intervals, you can probably do all your work at the toe with a rasp. Keep toe wall under 3½ inches long if possible (Chapter 10). If right-handed and trimming the horse's left hooves, try rasping forward on a diagonal from outside heel-buttress to the inside toe wall, and, from the outside toe wall backward towards the inside heel-buttress; reverse for right hooves. The rasp should not make contact with the concaved sole (Figure 8-5). Finish toe wall by rounding off outer edge with the mustang roll.

Don't be bashful — if you don't fit under the horse, kneel beside him and you can still do a good job.

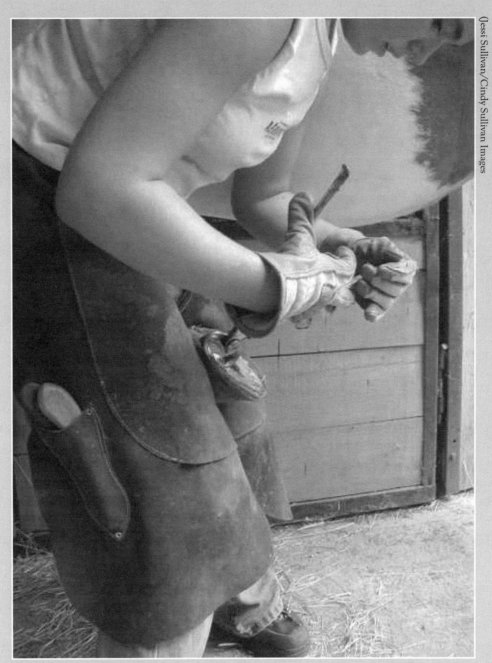

14 year-old Jessi Sullivan executes quintessential form as she nips the outer wall.

(Continued from page 117)
Still other hooves had hoof walls that were entirely active on one side of the capsule, but only partially active (the heel-buttress) on the opposing side. In all hooves, I should point out, both heel-buttresses were found to have active contact with the ground.*

Before I explain how to trim the hooves relative to active and passive wear, I want to say that it would be a misperception to think that the horse is walking around on a "3-Point" (or 4-Pt., or whatever the case) "base" of support. The horse uses its entire hoof base—including the sole and frog—to support itself, although some points definitely bear weight more than others, at least on a flat, relatively firm stretch of ground. Further, I do not believe that the horn structure of the quarters, or any segment of the outer wall exhibiting passive wear, is inherently weaker or is any less capable of absorbing compressional or concussional shock than the active points.

In all likelihood, the active points are biomechanical responses to specific conformation and locomotive peculiarities of the individual horse. Horses, in other words, wear their hooves in diverse patterns no differently than we wear our own shoes (or bare feet). Accordingly, I don't consider it too much of a stretch to suggest that the equine "toe and heel-buttresses" are tantamount to the "ball and heel" of our own species' foot. In this interpretation, the heels (joined by the passive quarters, the bars, and the concaved sole, frog, and heel-bulbs) are involved principally with "feeling" the ground during the landing phase, and absorbing enough body weight at the onset of the hoof's support phase to absorb concussional shock. Very soon after, the toe picks up the majority of body weight during the hoof's middle and late period support phase.* All in accordance with the hoof mechanism.

My recommendations for trimming the hoof wall for natural active/passive wear are as follows:

First, trim all excessive horn from the hoof wall, consistent with the previous guidelines in Figures 8-1 and 8-2.

Second, using your rasp, level the hoof wall such that both heel-buttresses and all or part of the toe wall align in a single plane. If both quarters and one side of the toe wall fall below the plane, go with it. If only one quarter and half the toe wall are passive, then go with that. In other words, if any part of the hoof wall forward of the heel-buttresses is "passive," then that is your starting point. On the other hand, if the entire hoof wall levels into a single plane (called the "shoer's trim"), then go with that. The hoof wall has simply lost its signature from the adverse effects of shoeing and needs the barefoot experience to bring its active-passive wear patterns to the surface. Give the hooves time.

Test your trim by holding the hoof in your hand and sighting it from behind: the heel-buttresses and toe wall should align in a single plane. One or both quarters should lie in the same plane or fall below it (i.e., become "passive"). I show you how to do this with a number of hooves in my companion video, so review those sequences now. In no instance should the quarters rise above the plane — typical in shod horses with "rolled toes." At least one segment of the toe wall should protrude actively above the quarters — or the hoof is not trimmed properly.

HOOF WALL: LENGTH X DURABILITY

Needless to say, having a tough hoof wall to work with is of paramount importance. A weak hoof wall threatens to give out and invert its active relationship to the naturally passive sole, frog, and heel-bulbs, thereby impeding the hoof mechanism.

The wild horse hoof model demonstrates unequivocally that the best way to sustain a tough, durable hoof wall is to keep it short. Actually we want the hoof wall *short* for a variety of interrelated reasons. A long hoof wall can snag and split more easily. It can impede the mechanism and delay breakover, thereby obstructing locomotive efficiency. Long toe walls stress and inflame the support lamina and the laminar corium, predisposing the horse to *laminitis* (I will discuss this at length

*This makes sense in view of the Swedish study cited earlier, which found that both heel-buttresses, flexing together, initiate the first phase of the hoof mechanism.

*Once more, the Swedish study.

in Chapter 16). Long heels pressurize the navicular bone, the navicular bursa, and the deep digital flexor tendon, and indirectly clamp off blood flow into the sub-coriums, the hoof now at risk of *navicular syndrome* (also discussed in Chapter 16).

A short hoof, in contrast, tamps efficiently against the ground, hardening off the hoof wall, sole, and frog, at the same time facilitating the mechanism and optimal breakover. A short hoof thus is a more durable one.

So, the first question obviously is "how short" do we want to trim the hoof wall? My studies of wild horses and years of personal experience provide specific answers. As a rule, I start by reducing the toe of the hoof wall down to 3¼ to 3½ inches. Most hooves, laminitic hooves being the principal exception in some instances, will, regardless of the horse's breed, including Draft horses as well as the ass and hybrid mule (Chapter 11), shorten to that length range readily. Of course, I wouldn't trim the toe that short if it meant that the sole behind the toe must be thinned so excessively as to render the hoof tender or "quicked". If I may speak with candor, intentional quicking, bleeding, or rendering the sole unnaturally thin or soft are inhumane procedures that violate the principles and ethics of natural hoof care.

As explained in Figure 8-1, begin nipping or rasping at the toe and work back to the heel-buttresses. Refer to Figure 8-4 to help gauge your depth in terms of the hoof's relative concavity (discussed in next section). Preferably too, review the trimming sequences in my companion video which visually demonstrate this reduction. I customarily leave a base of wall one-sixteenth to one-eighth inch above the adjacent white line and sole. This assures that the sole, barring incompetence, will not be quicked and will remain ensconced passively within the protective periphery of the hoof wall as nature intended.

RELATIVE CONCAVITY

A third dimension of much importance in natural trimming concerns the hoof's *relative concavity*. As explained in Chapter 2, this defines the relative position of the hoof wall, the white line, the sole and frog to each other in the hoof's vaulted solar dome.

Natural relative concavity, based on the

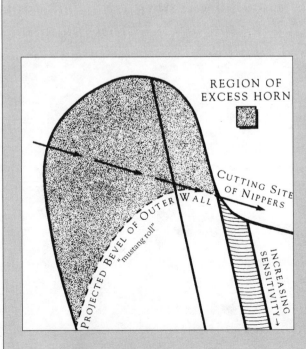

REGION OF EXCESS HORN

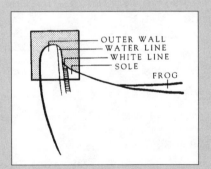

FIGURE 8-4

RELATIVE CONCAVITY

We want to work the outer wall (grayed area) to form the mustang roll with the rasp. As shown, keep the white line and sole passive. Don't gouge the sole to do this; let natural wear lower the sole if possible. Leave a little extra outer wall if necessary to sustain the hoof's natural relative concavity.

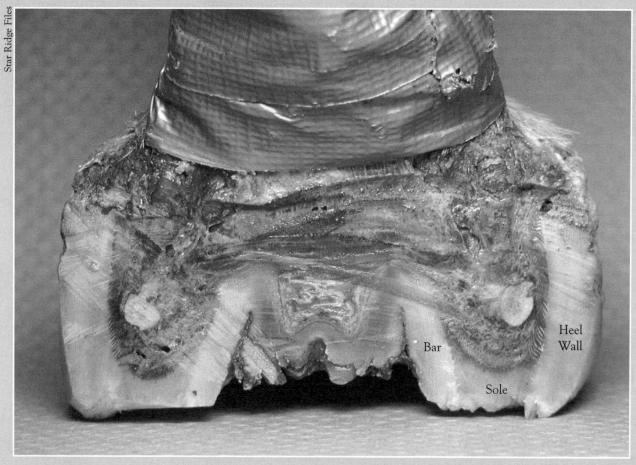

Bar

Heel
Wall

Sole

FIGURE 8-5

THE "SOLE" TRUTH

Cross-section of white wild horse hoof viewed from the rear. Note the thickness of the sole — ¼ inch — as thick as a horseshoe and about as hard! It is solid horn . . . not flaky or soft. It has been my observation that the thickened sole naturally develops without a corresponding increase in hoof length (e.g., toe length). Nor does the thick sole impair the hoof mechanism since its vaulted form is still molded after the arched solar corium from which it grows. For cross-sectional view of the sole at the toe, refer to Figure 2-11.

WHY THE "BARS"?

The same cross-section reveals another important characteristic of naturally shaped hooves — and another vital lesson from the wild: the importance of the bars. What are they and why are they there? Although not at all obvious when the hoof is looked at from below, it can be seen here that they are extensions of the hoof wall. They are technically part of the heel-buttress system. The bars in this white hoof are one inch long at this point; the corresponding outer wall at the quarters is 1½ inch long. Interestingly, if you add the two together, which totals 2½ inches, the sum equals the length of the toe wall of this hoof. What does this mean? Could it be that the sum of the wall length of the bars and quarters always equals the length of the toe? If so, then the bars may become increasingly longer as we approach the ends of the heel-buttresses — reflecting their contribution to weight bearing during the first phase of the mechanism. Thinning the sole at the bars, therefore, could weaken the brace effect on the bars by the heel-buttresses, in effect, enabling compressional forces to drive the bars up into the navicular pulley — causing navicular pain. On the other hand, removing the bars through aggressive trimming obviously removes an important cog in the weight bearing function of the heel-buttresses. The effect, a pathological one which I have seen in some "ersatz" natural trims, is to force the weakened buttresses apart (— forced "de-contraction" of the hoof, in other words). This sores the horse and, in what can only be viewed as inhumane trimming, obstructs the mechanism. The lesson from the wild? Don't remove what God and Nature put there for darn good reasons!

wild horse hoof model, can be stated as a generalized Principle (or the "Principle of Relative Concavity" as I think of it):

1. Each quarter will be level with or passive to the toe wall and heel-buttress on its own side.
2. Each bar will be passive to its own heel-buttress.
3. The white line will be at all times passive to its contiguous hoof wall.
4. The sole will be level with or passive to its contiguous white line.
5. The frog will be passive to the heel-buttresses, bars and sole, except around the point-of-frog, where frog and sole may or may not be level with each other.

As long as the hoof's natural gradations of concavity are sustained, the mechanism is rendered most efficient and the bare hoof is best prepared to withstand the ultimate test of high performance barefootedness.

SOLE

Avoid excessive thinning of the sole after roughing out the hoof (Figure 8-1). We want the sole to thicken, harden off, and form its own concavity as much as possible from natural wear. To give you an idea of how thick that sole is in the naturally worn hooves of wild horses, take a look at Figure 8-5.

When trimming the sole, follow the "active" and "passive" convolutions of the outer wall, staying even with or just below the white line if possible without quicking the sole or removing desirable calloused horn. You've trimmed too much if the sole becomes soft and moist, yields (gives) to thumb pressures, or bleeds.

What if you quick the sole? Well, it's not the end of the world — it simply means you've been too aggressive, that you've removed too much horn. Regrettably, quicking comes with learning, but it is much less likely to occur if

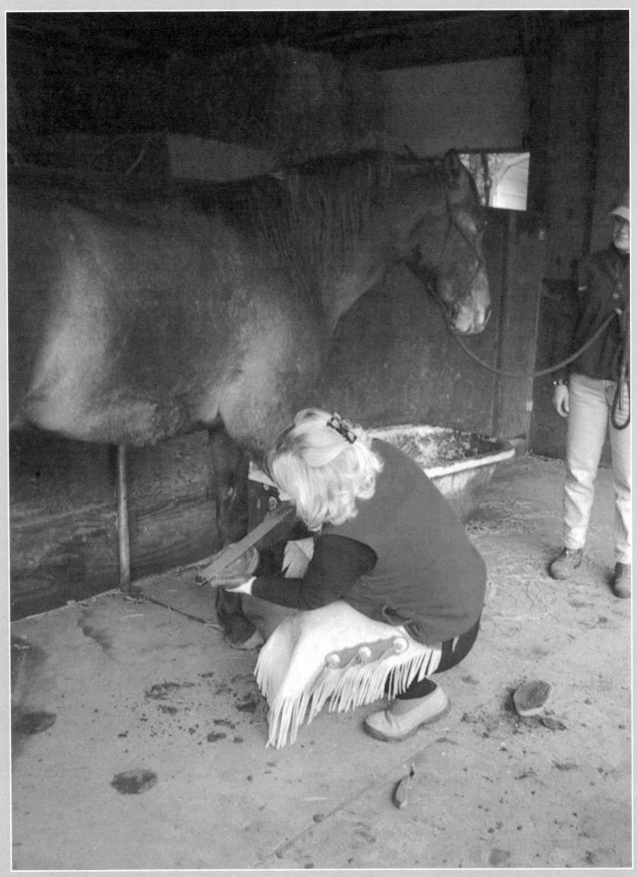

Debbie Dutra/Star Ridge Files

(Continued from page 125)

you follow the principle of relative concavity. It is also much more likely in close trimming for conventional horseshoeing, fortunately, a non-issue in this *Guide*. I will add that some of the ersatz "natural trims" in vogue now purport that "bleeding" of the sole and/or ablative resections of the bars is necessary for healing contracted hooves. This is nonsense. Hooves need not be "close trimmed" to the bloodline to de-contract them (discussed in detail in Chapter 16).

If you do quick the sole, consider calling in a vet if there is reason to believe that a tetanus shot is warranted; otherwise, clean the wound with propolis tincture (see Resources) and leave it alone. Within hours, new epidermal horn will commence to layer in, forming a natural band-aid. And in days the hoof should be well along in its healing.

"MUSTANG ROLL"

To finish our work at the bottom of the hoof, we want to impart a turn to the bearing surfaces (both active and passive) of the hoof wall, just like those wild horse hooves in Figure 2-1.

Step 1. To begin mustang roll, use the rough side of the hoof rasp with the hoof secured between your legs. Simply rasp away at the outer edge of the hoof wall to round it off. Don't include the white line in this rasping — stay a full ¼ inch outside of it if possible, depending how thick your horse's hoof walls are.

The action of the rasp is downward at an angle of approximately 45°; the action is in one direction, in other words, not up and down, or back and forth as though playing a violin. This puts the sharp edges of the tines or "teeth" of the rasp against the horn grain.

The teeth are mini-chisels designed to gouge evenly into the horn, rather than abrade it back-and-forth like sandpaper.

I advise strongly that, when first forming the mustang roll, be fastidious about keeping the outer wall slightly above the white line and sole (Figure 8-4), or, at most, even with them. This assures that the hoof wall, rather than the sole, will endure the main compressional forces during support.

Recall again from the wild horse hoof in Figure 1-1 that the "slant" of the turn is rounded rather than flat, like the cutting edge of a chisel. So you want to "round" off the edges. Which will require some practice to achieve a professional's "touch." This rounded edge — hence the name mustang "roll" — aids in the prevention of wall ravel, a sharp edge being at risk of splintering. Ravel is also minimized by the presence of keritinized intertubular horn which "glues" together the mass of horn tubules composing the hoof wall. When the hoof is properly balanced (Chapter 10), the tubules are aligned in the direction of impact, and the ends of the tubular horn are pressed against the ground — tamping them into a rock hard mass. In this case, a protective hard and rounded edge.

I personally find it cumbersome if not impossible to complete the mustang roll while working the hoof from the bottom (i.e., in my lap). For this reason I complete the roll with the hoof up on the hoof stand where I can wield my tools freely to do the job. Let's move to the next chapter then to complete the mustang roll and also finish the upper reaches of the outer wall that may need attention. We're almost done!

The author deep in concentration.

CHAPTER NINE

SHAPING THE OUTER WALL

"Once the wall has been leveled, its outer edge should be well-rounded. The wall should have a smooth curve to it; any sharp edges might cause it to split away, particularly at the quarters. It also makes the trim job last longer and such trimming stimulates natural wear." Emery, Miller, and Van Hoosen, Horseshoeing Theory and Hoof Care

With the bottom of the hoof now finished, it's time to move on to the outer wall. This phase of the trimming takes place on the hoof stand. We're now faced with less than a minute more of actual work!

Finishing the outer wall means rasping away flares and bulges in the hoof wall, in effect simulating natural wear. If you refer back to any of the photographs of wild horse hooves in Chapter 2, you'll see that the outer walls of their hooves are very "straight", neither concave, convex, or "bulging" with areas of excessive growth. Accordingly, using our rasps, we want to simulate natural wear as part of natural trimming.

Let's go ahead and begin that work now, beginning with introducing your horse to the all important hoof stand (facing page, see also Resources), the "work center" for natural hoof care practitioners.

SET HOOF ON GRIP HEAD OF HOOF STAND

Once more, balance the horse on his "diagonal." Then put the hoof you're going to start with on the hoof stand. I advise setting the grip head at or above knee level — horses, it may come as a surprise, seem more comfortable when the hoof is positioned at this height. It's also a whole lot easier on one's back. Many horses, I've also observed, seem to enjoy (or are at least very tolerant of) putting their hooves upon the stand. Few will offer to give you trouble once they understand what you want of them.

To put the hoof on the grip head, try placing the hoof first on your knee and positioning your knee where the horse seems most balanced and comfortable. Then substitute the hoof stand in place of your knee. Set the grip head against the sole forward of the point-of-

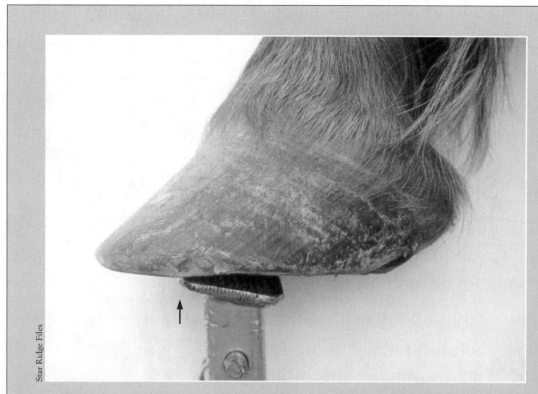

FIGURE 9-1

USING THE "HOOF GRIP"

Position hoof upon grip head of hoof stand. Arrow points to active point of contact between grip head and tough toe sole just forward of point-of-frog. Avoid placing frog over grip head as this may cause tenderness.

frog, as shown in Figure 9-1. Please refer also to my companion video (see Resources) for many live action sequences showing how I put front and hind hooves on the hoof stand.

REMOVE GROWTH IRREGULARITIES FROM OUTER WALL

Once your horse becomes accustomed to having his foot placed on the hoof stand, check the outer wall for any unnatural growth irregularities. This would include bulges, flares, unnatural wall angles, or any other irregular growth salient which compromises the natural conformation and functioning of the hoof. These generally result from insufficient natural wear of the outer wall, unnatural trimming practices, and certain lamenesses such as laminitis. They are important to remedy since unnatural growth, in addition to impacting hoof balance, the gaits, and the general comfort of the horse, also influences new growth. In this respect, working the outer wall is tantamount to "aiming" the hoof and setting the stage for an improved foundation for the horse to move upon.

Gross protuberances, such as flares and "seedy" (i.e., founder) toes, can be removed or worked back gradually with the nippers, followed by concentrated strokes with the coarse side of the rasp. The entire hoof wall is first surveyed from below and the growth irregularity identified (Figure 9-2a). Nip or rasp back

Dressing the outer wall in Colorado (Lisa Simons)

(*Overleaf*) Figures 9-2 and 9-3

FIGURE 9-2

REMOVING WALL FLARE

WORKING IN THE VOLAR VIEW

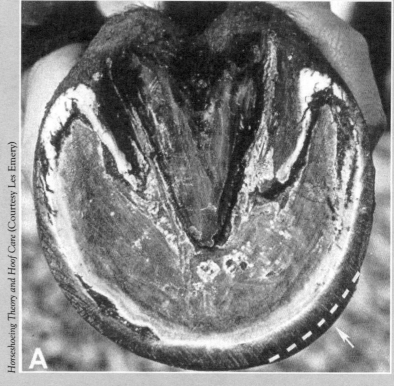

Figure 9-2a Flare identified.

Figure 9-2b Flare removed.

FIGURE 9-3

REMOVING WALL FLARE

WORKING THE OUTER WALL

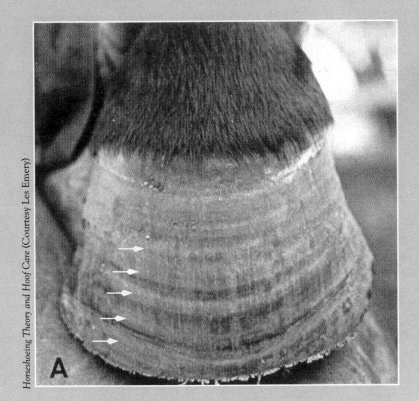

Horseshoeing Theory and Hoof Care (Courtesy Les Emery)

Figure 9-3a Ripples identified.

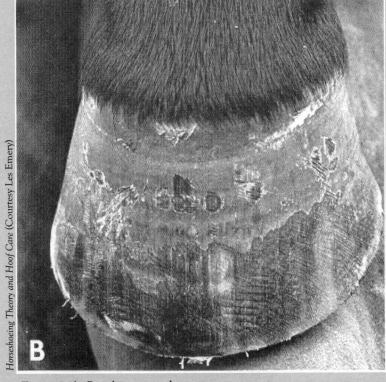

Horseshoeing Theory and Hoof Care (Courtesy Les Emery)

Figure 9-3b Ripples removed.

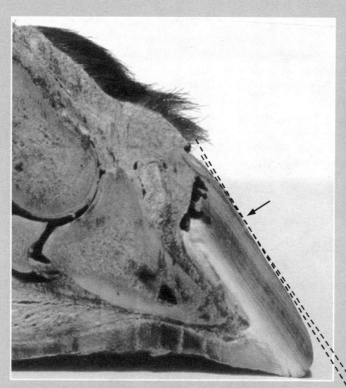

FIGURE 9-4

WEAR OF HOOF WALL

In this wild hoof cross-section, the impact of natural wear on the outer wall is evident. Line "a" is the hoof's actual angle of growth. Line "b" is the "angle of wear." The arrow marks the approximate point at which the outer wall begins to significantly wear; clearly, two thirds of the outer wall is abraded from natural wear.

a

b

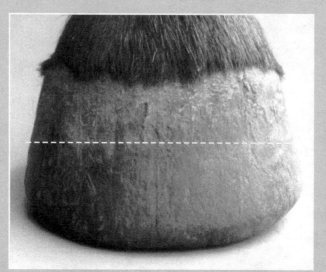

FIGURE 9-5

WEAR OF HOOF WALL (PERIOPLE)

Front view of a wild horse hoof showing abrasion of periople. Even in the wild, where horse's hooves undergo extraordinary wear, the upper one third of the outer wall (indicated by dashed line) has still retained much of its perioplic skin. The lower two thirds is abraded clean of all periople; the same two thirds of the outer wall is also worn thinner than the upper one third (compare with Figure 9-4).

(Continued from page 130)

the salient (Figure 9-2b). Figure 9-3a,b shows how to remove outer wall "ripples" using the rasp.

Clearly, our objective is to render approximately the same wall thickness to all stretches (toe, quarters, heels) of the outer wall. Gauge this thickness from the outer edge of the mustang roll to the outer perimeter of the white line. In other words, the quarters should be as thick as the toe wall, and as thick as the heels, and vice versa.

Many amateur and professional farriers, regrettably reinforced by many farriery and veterinary texts whose authors are unaware of genuinely naturally shaped hooves, believe that the thickness of the hoof wall at the quarters is naturally thinner than at the toe wall. However, in the thousand or so wild horse hooves I have examined at arm's length, I've not found this to be the case at all. The thickness is the same. The photograph of the wild horse hoof (secured by a rope) at the beginning of Chapter 2 clearly shows this. For me, this is ample justification to abrade the outer wall, either all at once if possible, or gradually in multiple trim-

ming sessions (most common), until such time that all unnatural growth irregularities are removed.

Another objection one commonly hears in conventional hoof care circles is that we shouldn't be rasping or "thinning" the outer wall at all. That this removes the periople, causing the hoof not only to dehydrate, but to weaken from the loss of horn — leading purportedly to wall ravel. Again, evidence from our wild horses — and, ever important, practical experience — proves that neither concern is justified.

Figure 9-4 shows a typical wild hoof in cross-section. Line "a" represents the hoof's true angle-of-growth. Line "b" is the actual wear line of the lower hoof wall. Nearly two thirds of the lower outer wall — the area between the intersecting lines — has been lost to natural wear! Moreover, the absence of periopic horn in the same general wear area, ostensibly ushered out by natural wear, seems inevitable (Figure 9-5). With tens of thousands of sound wild horses with hooves worn just like these — thinned outer walls with no periople — clearly it is a non-issue.

Rolling the toe in Florida (Steve Dick)

Steve Dick/Star Ridge Files

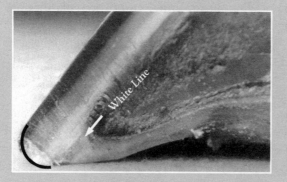

FIGURE 9-6

MUSTANG ROLL: THE RIGHT ROLL

The mustang roll outlined on the cross-section of a wild horse hoof biospecimen. (*Left*) This is the natural way to do it: minimal hoof wall is removed, the outer wall is turned to prevent ravel, and the sole is passive. White arrow marks position of white line.

The outer wall is "banked"—also called "snubbing" the toe—and thinned backed to the white line. This weakens the hoof wall and leaves too little to support descending body weight. I've never seen this in the wild.

The outer wall is cut back too far. The sole now endures descending body weight actively, the hoof wall passively. I've never seen this in the wild either.

I do not, however, recommend "banking" or "snubbing" the outer wall, "squaring" or "close cutting" the toe, all common farrier practices that, in my estimation, can weaken and harm the hoof wall (Figure 9-6). The natural alternative is the mustang roll.

FINISH MUSTANG ROLL

With the lower two thirds of the outer wall evened out by judicious use of the rasp, it's now time to finish the mustang roll.

Use the fine side of the farrier's rasp to do this work. The action of the rasp is now a sideways "back-and-forth" action, like you were using sand paper, following the along entire circumference of the outer wall from the toe to

(Continued on page 138)

Matt Worley diligently dressing the outer wall in Georgia

SHAPING THE OUTER WALL

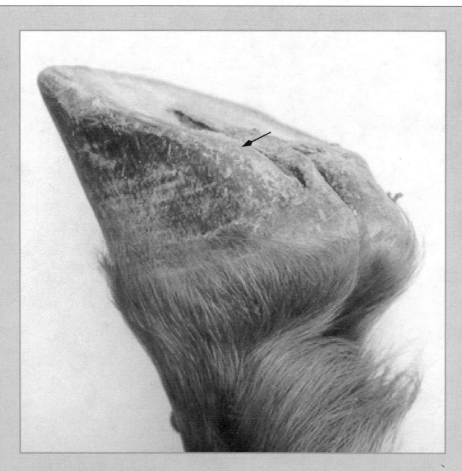

Figure 9-7 MUSTANG ROLL

Render the mustang roll everywhere around the hoof wall, including the heel-buttresses as shown here. This will help build stronger and more massive buttresses — a key signature of naturally shaped hooves.

(Continued from page 136)

each heel-buttress (Figure 9-7). Figure 9-8 shows the direction of the rasp. Refer also to Figure 9-9 for further suggestions on how to balance your horse, secure his foot both on and off the hoof stand, and wield your tools efficiently while doing the mustang roll.

This action really rounds and smoothes the otherwise sharp turn of the outer wall. I do this work fairly fast. I may hold the rasp in one hand, while securing the hoof on the grip head with the other, as I put pressure on the turn of the outer wall. Now, remove your gloves and feel the finish of the mustang roll. It should *look* and *feel* smooth and well-rounded — no

jagged edges! — with a radius of at least one quarter inch.

Study the trimming sequences in my companion video to see how I do the mustang roll. Refer too to Figure 9-6 to see the roll in cross-section. Also, I mentioned above the practices of snubbing and backing up the hoof wall. Since these can adversely impact the mustang roll, I've included some comparative discussions and diagrams to help you avoid doing them inadvertently.

ABRADE AND POLISH THE OUTER WALL
TO SIMULATE NATURAL WEAR
With all major growth irregularities in the

(Continued on page 142)

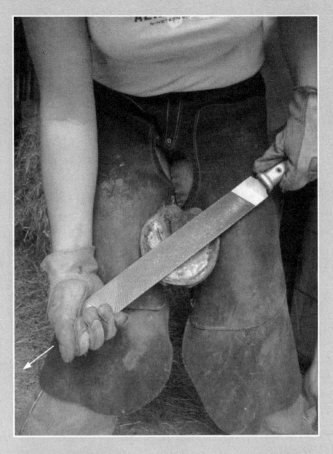

FIGURE 9-8

MUSTANG ROLL

INITIATING WITH RASP

Jessi Sullivan lays rasp to hoof, first to her right (*top*), then the left — initiating the mustang roll.

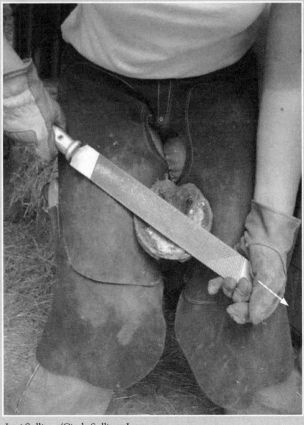

Jessi Sullivan/Cindy Sullivan Images

(Over) Figures 9-9

FIGURE 9-9

DOING THE MUSTANG ROLL

WIELDING YOUR RASP

Right front on stand: work the outside of hoof. I've got my left foot pressed down on leg of stand while my left thigh, arm, and chest help secure and balance the horse's foot.

Right front on stand: work the inside of hoof from same position as for left front hoof. My arms are free to work — I'm done in a minute. Repeat with left front hoof.

There are several ways to approach the hind hooves. Sometimes I'll do the roll on the stand, as seen on the facing page of this chapter's heading, I am working the hoof from the outside. All the horse's weight is on the stand — so the job is easy. Note that I've got the stand secured with my left boot.

In some instances, where space is "tight" because of the horse's size, I actually find it easier to do the hind hooves right on my knee (*left*). It's not hard if the horse is balanced on the diagonal. Here, I'm working the outside toe and outside quarter of the right hind hoof from the inside, that is, kneeling between the horse's leg and torso. Reverse for the left hind hoof.

Now I'm working the toe wall and inside quarter while supporting the horse's hoof on my left rather than my right knee as above. The hoof has simply swiveled from knee to knee and never touches the ground, which is demonstrated on my companion trim video.

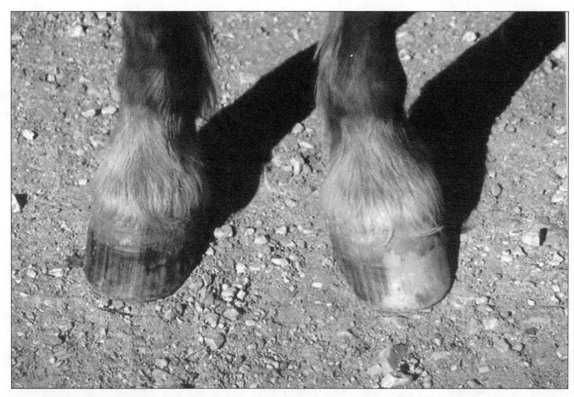

Figure 9-10 White and black hind hooves polished and ready to take on any gravel road or back country trail they might encounter. (Jaime Jackson/SRP Files)

(Continued from page 138)
outer wall now trimmed back, and the final turn of the mustang roll complete, I recommend lightly "roughing up" the entire lower stretches of the outer wall below the perioplic horn "zone" (upper one third of the outer wall) to simulate natural wear.

Use the fine side of the rasp, working it downward at a slant from the bottom edge of the perioplic horn to the turn of the mustang roll. Consider also polishing the outer wall further by abrading it with sandpaper. I liken this step to having your teeth cleaned and polished by the dentist! Polish the hoof from toe to heel-buttress. The neat, handsome hooves seen in Figures 9-10 and 9-11, the work of myself and

several of the natural hoof care practitioners featured in Chapter 17, suggest a standard you should work towards.

SUMMARY

As this chapter completes the trimming guidelines, you can see by now that performing a natural trim isn't really that hard to do. The real issues are whether or not you know what you're doing, that you are in relatively good shape to do the job, and that you can manage your tools effectively and efficiently. Beyond these prerequisites, it's a 20 to 30 minute job for all four hooves.

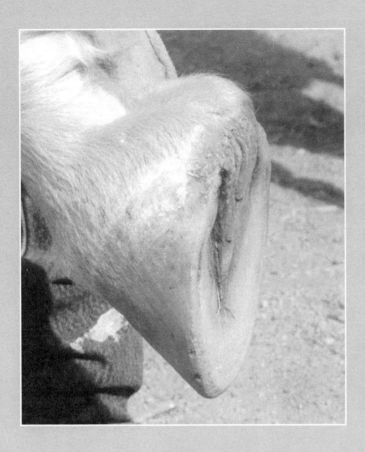

FIGURE 9-11

MUSTANG ROLLS

THE LAST STEP

Immaculately finished hooves with mustang rolls by (*top*) Kenny and Lisa (Ross) Williams and (*below*) Pete Ramey.

Sighting a hind hoof.

CHAPTER TEN

ASSESSING YOUR WORK

for HOOF BALANCE

"The feet should first be tested by examining the horn; thick horn is a much better mark of good feet than thin. Again, one should not fail to note whether the hoofs at toe and heel come up high or lie low. High ones keep what is called the frog well off the ground . . . ." Xenophon, Art of Horsemanship (c. 450 BC)

What do we mean when we say that a hoof is naturally balanced?

A balanced hoof is one whose size, shape, and proportion correspond precisely to its own unique, natural conformation.

Studies of wild horse hooves provide us with vital evidence of what this means exactly. For example, their hooves provide us with specific information about natural toe lengths, toe angles, front and hind hoof shapes, and how the hoof's angle-of-growth intersects the ground. Hoof balance must be evaluated through a knowledgeable assessment of these and other factors.

Natural hoof care practitioners gauge hoof balance in a combination of ways:

They measure the hoof along its various growth axes, such as toe length, hoof width, and hoof length, in order to ascertain the *size* of the hoof. They measure the angle of the hoof wall, for example, toe angle, to determine *proportion*, that is, how the hoof's angle-of-growth intersects the ground bearing surface or "volar plane" of the hoof wall. They measure the ground bearing width of the entire hoof wall ("Hoof Width") versus its length ("Hoof Length") to contrast front and hind hoof *shapes*.

After measuring and studying the shape of the hoof, natural hoof care practitioners evaluate this information relative to known data for wild horse hooves, and also relative to their personal experience with trimming many domestic horses. Generally, trimmed hooves are said to be naturally balanced when they meet the criteria summarized in Figure 10-1. Let's

FIGURE 10-1

BALANCED HOOVES

ASSESSING YOUR TRIM JOB

HOOF BALANCE CRITERIA		DESCRIPTION
1	Data versus wild hoof standard	The measurement data for the hoof falls within the known statistical ranges for wild horse hooves, our standard for natural hoof state.
2	Angle-of-growth	The outer wall's angle-of-growth aligns at approximately 90 degrees to the ground when the hoof is viewed from the front.
3	Active wear	The hoof wall has at least 3 active points of support, including both heel buttresses.
4	Frog pressure	There is passive frog pressure.
5	Hind versus front toe angles	Hind toe angles are greater than front toe angles.
6	Front versus hind hoof size	Hind hooves are not larger than the front hooves.
7	Sorefootedness and natural trim	The horse is not foot sore following the trim.
8	Natural trims and interference	The horse experiences no hoof or limb interference following the trim.
9	Measurement consistency	The measurement data for the hoof does not change significantly from one trim session to the next.

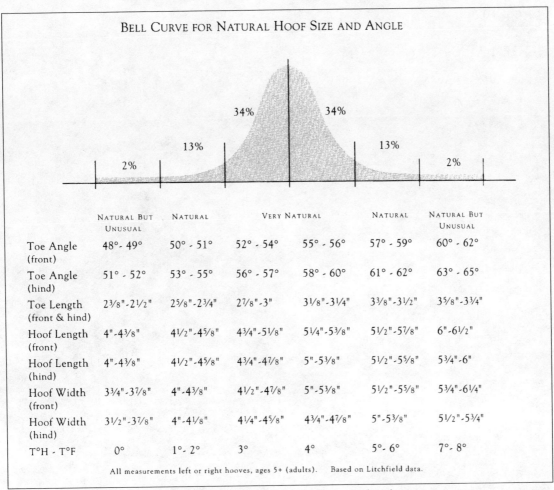

BELL CURVE FOR NATURAL HOOF SIZE AND ANGLE

	NATURAL BUT UNUSUAL	NATURAL	VERY NATURAL		NATURAL	NATURAL BUT UNUSUAL
Toe Angle (front)	48° - 49°	50° - 51°	52° - 54°	55° - 56°	57° - 59°	60° - 62°
Toe Angle (hind)	51° - 52°	53° - 55°	56° - 57°	58° - 60°	61° - 62°	63° - 65°
Toe Length (front & hind)	2⅜"-2½"	2⅝"-2¾"	2⅞"-3"	3⅛"-3¼"	3⅜"-3½"	3⅝"-3¾"
Hoof Length (front)	4"-4⅜"	4½"-4⅝"	4¾"-5⅛"	5¼"-5⅜"	5½"-5⅞"	6"-6½"
Hoof Length (hind)	4"-4⅜"	4½"-4⅝"	4¾"-4⅞"	5"-5⅜"	5½"-5⅝"	5¾"-6"
Hoof Width (front)	3¾"-3⅞"	4"-4⅜"	4½"-4⅞"	5"-5⅜"	5½"-5⅝"	5¾"-6¼"
Hoof Width (hind)	3½"-3⅞"	4"-4⅛"	4¼"-4⅝"	4¾"-4⅞"	5"-5⅜"	5½"-5¾"
T°H - T°F	0°	1° - 2°	3°	4°	5° - 6°	7° - 8°

All measurements left or right hooves, ages 5+ (adults).   Based on Litchfield data.

Figure 10-2 Wild horse hoof data. (*The Natural Horse*/1992/Jaime Jackson)

discuss these now:

1. THE MEASUREMENT DATA FOR THE HOOF FALLS WITHIN THE KNOWN STATISTICAL RANGES FOR WILD HORSE HOOVES.

What this means is that after you've trimmed your horse, and measured his hooves carefully, each of his measurements will fit into the ranges for specific measurement categories determined for wild horse hooves. This comparative data has been published in its entirety in my book, *The Natural Horse* (see Resources). Figure 10-2 is copied here for your quick reference. Now, let's explain what these measurement criteria are so that you can assess your own trim job for hoof balance.

The measurement categories natural hoof care practitioners use are Toe Length, Toe Angle, Hoof Width, and Hoof Length. Figure 10-3 illustrates how to take these specific measurements. Go ahead and measure your own horse's feet as shown and then compare your results with the ranges given in Figure 10-2. [Note: the data does not apply to foals; young horses still maturing (Figure 10-6); ponies, donkeys, or draft breeds (see

(Continued on page 150)

(Overleaf) Figures 10-3

FIGURE 10-3

HOOF BALANCE

TAKING MEASUREMENTS

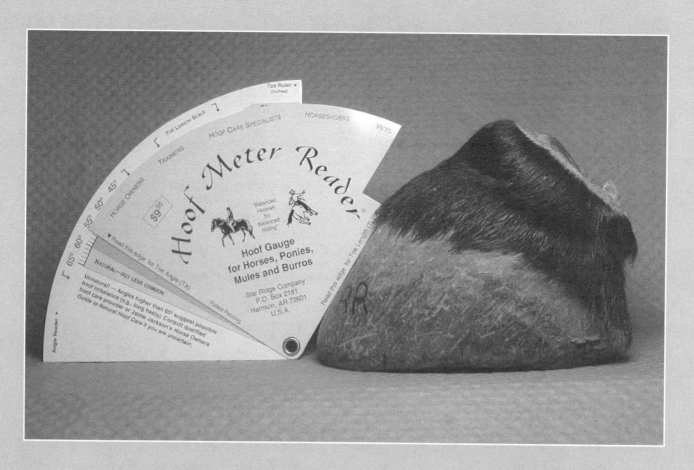

TOE LENGTH (TL) AND TOE ANGLE (T°)

I have invented a very simple and inexpensive gauge for measuring these two very important dimensions of the hoof. See the Resources section for ordering the "Hoof Meter Reader". Follow the instructions closely that come with the gauge. Toe Angle is recorded in degrees, Toe Length in inches. The T° for this wild horse right hind hoof is 56 degrees. Record your data at each trimming section into a notebook or use the "Record Keeper" also available through the Resources section. Incidentally, these measurements are also important when fitting horse boots (Chapter 14).

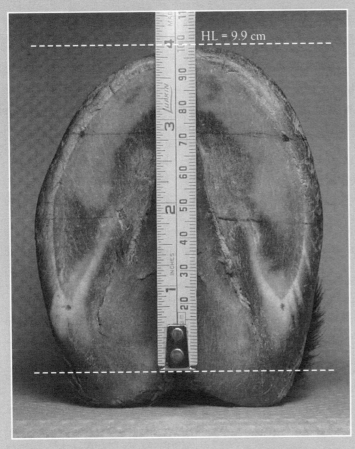

HL = 9.9 cm

HOOF LENGTH

"Hoof Length" is a measurement of the *ground bearing surface* of the hoof wall extending from the tip of the toe to the end of the heel-buttresses. Select the heel-buttress which is furthest to the rear of the hoof (often they are not symmetrically located across the centerline of the hoof). You want to identify the most posterior point of active ground contact. If it helps, mark this point with an indelible marker (I've used a dotted line here to demonstrate where I would have marked this hoof). This measurement is also important for booting horses. I advise using metric equivalents for this purpose.

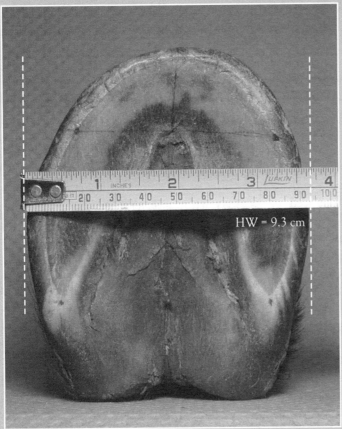

HW = 9.3 cm

HOOF WIDTH

"Hoof Width" is the widest expanse of the hoof. Normally this is across the quarters. Use a metric tape for this measurment. You can measure in inches but metric is preferable if you are going to boot your horse.

(Continued from page 147)

Chapter 11)]. If your measurements fall outside the ranges given, I recommend either re-evaluating your work and re-trimming your horse, or solicit the services of a professional natural hoof care practitioner and have that person show you how to trim your horse correctly.

2. THE OUTER WALL'S ANGLE-OF-GROWTH ALIGNS AT APPROXIMATELY 90 DEGREES TO THE GROUND WHEN THE HOOF IS VIEWED FROM THE FRONT.

A balanced hoof does not sit on the ground in a "lop-sided" configuration. Indeed, the direction of growth of the outer wall is naturally aligned (relative to the ground) so as to offset potentially damaging concussional forces (trauma emanating from the ground) rippling upward into the hoof at impact. At the same time the wall simultaneously endures powerful compressional or weight loading forces.

Again, wild horse hooves speak very clearly to us about what that natural alignment is. Go ahead and review Figure 2-14. The idea behind natural trimming of course is to simply encourage these normal and natural wall growth patterns. When this is done, the hoof will "balance" itself. A word of warning, however: it has been my observation that the criteria here for natural hoof balance may conflict with some of the arbitrary farriery and veterinary standards for purportedly balanced hooves. Most horse owners at one point or another become familiar with them, so they are worth discussing here.

For example, some hoof care practitioners ascribe "balance" relative to the slope of the hairline above the outer wall, rather than the hoof wall itself; they may attempt to trim the hoof wall to influence the position of the hairline, even if this means lengthening or shortening the outer wall in contraposition to natural hoof balance.

Others may define hoof balance relative

to how the toe wall aligns with the slope of the pastern or with the vertical axis of the legs below the knee joints, trimming accordingly to make sure they are one and the same.

Equally common, some practitioners will base their decisions on how the hoof lands on the ground, or takes off following support, or how the hoof itself travels through the air between support phases. They may trim (and shoe) the hoof so that it breaks over a particular way, or so that it doesn't "wing" or "paddle" (or in some instances, so that it does!), or so that the heels land first (or not first!), or that both sides of the hoof impact or depart the ground simultaneously. There are many, perhaps countless, criteria that influence the trimming of the capsule, each depending on how the practitioner believes the hoof should move and support the horse's weight.

But so far as "natural balance" is concerned, the hoof's angle-of-growth (viewed from the front, as in Figure 2-14) is very specific. How the hoof lands, supports the horse's weight, leaves the ground, or flies through the air, are certainly dynamic influences that shape the hoof capsule. But none is a hallmark of hoof balance per se, rather they are biomechanical variations of balanced motion. The shape and growth patterns of the capsule, in contrast, are legible fingerprints of the balanced hoof.

3. THE HOOF WALL HAS AT LEAST 3 ACTIVE POINTS OF SUPPORT, INCLUDING BOTH HEEL BUTTRESSES.

Very closely related to the hoof's angle-of-growth is the hoof wall's "active and passive" support points. These were discussed in Chapters 2 (theory) and 8 (practice). Briefly, for a hoof to balance, both heel-buttresses and at least one other point forward of the quarters must always endure active contact with the ground.

The precise position and extent of these

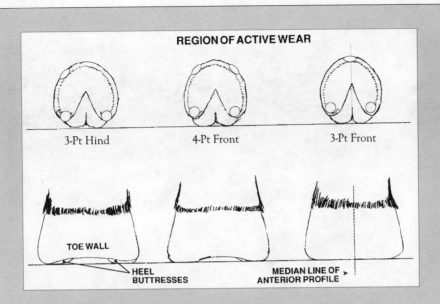

REGION OF ACTIVE WEAR

3-Pt Hind   4-Pt Front   3-Pt Front

TOE WALL

HEEL BUTTRESSES   MEDIAN LINE OF ANTERIOR PROFILE

Figure 10-4   ACTIVE & PASSIVE WEAR

(*Top*) Examples of active/passive wear patterns. (*Bottom*) No matter how hooves are worn across their bearing surfaces, they all rest balanced upon the flat ground in essentially the same way. (*The Natural Horse*/1992/Jaime Jackson)

active wear points along the hoof wall is virtually impossible to predict in advance of trimming a hoof naturally the first time — given our current body of knowledge and research. Figure 10-4 gives but three examples of what are endless possibilities (including all points of the hoof wall enduring active contact). As noted too in the illustration, regardless of the position or extent of the active wear points, the criteria for the balanced outer wall's angle-of-growth (#2) is not compromised.

Natural hoof care practitioners astutely observe subtle changes in the bearing surface of the hoof wall resulting from natural wear and previous trims to determine which points appear to be active and which recessions seem to be passive. The closer the trim intervals, the more natural the horse's living conditions and opportunity to move naturally on his bare feet, and the greater the experience of the practitioner, the easier it will be to coax into

prominence these fascinating convolutions of the naturally shaped hoof wall.

Horse owners should be aware that conventional horseshoeing effectively eliminates all patterns of active/passive wear by virtue of the fact that the hoof wall must be leveled if the shoe is to be fastened securely to it. Moreover, the presence of the shoe precludes all natural wear, thereby rendering impossible the formation of natural active and passive support points.

It has also been my observation that some ersatz "natural" trimmers advocate ablation (tantamount to surgical removal) of one or both heel-buttresses to de-contract hooves. Others recommend buttress reductions so as to manipulate the support peculiarities of the capsule, and solely with an eye to subverting the natural flight biomechanics of the hoof and limbs. But in all such cases, none of which I advocate, the result is inevitably an aberration or obstruction of the natural gaits, and an invitation to lameness.

Figure 10-5 FROG PRESSURE

The frog endures passive contact with the ground
in a balanced, naturally trimmed hoof.

4. THERE IS PASSIVE FROG PRESSURE.

Consistent with the trimming guidelines in Chapter 8, the frog will fill the space between the heel-buttresses and, at most, passively make contact with the ground. Although much to-do has been made about the supposed importance of "active frog pressure" for healthy hooves (blood circulation and shock absorbency), the natural model clearly shows that the frog is a passive player in the hoof capsule, serving "actively" as a hinge between the heel-buttresses and as a key player in the mechanism.

Figure 10-5 shows a healthy, naturally trimmed hoof with passive frog pressure.

5. HIND TOE ANGLES ARE GREATER THAN FRONT TOE ANGLES.

The wild hoof model also demonstrates that hind toe angles are never less than front toe angles (Figure 10-1). The explanation for this lies in the biomechanical roles played by front and hind limbs (and hooves), a matter discussed at length in my book *The Natural Horse.**

Of course, this natural angle differential is subject to exceptions among domestic horses whose hooves are pathologically or excessively unnaturally shaped. In this case, I recommend approaching the matter strategically over a period of two, three, or more trim sessions. In time, and with diligence, angle issues will naturally resolve themselves without "forcing" the hooves through over-trimming.

**The Natural Horse,* p. 95.

These mustang "twins" from BLM rangelands in Colorado bring to mind an important lesson from the wild. Two horses with seemingly identical upper body and leg conformations, can have entirely different feet. Variation is a key signature of Nature and natural hoof care practitioners should respect this. Same size horse, different size feet, different toe angles, different capsule colors, different everything. Even different boot sizes!

6. HIND HOOVES ARE NOT LARGER THAN THE FRONT HOOVES.

This is another characteristic of naturally shaped hooves. The front hooves will tend to be wider and longer than the hinds. Once more, the difference is explained by the biomechanical roles of front versus hind feet. The narrower hind hoof and major joints of the upper hind leg and pelvis favor lateral thrust; the broader front hoof (with only one major joint of propulsion — the shoulder) performs more of a support function.

Hind hooves invariably become larger than their corresponding fronts as a result of unchecked wall flares and excessively long toes. This is easy to remedy, however, bearing in mind that front and hind toe lengths are virtually the same in wild horse populations. Most domestic horse hooves yield their excessive size readily in two or three trim sessions, resuming their natural correspondence in relative size and proportion from front to hind.

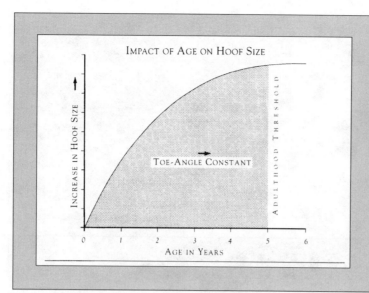

FIGURE 10-6

AGE VS. HOOF SIZE

Impact of age on hoof size. (Source: *The Natural Horse/*1992/ Jaime Jackson)

7. THE HORSE IS NOT FOOT SORE FOLLOWING THE TRIM.

It is a cardinal rule of genuine natural hoof care that the horse is not sored by the trimming process. This means that the sole has not been thinned until it either bleeds or is "soft" or "mushy" to the touch. The same applies to the bars and frog, in other words, all of the volar support structures of the capsule.

Indeed, an important feature of natural trimming is building in tough, dry, callused horn at the bottom of the hoof by not over-trimming the capsule. Without this veneer of dense protective horn, no horse could ever go barefoot without coming up footsore.

8. THE HORSE EXPERIENCES NO HOOF/LIMB INTERFERENCE FOLLOWING THE TRIM.

Logically, any horse that interferes following a trim session has not been naturally trimmed.

9. THE MEASUREMENT DATA FOR THE HOOF DOES NOT CHANGE SIGNIFICANTLY FROM ONE TRIM SESSION TO THE NEXT.

Horses coming out of horseshoes for the first time will undergo de-contraction of their hooves. Conversely, horses with unnaturally splayed (flared) feet will contract in hoof size as they are brought into the fold of genuine natural hoof care. But at some point, whether de-contracting from shoeing or contracting from splaying, every hoof's measurement data following each trim session will sooner or later "settle," that is, cease to change.

What this means specifically is that hoof size (e.g., Toe Length, Hoof Width, and Hoof Length) and proportion (e.g., Toe Angle and Front/Hind Angle Differentials) following a reasonable post-deshoeing transition phase, will tend to become static year round. This is to be expected when the hooves are managed by a competent, knowledgeable professional, and the horse owner is reasonably consistent in the care of his or her horse.

Data that does not settle may be suggestive of hoof (and non-hoof) based problems on the horizon. Horse owners, therefore, should keep data charts for their horses and learn to "read" them. Measurements that vary more than 2 to 3 millimeters or 1 to 2 degrees from one trim session to the next suggest either incompetent hoof care or other problems worth checking out.

The effects of aging, on the other hand, must be taken into consideration when interpreting your data. My studies of wild horse populations show that most hooves cease to grow in size past age five (Figure 10-6). So, expect your horse's data to change at about the rates seen in the chart before age five, and to quickly settle soon after that as he reaches maturity.

There is one other exception to consider as you assess your horse's hoof data. This is the impact of adaptation. Because the hoof is a relatively elastic subject — its physical form may vary somewhat from one kind of environment to the next — we can expect our data to change somewhat if his boarding environment is significantly altered. A horse living upon the soft and unnatural grass pastures of Lexington, Kentucky will not have the same hooves if he were moved to the natural rangelands of the Great Basin where our wild horses roam. Obviously, expect your horse's hoof data to change markedly if his living conditions change with this kind of significance.

Suffolk stallion is readied for his trim. (Author/Star Ridge files)

CHAPTER ELEVEN

DRAFT, PONY

DONKEY AND MULE

The principles of natural hoof care for the common saddle horse breeds apply equally to draft horses, miniatures, ponies, mules, and donkeys. No modern equid is exempt from the laws of nature (including the zebra!).

DRAFT BREEDS

The precedent for the draft breeds was apparently established in wild horse country during the Great Depression.* Draft horse enthusiasts are encourage to contact the BLM to locate wild bands in the Wyoming rangelands of the Great Basin, where the draft influence has been noted by wranglers in the field.

Figure 10-2 itemizes the hoof sizes I personally sampled years ago. In fact, the hooves seen in Figure 2-1, belonging to a five year old, 1500 lb. stallion, spanned nearly 6½ inches (Hoof Width)! In terms of shoe size, his feet transcended the common saddle horse limits. And this horse was captured in Oregon. But what is particularly interesting about his hooves is that his toe lengths measured shorter than 95 percent of all the adult horses I sampled: less than 2¾ inches! This is unheard of in the annals of modern hoof care.

Commonly, horse owners believe that the larger and heavier the horse, the larger and longer his hooves should be in correspondence. Yet, as the wild horse above proves, nothing could be further from the truth in the horse's natural world. I have trimmed draft horses according to the principles and guide-

*See related discussions in The Natural Horse (1992), p. 14.

(Continued on page 160)

(Overleaf) Figures 11-1

FIGURE 11-1

MULE HOOVES

SIMILARITIES AND DIFFERENCES WITH HORSES

Wild mule of the Great Basin and her hooves (*below*).

Jaime Jackson/Litchfield Corrals/American Farriers Journal

1 **Heels and heel-buttresses:** no different than with horses, so trim them short. The distinctive outward turn of the heel-buttress seen in domestic mules is also true in the wild, although it is not evident from this poor photograph—the only surviving photo I took of a wild mule hoof; I suspect that the degree of turn varies with the degree of ass influence in the hybrid offspring.

2 **Frog, Heel-bulbs:** same as horses — frog worn flat and passive to heel-buttresses, heel-bulbs compressed flat and just passive to the ground.

3 **Outer Wall, Mustang Roll** — follow directions for horse hooves.

4 **Sole** — follow same guidelines for "relative concavity" given for horses.

Mules live in and among wild horses in America's high desert country. They are found wherever wild ass herds (bands) mingle near wild horse herds. (Facing page) In 1983, I had the opportunity to examine the hooves of an 1100 lb. wild mare mule from central Nevada, just captured by the BLM in a gather. Her hooves were so extraordinarily perfect by industry standards that the entire mule and ass using community would be wise to completely re-think current hoof care protocols. This intelligent hinny — sound and tough, endowed with broad hindquarters, powerful shoulders, stout legs, soft but determined eyes, a bray only rivaled by the deep bellowings of monarch stallions calling in the night, and magnificent ears which beckon back to the ancient deserts of North Africa — was a true foot soldier of wilderness life. Yet, somewhere, at some time — conceivably the 18th century during Spanish exploration — one of her ancestors left a halter on some now forgotten remada to seek the natural path. In the moment my farrier's gauge first crossed her hooves, I was the first human being to re-kindle the old historical connection. Sixteen years later, I still ponder what became of this finest example of the mule's unique natural world. This is my only surviving photograph of her hooves, here reproduced from an article I wrote for the American Farriers Journal. I was caught by surprise by the many mule owners who were interested in natural mule hooves, or I would have taken a hundred photos. Mule owners are probably the most underserved persons in the domestic horse world.

(Continued from page 157)
lines of this book, including the Suffolk stallion on the frontis of this chapter. The only "problem" with such large hooves is trying to find boots large enough to fit them! Otherwise, I encourage owners of the draft breeds to embrace the natural trim for their horses with the same enthusiasm they would show for the other breeds.

PONIES AND MINIATURE HORSES

I have trimmed hundreds and hundreds of ponies and miniature horses with the method described in this *Guide*. As with their "giant" cousins, the natural trim applies equally to all of the diminutive breeds.

As you can see in Figure 10-2, I sampled hooves in the wild as small as 3½ inches in width (Hoof Width), smaller than the smallest Swiss Horse Boot designated as "Pony size." There is no doubt in my mind that the pony breeds have at some point entered wild horse country and found their place in history.

Hence, it is not surprising that Figure 10-2 also reveals that toe lengths (Toe Length) less than 2½ inches are not uncommon in the wild. And my experience with domestic ponies and miniature horses is that they too will trim close to this lowest range of natural toe lengths. It is worth commenting that many owners of ponies have discovered on their own that the tough hooves of their little guys readily go barefoot. Many of their horses have never seen horseshoes.

MULES AND DONKEYS

Donkeys and mules also have made their place in wild horse country, and have given us a clear example of nature's perfect model for their natural hoof care (Figure 11-1).

The earliest of these animals found their way into the Great Basin during Spanish exploration of the Southwest hundreds of years ago. According to Indian oral history,

Wild donkeys. *U.S. Department of the Interior (USDOI)*

Wild baby donkeys like this charmer can be adopted from the BLM's Adopt-A-Horse Program. *U.S. Department of the Interior (USDOI)*

Wild donkey. *U.S. Department of the Interior (USDOI)*

No longer free-roaming, wild donkey awaits her new human owner/companions, and, we all hope, a good home and natural hoof care! *U.S. Department of the Interior (USDOI)*

Wild donkey. *U.S. Department of the Interior (USDOI)*

mounted Blackfoot Indian warriors as early as the 1700's rode 1500 miles south of their haunts in the northern Montana Rockies to assault Spanish and Mexican pack trains in the lower Great Basin — to steal their much coveted mules and donkeys. Apache, Navajo and Ute warriors did the same, but even earlier in the wake of the great Pueblo uprising against Spanish colonial rule in 1690. Inevitably, many of these domestic asses and hybrids escaped their Indian captors and became feral.

Following the Great Basin gold rushes of the early 1800's, miners released countless donkeys into the wild, and they were no doubt eager to join their Spanish cousins braying for

their company in the distance. By 1900, tens if not hundreds of thousands of wild donkeys had pervaded the southern rangelands of the Great Basin. Thus, like their distant cousins, *Equus Caballus*, with whom they have bred wherever donkey and mustang homelands overlap, they showed that their hooves were also perfectly adaptable to the harshest of all North American environments.

I really encourage mule and donkey owners to get out into wild horse and "burro" country to see what it's all about. If you are such a person and have never been there, you will be quite surprised.

Natural hoof care practitioner Pete Ramey (bio/Chapter 17)) does a head count during trimming in the Smokey Mountains of Georgia

CHAPTER TWELVE

TRIMMING SCHEDULE

Now that your horse's feet have been given their first natural trim, it's time to turn your attention to the future. What happens next?

I urge you to inspect your horse's feet at three to four week intervals. If the hooves require trimming or touch-ups, trim them then. How do you know if they need trimming? While you can "eye ball" the hooves (Figure 12-1), it is much easier and much more reliable (especially for beginners or very busy professionals) to simply measure them and contrast the data you gathered in Chapter 10 for hoof balance. [Order one of my specially designed "Record Keepers" found in the Resource section of this book, and then faithfully enter your hoof measurements following each trim session at the designated trim interval.]

TRIMMING INDICATORS

There are several indicators that let us know the hooves are ready for trimming again. These are summarized in Figure 12-2. Use these criteria in conjunction with your measurement data when assessing the hooves. Let's discuss them here now:

EXCESSIVE WALL GROWTH

This will be the most obvious. Typically, the hoof wall grows longer than the adjacent sole and frog. You can use the Hoof Meter Reader to check the length of the toe wall also. If "Toe Length" has increased, trimming is certainly indicated.

EXCESSIVE FROG GROWTH

It may be that the frog itself has become overgrown. If this is the case, bring out the tools and trim the hoof.

WALL FLARE

One of the most obvious indicators of excessive growth is the existence of wall flare. We recall this from Chapter 9 (Figure 9-2). Once more, bring out the tools and trim the feet.

FIGURE 12-1

GAUGING EXCESS GROWTH

WHEN TO TRIM NEXT

Pete Ramey/American Association of Natural Hoof Care Practitioners

Jessi Sullivan/Cindy Sullivan Images

(*Above*) This handsome Percheron hoof has a modest ring of hoof wall in place above the solar dome, and does not require trimming at this time. Train your eye to see this "ring". You may have to "scratch" at the white line (*left*) with your hoof knife or a wire brush to see it. If the hoof wall has grown out much beyond the sole, which usually takes four weeks, it's probably time to trim again.

WALL CRACKS

This is an "iffy" one. If a hoof wall has a crack in it and it can be traced to shoeing or previous excessive growth, ignore the crack. It will grow out on its own gradually with normal trimming. On the other hand, if the wall is split forming an equine "hang nail," bring out the tools and trim off the offender. Be sure to finish off the remaining wall with the mustang roll.

NON-RELATIVE CONCAVITY

In this case, the principles of Relative Concavity discussed in Chapter 8 are violated. A classic example of this is when the sole protrudes below the hoof wall itself; in other words, the horse is walking on his sole rather than the hoof wall! If possible, trim the sole back if it is simply overgrown. Or, if it cannot be shortened back any further, then refer to Chapter 16 — this is a serious hoof imbalance issue that could foretell lameness, damage to the vascular and nerve structures above the sole, laminitis, or all the above. Excessive frog growth (discussed above) is another indicator, in this case the frog protrudes below (distal to) the buttresses and hoof wall, and the horse is walking on his frogs rather than the hoof wall.

PATHOLOGY

I will defer this section to Chapter 16. A lame horse may require special attention.

OVER-TRIMMING THE HOOVES

I will caution you against trimming the hooves too often, for example, less than three to four week intervals. Why? There are several reasons. First, by trimming too often we can remove too much horn and render the hooves hypersensitive and the horse lame. "Over-

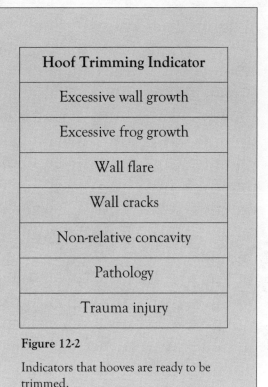

Figure 12-2

Indicators that hooves are ready to be trimmed.

trimming" the hooves leads to short-term and, if kept up, unnecessary long-term chronic lameness.

Second, we can interfere with the hoof's internal attempts to shape and balance itself as it "builds in" callused horn in the sole, hoof wall, and frog. The hoof capsule, a composite product of the coronary, laminar, solar, and frog growth coriums, must be allowed time and freedom to express itself through new growth and interaction with the environment — if it is to harden off, become balanced, and be adaptable to high performance barefootedness. Over-trimming and too-frequent trimming, tantamount to clear-cutting or stripmining the hoof, will interfere with this natural process.

Wild horse country provides a valuable model for natural boarding. [*U.S. Department of the Interior (USDOI)*]

CHAPTER THIRTEEN

NATURAL BOARDING

The key to healthy hooves and a happy horse attached to them is a regular schedule of natural trims *and* as natural a boarding arrangement as you can possibly arrange for your horse. Beyond this, horses need very little to sustain tough, naturally shaped hooves.

But what do we mean by "natural boarding"?

Ideally, it's what you see in the wild horse photographs peppering this chapter and book. Let's look a little closer at the photo of the family band at left, because everything we need to know and provide for is right there. We just have to learn how to see it.

EQUINE COMPANIONS

First, horses naturally *need* each other's constant companionship. They are not happy living alone or living in a stall by themselves. In fact, they don't like living in stalls period, and stall life isn't good for them either. Nasty and neurotic habits such as cribbing, head weaving, and stall kicking occur because horses are stir crazy from being cut off from each other. Aberrant behavior, like close confinement, can adversely impact the hooves — to say nothing of the horse's mental outlook. I have seen hooves worn into horribly misshapen disasters from both. A buddy to play around with can make a big difference.

FREEDOM OF MOVEMENT

Horses are built to move virtually all the time — 20 hours per day. They are curious animals by nature, and they like to explore their surroundings as much as eat from them. In addition to providing constant companionship, round out their lives by giving them things to do. A large pasture turnout out is ideal. Just let them go do their own thing. Let them move, move, move! Horses that can't move freely are most prone to problems — neurotic habits, colic, stocked up legs, ligament aches and pains, unhealthy hooves (lack of mechanism), and so forth.

DRY PASTURE

Green pastures are founder traps (as I'll discuss in Chapter 16), so if you've got your horse out in lush pasture, get him out of there as quick as you can put this book down. Wild horse country is a land of dry pasture, and at first glance, grass is apparently relatively sparse. Everyone who visits wild horse country is always amazed at just how little there seems to be to eat, yet the horses are well-nourished and in marvelously good health. The "secret" is, contrary to the untrained eye (which is invariably prepossessed with looking for green grass — which isn't there for the most part), an abundance of dry grass spread out over vast acreages of rangeland. In the words of Dr. Ric Redden, speaking at the annual Bluegrass Laminitis Symposium he founded in Kentucky, and who initiated his first study of wild horse hooves in 2000, "There is more grass growing on the paper I've written this report on than could be found on 100 acres of their natural habitat."* Movement is what "bundles" the forage together — again, horses must move to eat, and traveling distances of 20 to 30 miles per day to obtain food is not uncommon.

*The Wild Horse's Foot ," R.F. Redden, 2001 Bluegrass Laminitis Symposium, Louisville, KY

As can be seen in the photographs in this chapter, grass is principally of a dry forage type. If you will, high desert grass is not unlike fresh hay. Thus, "hay" in a very real sense, is a staple ingredient of the natural equine diet. [In the words of the BLM, "Good quality grass hay is adequate for a wild horse or burro."*] And "hay x movement" is how it is consumed. There is a lesson from the wild in this for horse owners. Or at least for those who are boarding their horses in paddocks (discussed below).

One, either minimize or prevent altogether the grazing of green grass, especially lush spring

*See BLM web site: http://www. adoptahorse.blm.gov/ adopt-bok.htm

> There is more grass growing on the paper I've written this report on than could be found on 100 acres of their natural habitat.

and fall pastures. Two, make dry grass hay (not legume hay!) the main course of your horse's diet. Moreover, feed your hay at ground level and distribute it widely across your horse's living quarters. In other words, encourage your horse to walk to eat, that is "hay x movement." As in wild horse country, your horse should have as much incentive to move constantly to find food too. Horses are natural browsers and are genetically unprepared to eat "set meals" once or twice a day without dietary complications leading to such metabolic disorders as laminitis and colic.

Feed more than one kind of hay. There are many grasses in wild horse country (among other things). Until these have been identified and, hopefully, made commercially available one day, I recommend instead any of the following: Timothy, orchard, brome, and most other non-leguminous hays. These seem to be compatible with the horse's digestive peculiarities while fulfilling his nutritional needs for graze. Avoid all legumes, particularly Alfalfa, clovers, and vetches; and do not feed any member of the fescue family of grasses. All of these seem to be dangerous founder traps (see Chapter 16, "Laminitis").

PASTURE OR PADDOCK?

The pasture obviously is potentially more than just a "dining hall" for the horse. It's also where he lives and exercises. For this reason, pastures are the ideal horse home. However, if your horse lives in a sea of green grasses (or legumes), rather than dry grasses (like wild horse country), in the name of founder prevention, move him into a "dry lot" paddock and feed him grass hays. Figure 13-1 shows a rental horse stable facility that dry lots their horses

(Pages 172-173) **Figure 13-1** A reasonably natural boarding facility for rental horses in the Smokey Mountains of Georgia.

Horses always need buddies. Here a family band roams together; note the father and his son at left.
U.S. Department of the Interior (USDOI)

Horses need room to move. *U.S. Department of the Interior (USDOI)*

FIGURE 13-1

A SIMPLE MODEL FOR NATURAL BOARDING

A VISIT TO PETE AND ANNETTE RAMEY'S RIDING STABLE IN N.E. GEORGIA

(*Across/top*) String horses, all barefoot (including several rehabilitated founder and navicular cases, are on line and ready for work. (*Across/bottom*) The string heads out at a canter on the gravel road before heading off onto mountain trails. (*Above*) Annette Ramey pitches hay to the string during a feeding respite. The grass hay is supplemented with a light ration of oats, mineral blocks, and free-choice water.

NATURAL BOARDING

Horses naturally stand in the water they drink. It's good for their digestion and it's good for their feet.
U.S. Department of the Interior (USDOI)

Chincoteague ponies of the Virginia barrier islands munch their dry marsh grasses. *(National Park Service)*

Wild horses romping through a giant "paddock" of dry grasses. *U.S. Department of the Interior (USDOI)*

24/7, yet meets all the horses' nutritional and exercise needs.

This would be the only reason to board your horse in a paddock — because the threat of grass founder is not worth playing "fescue foot" with. If you do this, then in addition to providing him with equine companions, he will require a regular exercise program.

OTHER DIETARY CONCERNS

Although no reliable comprehensive study of wild horse diet has been conducted to date, at least one research project I'm aware of has shown that wild horses do eat many things besides dry bunch grasses.* Obviously, as with humans, a balanced equine diet is complex and necessarily varied. I will refer you to my diet recommendations given in my book *Founder: Prevention and Cure the Natural Way* (See Resources). This text addresses vitamins, minerals, watering and so forth from a holistic perspective and is not just an anti-laminitis diet.

At issue is supplying the horse's nutritional requirements without going to extremes: rich grains, harmful grasses and legumes, overfeeding, and starving the horse's temperamental digestive system by withholding feed when he should be eating — a reminder that "free choice" hay is probably the single most important thing you as a horse owner can do to help your horse's digestion. The hooves are a deadly repository for digestive toxins when the diet isn't right, hence naturalizing the horse's diet is a critically important dimension of natural boarding.

WATERING

Just look at those healthy wild horses at the water hole above! That's exactly how nature intended your horse to drink. Mouth to the ground and standing in what he's drinking. It doesn't require much imagination or expense to provide your horse with a small watering hole. In the wild, this is the time when horses soak their feet — a real foot bath and conditioning process. Do the same for your horse every time he goes to get his fill of water.

(Continued on page 177)

See U.S. National Research Council. Wild and Free-Roaming Horses and Burros Report No. BLM–TE-82-001-4700/Oct. 1982. National Academy Press (Washington, D.C.).

Knee deep in non-edible plants, wild horses know how to find what's edible to be healthy. Trust your own horse's instincts.
U.S. Department of the Interior (USDOI)

Elements of Natural Boarding	Unnatural Equivalent
Equine companions	Isolation
Space to move naturally in	Stall life & close confinement
Dry pasture	Lush, green pasture
Paddocks	Stall
Simple diet	Rich grains and hays
Unlimited grass hay	Limited or no grass hay
Free-choice feed	Scheduled meals
Water hole	Water above ground level
A place to roll	No place to roll
Winter coat	Body blankets

Figure 13-2 Elements of natural boarding.

Some horse owners simulate a natural watering hole by letting their water tank overflow until a large muddy area surrounds the tank. The horses stand in the mud while drinking.

Others use natural streams, springs, ponds, and lakes. In wild horse country, horses most often frequent small, spring fed ponds. The large pond on page 174 is located high in a mountain range and is frequented by a wide variety of wildlife and many different wild horse bands. When winter arrives, water holes like this one may freeze over. The horses will then either chop through the ice with their hooves, eat snow instead of drinking water, or move to lower elevations. The message is that horses are very adaptable.

One concern horse owners have expressed to me is how healthy it is for their horses to be drinking from ground water. Water they've been standing in, bathing in, and so forth. If their digestive systems are that sensitive — bacteria setting off laminitis, sand causing colic — how can we let them drink from what must be contaminated sources? My only answer is that horses do it in the wild and they are healthy. Certainly this could be another invaluable research project to conduct in wild horse country (Chapter 18).

Some horse owners have also expressed concerns about their horses standing too often or too long in water or mud, especially in moist climates. The concern being that the hooves will ravel under the constant moisture. But wild horses walk in mud frequently during winter at the lower elevations, where alluvial soils quickly turn to gumbo with rain or melting snow. Significantly, it does not seem to bother their hooves or the ability to move efficiently through their home ranges. Even after months of daily walking in mud to their fetlocks.

I've thought long and hard about the effects of moisture on the hooves. And whether horse owners should opt for dry boarding conditions or wet. Experience and observation has lead me to this conclusion: let your horse take his water while standing in it (or mud); this happens in the wild every day and causes no harm. Don't worry about his hooves being wet or muddy during the rainy season; this is also natural for horses, at least within a three month window of wintry weather.

In short, don't worry about moisture at all, at least if your horse isn't boarding in a swamp! Hooves can take it dry or wet within reasonable limits — thrush (see Chapter 16), in case your are protesting, has its pathogenesis in unnatural hoof form rather than moisture per se. If you're going through a long rainy season, and your horse's feet seem a little too soft or ouchy to go down a gravel road, then use hoof boots for the ride. End of problem. If your climate is very dry, like the high desert, and his hooves never get moisturized, then let his watering tank overflow on to the ground so he is standing in mud while drinking. End of problem, if there ever was one.

PUTTING IT ALL TOGETHER

Figure 13-2 outlines the essentials of natural boarding based on our wild horse country model. I've included some things not discussed in this chapter. Now think about these things in the context of domestication. What little things can you do to make your horse's life more natural? That's the challenge we all face. But with success comes a healthier horse with healthier hooves.

Figure 13-3 explains what one boarding facility did in Colorado — right at the edge of wild horse country. Before the owners made systematic changes to naturalize the horses' lifeways, it was a pretty bleak environment for horses to live their lives out in. So check out what they did to change all that, and see if you can borrow some of their ideas for your own horse's boarding situation. Good luck!

(*Overleaf*) **Figure 13-3** What one natural boarding facility in Colorado has done.

FIGURE 13-3

A SIMPLE MODEL FOR NATURAL BOARDING

A VISIT TO ELOISE JODER'S BOARDING STABLE IN BOULDER, COLORADO

(*Across/top*) View to east overlooking ranch facilities. Owners keep grounds as natural as possible: little pavement, horses constantly in sight of each other, regular pasture rotation in small bands, limited boarding to prevent overcrowding, riding trails, quiet, and plenty of fresh air. In addition, there are longing areas, cross country courses, jumping arena, indoor arena, space for trailers, and other amenities.

(*Across/middle*) Let's turn around to look behind us. This is the 100 acre southwest pasture, as inviting a stretch of land to a horse as any I've seen in wild horse country. Horses, grouped in small bands, are rotated daily through this and adjacent pastures, each of which offers something different in terms of equine needs.

(*Across/bottom*) Tack rooms, left, and holding paddocks, right, where horses are brought from outer pastures and await their owners.

(*Below*) Serene east pasture with jumping arena; riders must walk their horse a ¼ mile to reach this quiet corner.

Riders of the Joder Ranch out with their horses

CHAPTER FOURTEEN

RIDING YOUR

BAREFOOT HORSE

I've thought a lot about what I want to say here in this chapter. But no matter how I say it, or dress it up with photos so it will be palatable to the reader, it will be viewed by my past profession — I was a twenty-year-plus veteran farrier as you recall — as subversive and heretical. In fact, no one in the conventional horse world will tell you to do what I'm going to tell you here and now. It's the final bridge we can burn — or build — together in the stream of natural hoof care.

The purpose, my mission, in writing this book was to bring you to this point. Namely, to ride your horse unshod, barefooted, and let the chips of convention fall where they may. And above all, have fun doing it!

There's a responsible way to go about doing it. Obviously, if your horse was previously shod, or lame from unnatural hoof care, he will probably need a measure of time to get

ready. We call it "transitioning", or conditioning if you like. Horses require time for their hooves to adapt to the environment. During transition, I urge you to boot your horse (Chapter 15) so that you can ride him through transition. There's no reason to put off riding, unless, of course, he is suffering from lameness. Even then, we'll want him to move as much as he can, and become rideable just as soon as possible too.

Stop for a moment, and take a look at the photos of the horses being ridden in this chapter, and elsewhere in this *Guide*. Now compare them to the numerous photos of wild horses sprinkled throughout the book. What do they all have in common? They are barefoot. And they are sound. It's no mystery. It's what Nature intended.

Let's see if we can't distill from the natural hoof care process the responsible and humane

(*across*) Riding along an ice-cold mountain stream in the serene Ozark Mountains of Arkansas

181

Forgive the blur, but one of these galloping (barefoot—what else?) horses prove an interesting and important point. The pinto at left was a chronic founder case until he was de-shod and given natural trims. Proving, as many barefoot horses have proven beyond all doubt, that ro-tated coffin bones do not require horseshoes or pads or anything but natural trims and barefoot-edness to heal and return the afflicted horse to soundness. See the discussion on laminitis in Chapter 16 for more detail.

steps you'll want to take with your horse to arrive at true "high performance barefooted-ness."

First, his hooves must be given a genuine natural trim. This we've done! Second, you must have him properly fitted with riding boots. You'll learn how to do this by reading the next chapter. Third, and last, you'll want to condition his feet by gradually riding him without his boots. Taken together, these three steps constitute "transition."

In this chapter, our focus is step three. Conditioning your horses feet — and by exten-sion, riding your horse barefooted. Let's get right into the process!

TRANSITION TO BAREFOOTEDNESS

Our immediate objective is to condition your horses feet so that he can be ridden at least 15 to 20 miles per day. This is a reason-able goal, one easily attainable by most domes-tic horses, and should meet the needs of aver-age horse owners.

The "key" to conditioning is to gradually build in tough, hardened-off horn across the hoof wall, sole and frog. Unless these struc-tures, particularly the sole, thicken and harden off, high performance barefootedness is not possible. By "thicken" I mean the horn at the

(*across*) All the horses seen here galloping across a mountain trail, barefoot of course, would not be particularly remarkable were it not for the white horse — over 40 years old.

"Here's my horse Shiloh smooching with his pal – a range bull we sometimes meet while trail riding."
Cathy Ritlaw
Arizona

bottom of the hoof becomes dense as opposed to simply "longer," like an overgrown hoof capsule with a horseshoe nailed to it. By "hardened off" I mean the horn itself gets so tough that it is nearly impossible to rasp or nip, especially in summer or in arid climates (like wild horse country). We call this *callusing*.

For the hoof capsule to thicken and callus, *it must be worked*. Standing around in a stall all day won't do it, but will delay or impede the process! Your horse must hit the trail and work his hooves. The more he works his hooves, the more they will thicken and callus. This is how nature intended the process to work.

Begin by observing your horse at liberty. If he was just de-shod, and is mincing his steps, you can't expect him to go barefoot under sad-

dle right then and there. He'll need time, because the effects of horseshoeing have been so damaging that he can barely move under his own weight. Commonly, when the shoe is removed, and the blood vessels and nerves begin to function normally again, the horse feels pain. The hoof capsule, weakened by the shoe, is still inadequate to protect the inner sensitive structures. If this is the case, then go ahead and ride him with boots.

Of course, if he is lame — as opposed to being simply tenderfooted, such as on gravelly surfaces — don't ride him at all, even with hoof boots, until he is sufficiently healed. Hoof boots are not intended to hide underlying problems or to give us reason to ignore actual lamenesses just so we can ride.

(Continued on page 188)

RIDING YOUR BAREFOOT HORSE

All of the horses above are barefoot and have been out on an extended 20 mile ride over pretty rough ground in northeastern Georgia with their lady riders. Now there's nothing unusual about that except for one thing: these sound, powerful moving horses are adapted to one of the highest rainfall climates in the United States. Proving that "moisture" is no excuse for not having high performance barefooted horses. *(Star Ridge Files/Cindy Sullivan Images)*

(Across) Not all natural hoof care aficionados are "serious" types. Many of us have a sense of humor as testified to here. This gelding has been barefoot for years and enjoys his unusual life in the foothills of the Rocky Mountains. *(Project Equus)*

HORSE OWNERS GUIDE TO NATURAL HOOF CARE

A BAREFOOT MARVEL

A LOOK AT A CLIENT'S HORSE: LEXUS

Many horse owners like to gauge the success of their barefoot program by their horse's capacity to take on a rugged trail or mountainside full of sharp rocks (across, bottom). "Lexus," whose owner is a client of mine, has been doing it five years now (across, top). She is a Missouri Fox Trotter, weighing in at just under 1100 pounds. Words can't describe the speed at which she moves along through our rugged back country here in the Ozarks – with toe lengths (TL) only 3 inches. I'm actually too intimidated to ride her! On one fifteen mile trek across the mountains last year, this horse led a pack of 60 shod horses. There would be nothing unusual about this except that she finished one hour ahead of everyone else. And there would be nothing unusual about that except that not one of the other riders realized this horse was barefoot!

While I've got her in hand here at left, following such a ride, let me brag on her a bit more. Just look at her bright eyes and attentive look. Of the thousands and thousands of horses I've trimmed over the years, this one has been my favorite: cooperative, intelligent, helpful, strictly business, tolerant of my shortcomings, and more patient than 99 percent of humans I know. Incidentally, she wears a #2 Swiss Boot up front, but I've been unable to persuade her owner to use them once! Nevertheless, begin your transition with hoof boots and eventually your horse can graduate to this spectacular level of high performance barefootedness without them.

RIDING YOUR BAREFOOT HORSE

(Continued from page 183)

Once your horse is moving comfortably at liberty, it's time to start riding him under saddle. Again, he will walk "gingerly" if he isn't ready. If he seems at all tender or hesitant about moving — use the boots, at least over rough ground. Remove the boots over soft ground. Eventually, he won't need them anywhere.

In short, gradually introduce your horse to being ridden barefoot. Rely on the boots, and be aware that some horses will transition quicker than others. Whatever his rate of transition is, go with it — and never forget that "going barefooted" is not harmful but *natural*.

The owner of a horse rental outfit in the mountains of northeastern Georgia, Smokey Mountain Stables, wrote me about his natural barefoot program. His comments on transitioning his own riding string and as well as his "outside" trimming clients over a two year period are worth sharing:

> For trail riders, a period of time ranging from a week to two months (or more if hoof problems are present) will have to pass before your horse will be ready for barefoot riding in rocky terrain. Most horses with fair feet will be ready to ride immediately in the show ring, pasture or wood trails, but for horses with problems to be rehabilitated or for those which are ridden on terrain much harsher than their home, we [use hoof boots].

This fellow was once a farrier but is now a full-time natural hoof care practitioner. Note that he wisely has given each horse the individual leeway needed to transition, and that hoof boots are integral to his program. Very important, he makes a clear distinction between horses that are essentially "fine" versus those that are lame and in need of "rehabilitation."

Obviously, it may be that the services of an expert hoof care practitioner will be necessary to distinguish between "normal tenderfootedness" in the wake of de-shoeing from abnormal hypersensitivity or lameness due to pathology. It is not uncommon that horse owners deshoe-

ing their entire string discover to their surprise that one horse "moves out" immediately with little or no transition, while another is still foot sore a month later. Invariably, what they learn is that the horseshoes were masking some developing problem they had no idea even existed.

Indeed, natural hoof care practitioners often pull shoes only to discover insidious infections of the white line, "sub-clinical" laminitis, mushy soles, and other abnormal conditions unknown to the horse owner because they were hidden under the shoe. Going barefooted, thus, has saved many a horse's life because transition revealed to their owners in the nick of time the presence of insidious pathologies.

Barring pathology, however, some horses simply require more time than others to transition. All that is required is your patience. But the rewards will be great. Once more our friend from the Smokey Mountain Stables:

> Fully transitioned barefoot horses are something to behold. They move with freedom and agility. They are faster, more maneuverable, and more sure-footed on any surface with a longer, more comfortable stride at any gait. They don't tire as quickly and have way fewer sprains and stone bruises than shod horses because they can feel where they are putting their feet. They are always ready to go. No more frantic searches for the farrier on the day of the show! Since most horses' careers are ended by hoof problems, a natural horse will almost always enjoy a much longer, useful life.

Above all, exercise common sense. Imagine if you were removing your own shoes to go barefooted yourself for the first time. How far and how long could you go? Probably not very far because your shoes have rendered your feet weak and unprepared. In exactly the same way that you would afford yourself the necessary time to transition, show the same generosity to your horse. Do this and you will succeed. Now, let's move to the next chapter and learn something about booting.

THE STATELY 300 YEAR OLD SPANISH RIDING SCHOOL of Vienna, Austria (Above); impeccable riders and barefooted stallions in Quadrille. Few of these horses are shod, except during the two-month summer break when, ironically, they shoe them for pasture time! Regrettably, all the performance stallions live in "tie-stalls" the rest of the year. I've just been informed that carpenters are getting ready to replace these with box stalls – after several hundred years, change certainly comes slowly! But even this is neglectful, isn't it? Could you suggest a natural alternative that would preclude this type of close confinement and still facilitate the School's performance agenda?

DRESSAGE — ART OF NATURAL RIDING

IMPORTANCE OF BAREFOOTED HORSES

FOR THE LIFE OF ME, *I can't understand why the entire dressage community hasn't taken the SRS's lead and de-shod itself yet. At least one lady has (above), and rumor has it that one member of the German Olympic dressage team is now barefooted.*

Dressage is alleged to be the riding discipline of "feeling." But how can it be when the horses themselves can't feel the ground through their shoes? I have watched many levels of dressage competition and performance over the years, and can personally testify to the widespread "resistance" seen in so many horses — the result of hock, back, and ligament pain caused by hoof dysfunction.

I witnessed the 1984 Gold Medal Individual Dressage ride by Rinehart Klimke of Germany on Alderich. The poor horse's toes were so long, it amazed me that he could even raise his feet at piaffe as high as he did. I wouldn't have known better, but the very same year I entered wild horse country where I observed feats of locomotion—from piaffe to movements yet undiscovered by dressage experts—with such perfection, impulsion and enthusiasm as to bring into question what dressage riders think they are trying to accomplish.

Virtually all the great riding masters of classicism, upon whose shoulders modern "dressagists" owe their colors, espoused the significance of nature — now "words without meaning" according to one distinguished SRS chief rider I interviewed.

RUNNERS & JUMPERS

*BUILDING BETTER EQUINE ATHLETES
THROUGH NATURAL HOOF CARE*

Of all the horse sport activities that come to mind, racing and jumping, in my opinion, should consider the benefits of barefootedness. That's because these powerhouses of the domestic horse world are more than any other horses pushed to their limits in extremely measured expanses of time. That translates to ligament, tendon, and joint injuries – not to mention hoof breakdown due to stress. These horses really need to "feel" the ground as they hustle along–and they need as much hoof resilience as possible to take the concussional and compressional beating their hooves are inevitably going to get. There are two very good reasons for de-shoeing track, harness, and jumping horses: one concerns the hoof itself, the other the horse's upper body.

First, by feeling the ground, the de-shod, naturally trimmed hoof can adapt to the surface it's going to work on. With each practice session, and each race, the hoof's balancing forces will kick into high gear and optimize growth for high performance: toe angles will modulate and become more natural (I predict higher), the frog will widen (on soft turf tracks – and become narrower on firmer turfs) and offer more traction, and the outer wall and sole will thicken and get tougher to take the beating. Moreover, the hoof mechanism will assure the hoof capsule of greater flexion and the growth coriums of better blood flow. The result will be stronger, more resilient hooves – exactly what's needed for optimal performance.

Which brings us to the second reason: as the naturally trimmed hoof unfolds, forming a tough, yet flexible and springy foundation for the horse, the horse's lower limb and upper body – the horse's overall conformation, in other words – will resonate with the hooves. Pain and inflammation in the upper body abates as unnatural concussion blasts caused by unnatural hoof form are absorbed by the reconstituted, flexible hooves.

The detrimental influences of shoe caulks, toe grabs, bars, pads, and other devices would be supplanted by the hoof's own native support and traction structures. And so too the debilitating habits of forging, clipping, and cross-interference replaced by natural stride extension. Blood flow to the horse's heart—and badly needed oxygen—would be restored by the hoof mechanism. Horses will run faster, further, and with fewer problems.

• Breeders should lead the way by keeping their young horses unshod from the beginning.

• Carefully thought-out hoof conditioning exercises on surfaces simulating turf conditions are a first step.

• At the track, or jumping concourse, surfacing would be altered to intensify footing—rather than subvert it as is, in my opinion, now the custom with excessively soft footing.

• Trainers could have horses trimmed at any time, any place, and at any frequency for optimal hoof form and function with zero risk of "overworking" the hoof.

• Innovative "speed" boots would be used for horses in barefooted transition, to compensate for poor track conditions, and for any reason that trainers, owners, and racing officials thought necessary.

I believe a solid program of high perfromance barefootedness would benefit the racing and jumping industry in savings of tens of millions of dollars in shoeing, lameness treatment, and ruined horses. But track stewards and competition guidelines today are steeped in the centuries-old traditions of racing. Horse owners themselves must rally to the cause and compel the industry to change.

WESTERN & TRAIL

ALL NATURAL

I know some readers are cowboys and cowgirls. Did you know
that South American gauchos have never heard of horseshoes? Do
you think that not having shod horses is going to prevent them
from doing their work? I don't think so, and it's not going to stop
the wrangler above either. You'll get better action barefoot and
without the risks of interference and limb cuts from up close,
quick work. Use your boots for longer trail rides if you think you
need them. Check out the old rancher in the next chapter riding
along the Buffalo River here in Arkansas. If that old guy can
adapt with a smile on his face (he's smiling because he's saving
on shoeing bills), so can you!

Now and then I hear concerns about bare-footed horses moving in water over a rocky bottom. Whether you are going barefoot like the horse above, or with the flexible Swiss Boot (next chapter!), your horse is going to be at a real advantage over a shod horse. Steel shoes, dangerous on pavement, aren't much safer on wet rock. You might consider this in making your decision to go barefoot.

Steve Dick – Florida. *(Star Ridge Files)*

CHAPTER FIFTEEN

BOOT YOUR HORSE!

Hoof boots, and by that I mean "riding boots" as opposed to medicinal boots, are a Godsend to the natural hoof care movement. Without them, the task of transition can become a cumbersome and time-consuming calamity. Fortunately, that problem is now moot because at least one good product is now in the marketplace which meets the transition and riding needs of all saddle horses. And I'm sure by the time this book goes out of print, others will have joined it.

Interestingly, most horse owners don't de-shoe their horses at this point in time because they want to use hoof boots. Most de-shoe simply to garner the benefits of barefootedness, and having sound horses is the real motivation. Not until they face transition do they awaken to the need, and blessing, of horse boots.

Horse boots, in one form or another, have been around for centuries. The ancient Romans used a type of strap-on sandal made of metal with leather thongs (Figure 15-1). It must have been a cumbersome affair, but apparently its use was limited to draft horses in their inner cities with paved roads. Otherwise the Romans, like the ancient Greeks, went entirely barefooted. Shoeing, still unknown, did not arrive until the 10th century (Figure 15-2), 600 years after Rome fell to the Germanic tribes of northern Europe.

Hoof boots continued to develop even after the advent of fixed shoeing. By 1800 modern prototypes surfaced in both Europe (Figure 15-3) and England (Figure 15-4). By then, forward-thinking vets like Bracey Clark, the British veterinary surgeon whom I quoted

(Continued on page 201)

(*Overleaf*) Figures 15-1 through 15-4: Horse boots, shoes, and sandals from antiquity.

FIGURE 15-1   ROMAN SANDAL

Roman "hipposandal" sans leather thong, c. 4th Century AD. Can you imagine strapping one of these to your horse's feet? I don't think so, and you don't need to. Modern hoof boots provide an excellent "contemporary" alternative!

FIGURE 15-2   EARLY EUROPEAN HORSESHOE

Early 1st Millennium horseshoe unearthed in Europe. They actually nailed these crude things onto horses' feet, so desperate were the feudal kings of medieval Europe with their close confined horses.

FIGURE 15-3 WOODEN SANDAL

19th Century horse sandal with wooden base and leather "upper" with straps. Although by now shoeing was entrenched across Europe (and much of the U.S.) early natural hoof care practitioners struggled with limited technology to create an alternative to a practice they knew was harmful. If you look closely, you can see the single leather loop attached at the back of the base, through which was passed a buckled strap. The latter, fed through a reinforcement strap stitched to the toe wall of the boot, could be secured in three positions.

FIGURE 15-4

FIRST MODERN HOOF BOOT

Still another 19th Century (c. 1800) horse boot. This one, however, is beginning to take on the shape and utility characteristics of its modern descendent, the Swiss Horse Boot: full front and back outer wall covering, adjustable keeper strap at coronet height, and natural hoof shaped base.

(Continued from page 197)

in this *Guide's* Introduction, recognized the fixed shoe's harmful effects upon the hoof — particularly obstructing the mechanism and causing hoof contraction (Chapter 16), and struggled to find alternative ways to protect the hoof. An angry and frustrated Clark would write in 1831:

He who first began the practice, whoever he may have been, little suspected he was laying the foundation of more animal suffering than ever it fell to the lot of one man to originate; for not only have countless myriads of feet, during the twelve or thirteen centuries or more that this practice has been in use, been injured with the suffering, which in a greater or less degree must necessarily attend it from the changes and reduction of the feet that we have pointed out [Clark is referring here to hoof contraction — JJ], but chastisements also for offences in going, still more hard to endure, it not being their fault, are to be added to it along with the cruelly severe bittings, or gaggings rather, and unmerciful usings up attended with scourgings and cruelty, of a description almost too atrocious and cruel for any pen to describe.

Clark pursued a shoe hinged at the toe (to help facilitate the mechanism) rather than a hoof boot as we think of it today, but failed in this effort. Yet his writings unquestionably influenced the early experimenters with booting technology, so it is my intent here to keep the

Tennessee Certified Journeyman Farrier Charles Hall, who has organized a barefoot riding club among his ex-shoeing clientele — over 100 members strong and growing — heat-fits a boot while the recipient waits eagerly at the door. No horse likes to be shod, but booting is another matter. Horse owners report horses getting excited when they reach for their boots for a ride.

(*across*) Booted horses along the Buffalo River, Arkansas.

spirit of this pariah's grand insights alive two centuries later.

Clark's writings are also interesting because they anticipated the motivations we see horse owners engaging in today to enter the barefoot culture. Namely, to escape the terror of lameness and losing one's treasured equine companion. So it is that horse owners enter the doors of natural hoof care, not to get booted, but from "fear of lameness" and only afterwards discovering the latent booting culture. They had no idea it existed, and certainly their farrier practitioners never intended to tell them about it, if they were even aware of it.

The first modern horse boot arrived one hundred years after Clark during the late 1960's, following the plastic extrusion revolution. Dr. David Glass, a nuclear physicist at Los Alamos, New Mexico, created the EasyBoot. Glass was inspired after his daughter's horse had developed a debilitating lameness, navicular (or laminitis). He believed the shoes, which included "stacked heels," were at the bottom of the lameness and moreover, something better than a metal shoe was needed to protect the inflamed hooves. Glass himself rode in endurance rides with his invention, which became available to the public in 1972.

During this same period other horsemen also sought alternatives to fixed shoeing, often for the same reason (i.e., lameness). The late Olaf Mustad was one, and, ironically, he was head of one of the world's largest horseshoe supply companies! Mustad developed the "glue-on" shoe, familiar to many hoof care professionals (though few horses owners) as the "Glu-Strider." It was, and is, used mainly for weak-walled hooves. American farriers generally rejected it, however, since Mustad's adhesives failed in the field. Nevertheless, it is significant and interesting that this man, cut from the very

fabric of the farrier world, would make the effort against the grain of his very industry.

Also forsaking shoe, nail and glue, at this time were no less than half a dozen new boot manufacturers, each dedicated to finding an alternative to the harmful and problematic horseshoe. These inventors, every one, were either shoers, vets, or disgruntled horse owners. Most U.S. horse owners have never heard of their products: the Horsneaker (U.S.), Barrier Boot (U.S.), Dallmer Clog (Germany), Equiboot (England), Ribot Shoe (Italy), Marquis SuperGrip (Germany), Swiss Horse Boot (Switzerland), and most recently, Old Mac (Australia). I have checked them all out, tested those I felt had potential, and in Figure 15-5 you will find a brief opinion of each.

As you can see, I elected personally and professionally to go with the Swiss Horse Boot. At their invitation, I flew to Switzerland in 1999 to meet the owners of the company, Hubert and Ruth Rohner. They showed me how their product is made, explained the extensive testing it went through with the Swiss government, and personally demonstrated it on their own horses. I was impressed and decided to use my influence to promote it here in the U.S. where it was still unknown.

The riders in the photographs of this chapter are all using Swiss Horse Boots. Many of the subjects in other photos are professional natural hoof care practitioners who are certified in booting procedures. In 2000 I organized an extensive certification program for professionals wanting to incorporate the Swiss Horse Boot into their practices. You can refer to the Resource section of this Guide to learn more about it and see if one of these practitioners is available to serve you in your area.

The Swiss Horse Boot must be custom fitted to each horse. This is done through a com-

(Continued on page 206)

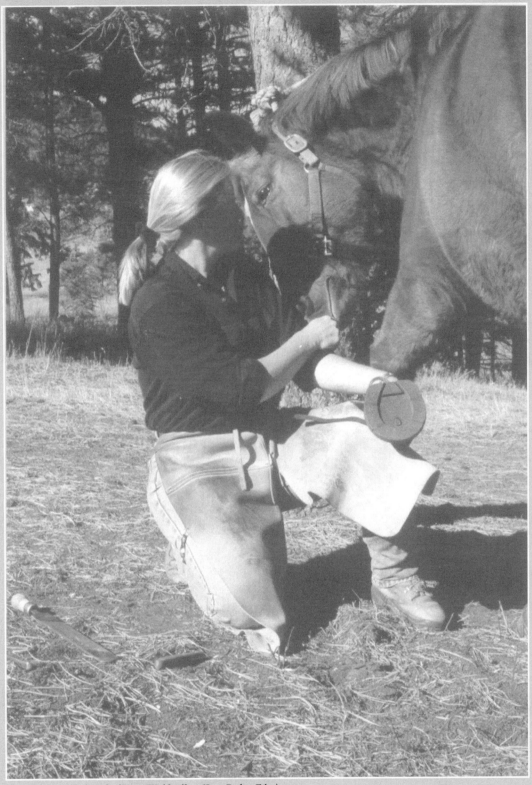

Booting up in Colorado (Eryn Wolfwalker/Star Ridge Files)

(*Overleaf*) **Figure 15-5** My assessments of current horse boots in the marketplace.

FIGURE 15-5

HORSE BOOTS

RECOMMENDATIONS

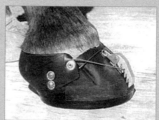

Easyboot

Horsneaker

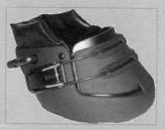

Marquis Supergrip

Old Mac

Swiss Horse Boot

Boot	Test Result	Recommendation
Easyboot (U.S.) $39.95/boot	I tested this boot vigorously on 20 horses. In my opinion, the quarter "grips" which help secure the boot on the hoof cause severe damage to the outer wall. If the grips are filed or bent down to render them less aggressive, then the boot will not stay on. When properly fitted, that is, the grips are set to aggressively grab the hoof wall, then the boot becomes next to impossible to remove! The boot has no way to conform to a naturally trimmed hoof, except by luck! There are other problems with it, far too many for me to delineate here.	This boot is not recommended for riding or transitioning horses.
Horsneaker (U.S.) $125/boot*	This custom boot is fitted via a mold process. Unfortunately, the molding method is cumbersome, unreliable, and expensive. The idea of custom fitting is attractive however. And, in those instances when it can be made to fit properly on hooves that have stabilized following transition, reports are that it works well.	At this time, this boot is problematic for riding or transitioning horses. However, if the molding process can be streamlined and rendered user-friendly, it may become a viable competitor in the future.
Marquis Supergrip Germany) $90.00/boot*	This is a very high-tech German boot. I tested it on several horses, as have several of my professional colleagues. So far, it seems to work very well, but the shape is not as natural as I would like, and this can present some fitting problems. However, the boot's unique "air cuff" compresses around the hoof to create a snug fit for most horses. There are also replaceable component parts — very attractive. Unfortunately, the boot is not yet available in the U.S. and the company has not put its promotional, fitting, and use instructions into English.	I plan to recommend and promote this boot as soon as the company supplies me with fitting instructions and support materials in English. *See Resource section which will lead you to contact information for latest on this boot.*
Old Mac (Australia) $62.50/boot*	The "Old Mac" horse boot is the brain child of David McDonald, an Australian farrier. There are pluses and minuses to this unique product. It is competitively priced and goes on and off very easily, hence its reputation for being "user friendly." Hoping for the best, I tested the boot with several of my clients here in the rugged Ozark Mountains. It literally fell apart after ten miles on the trail. Dr. Bridget Van Damsen of the Institute For Hoof Boots in Germany had similar results in her recent tests (2002). Nor is the fit secure against the hoof wall, but rather "baggy" by most accounts. I did meet with the manufacturer after my tests to make suggestions for changing the boot, including giving it a more natural shape. A recent letter from them wasn't encouraging: "We will not be altering our boots to suit your customers."	This boot is not recommended as currently designed.
Swiss Horse Boot (Switzerland) $64.95/boot*	In my opinion, this is the very best horse boot available to date. It's been thoroughly tested by the Swiss government and Van Damsen's institute, which rated it the "the best boot on the market" (1999 and again in 2002). It has been used by horse owners in Europe for years. I've booted hundreds of horses nationwide successfully and trained professionals to use them. Completely adaptable to naturally trimmed hooves, and very durable, but requires professional fitting.	Highly recommended if you can get your horse fitted properly. *See Resource section for leads on professional booters.*

*Prices are, to the best of my knowledge, accurate as of this writing (Jan./2002)

(Continued from page 202)

bination of special inserts (quarters/heel), toe slots, heat molding of the boot, and special pastern straps. The hoof is first measured accurately and a corresponding boot is selected from a range of six sizes. Most saddle horses can be fitted; larger ponies and the smaller draft breeds can also be fitted.

The unfitted boot is called a "blank." A blank has nothing done or added to it, except the standard rear pastern strap. Very few horses can be fit "straight out of the box" with a blank, consequently a trained professional is recommended to properly fit the horse — although a determined and diligent amateur can do the job too.* Figure 15-6 outlines the booting procedure used by certified professionals.

I urge readers to go to the Resource section of this *Guide* to learn more about the Swiss Horse boot and other new boots that will be coming onto the marketplace. These riding boots will see you through all your transition needs. They are the perfect adjunct to a humane program of high performance barefootedness.

Now, it's time to move on to Chapter 16. I know that many of you have come to the natural trim from having encountered serious and even life-threatening hoof problems with your horse. Chapter 16 was written to help you face and solve these terrible issues by using our natural model for the hoof. So far as treating and preventing hoof lameness is concerned, natural hoof care is the best thing to come along — maybe ever.

I have written a training manual and companion video for professional and serious amateur booters, Guide To Booting Horses For Natural Hoof Care Practitioners (see Resources).

You can take your horse boots into the water and not lose them. (Cathy Drewry/Star Ridge Files)

FIGURE 15-6

CUSTOM FITTING HORSE BOOTS

A "TOUR"

Richard Drewry, a booter from Arkansas, begins the process by freshly trimming the hooves. Fitting should be done immediately following the trim.

Richard next measures the hooves across two axes (here, Hoof Length, see Figure 10-3). Accurate measurements, taken preferably in metric, are critical for effective booting.

Booting tour continued next page.

Booting tour continued next page.

FIGURE 15-6

CUSTOM FITTING HORSE BOOTS

A "TOUR" CONTINUED

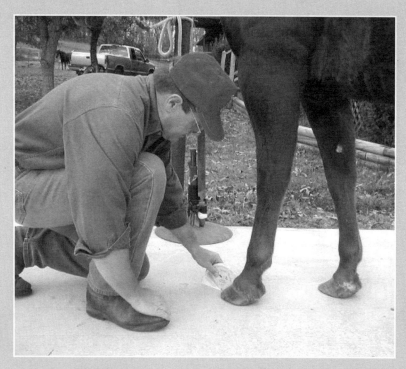

Continuing . . . Richard now measures hoof angle (T°). This measurement is also indispensable: if the angle is less than the front of the boot, the boot may require slotting; if higher, the toe of the boot must be heat fitted.

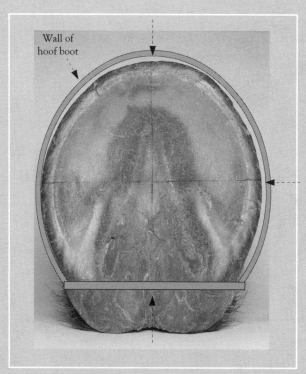

Wall of
hoof boot

Now comes the tricky part. The three arrows mark points of vital importance to a proper fit. At the base of the toe, there must be room for normal wall growth, yet the hoof wall above must be set firmly against the wall of the boot. At the quarter, the boot must be tight against the hoof wall to provide grip, but not so tight as to deform the boot or obstruct the mechanism. At the heel-buttresses a tight fit is sought — enough to drive the hoof forward against the front of the boot. All these, and other, custom fitting efforts are aimed at snugging the hoof into the boot.

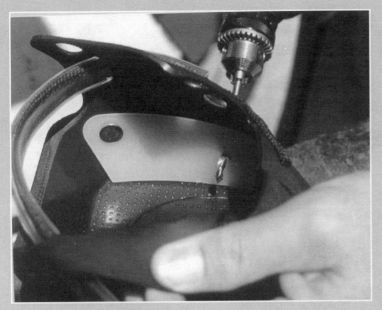

Quarter inserts are riveted to the sides of the boot as needed to provide grip for hooves too narrow for the boot. Similar inserts can be riveted to the heel of the boot for hooves that are wide enough for the boot, but are not long enough (Hoof Length).

Long and narrow hooves with low toe angles may require toe slotting of the blank: a narrow slot at the toe of the boot is created. The toe wall of the hoof can slip snugly into it and enable a perfect fit.

Some hooves, particularly those with steep hoof angles, will require that the boot blank be heated and then form fitted over the capsule. An excellent fit can be achieved in this way.

Booting tour continued next page.

FIGURE 15-6

CUSTOM FITTING HORSE BOOTS

A "TOUR" CONTINUED

With all the necessary custom fitting completed, Richard is now ready to test the fit. With a rubber mallet, he taps the boot onto the hoof. The mallet is necessary because the boot is fit snugly to the hoof. Horse owners also use the mallet to set the boot. Note that Richard is tapping the toe first . . .

. . . next Richard taps the boot over the heels. This "sets" the hoof into the boot firmly. Tapping the boot on is actually a very quick and trouble-free step. Don't feel daunted — most horse owners can set a boot in just a few seconds.

The last fitting step requires that a strap be snugged around the back and front of the pastern. This is insurance against the boot coming off while riding. Once the strap has been properly adjusted, the horse owner can set the strap in seconds.

Removing the boot involves another quick procedure. Richard demonstrates the easiest method. Simply press the heel of your hand against the back of the boot. Presto! Off it comes! If a boot can't be popped off in one second, it wasn't properly fitted to the hoof.

Booting tour continued next page.

FIGURE 15-6

CUSTOM FITTING HORSE BOOTS

A "TOUR" CONTINUED

Richard's entire family is booted and out on one of the many Buffalo River riding trails in northern Arkansas. The banks and beds of this river are covered
with gravel and sharp rock — as can be seen here. While shod horses are easily
sored by such terrain, booted hooves are obviously spared the ravages.

End of tour.

Cathy Drewry rifles her booted horse along the shores of the Buffalo River in Northern Arkansas. This five year old Paint mare was brought to me in shoes with a serious toe crack running down the toe wall of the left front hoof. We pulled the shoes and within one year the hoof had completely healed. Two years later this mare will ride any stretch of our rugged Buffalo River country with or without her Swiss Horse Boots. Cathy now does natural trimming for others. Her story is told in a new book we're collaborating on — *Boot Your Horse!*

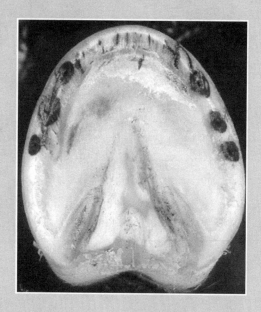

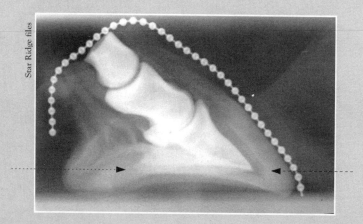

Star Ridge files

The objective in natural healing is to restore the pathological hoof capsule to its normal and natural shape. The wild horse hoof model is very clear about this healing pathway. For example, the (hind) laminitic hoof (*top*) is suffering from coffin bone rotation. The radiograph of the wild hoof (*center*) tells us that the coffin bone must be restored to a "base parallel" orientation if it is to heal. Professional natural hoof care practitioners have studied the natural healing sequences to restore the bone to its correct position. Once this has been effected a normal and natural hoof capsule is restored — just like the wild (hind) one at right.

CHAPTER SIXTEEN

NATURAL HEALING AND

PREVENTION OF LAMENESS

"First, cause no harm and respect the healing forces of Nature."
Quote from the Official Seal of the American Association of Natural Hoof Care Practitioners

When I first stepped into wild horse country in the early 1980's, my immediate impressions of the herds gave no thought to such matters as lameness. To the contrary, my attentions were focused on the lifestyles of healthy animals with sound feet. It wasn't until sometime later, as I recall, that a client just happened to ask, how do the wild ones deal with their lamenesses? "What lameness?" I responded in knee-jerk manner. And after reflecting further, it dawned on me that lameness wasn't a consequence of natural living. Indeed, lame horses are extremely rare in wild horse country.

The "black hole" of lameness here in the domestic horse world, in contrast, is a vast and dark realm. Our horses are commonly lame. The numbers are staggering. According to Walt Taylor, co-founder of the American Farriers Association, and member of the World Farriers Association and Working Together for Equines program:

Of the 122 million equines found around the world, no more than 10 percent are clinically sound. Some 10 percent (12.2 million) are clinically, completely and unusably lame. The remaining 80 percent (97.6 million) of these equines are somewhat lame . . . and could not pass a soundness evaluation or test. [American Farriers Journal, Nov./2000, v. 26, #6, p. 5.]

Horses become lame because they are overwhelmed by our demands — pressure to perform beyond their limits, pressure to digest foods and chemicals that are not natural and which overtax their systems, pressure to be something they are not. The remedy is simple, however, and cost-effective — if that is an issue— and it works well for all horses.

First, we make a commitment to educate ourselves about the horse's natural lifeways. This will prepare and enable us to identify the domestic sources of the conflict leading to his lameness. *Second*, with our new knowledge we make appropriate changes in the horse's lifestyle to remove the source of the conflict. Finally, we accord Nature time to do the healing work for us.

Prevention works in basically the same way

as healing, except that we take the same steps — the same measures to bring about a healing — in advance to preclude or minimize the problem from occurring in the first place. Treatment and prevention thus go hand and hand in the natural, holistic care of horses. And as with treating lameness, we must be patient and allow time for our holistic preventive measures to take hold and do their job.

Our human impatience often conflicts with Nature's healing forces, however. We want the lameness cured immediately and we are ever seeking a silver bullet to do the job. But the rate of natural healing often moves to the beat of a slower drum.

We see this, for example, in the frenetic onrush of conventional veterinary and farriery treatments for laminitis. Faster than a drum roll, out come the prescriptions for bar shoes, pads, drugs, surgery, and close confinement. If these do not bring relief or a cure soon enough, then a stop watch is set for euthanasia. We are impatient, frustrated, and oblivious to the latent healing forces of Nature suppressed within the hoof capsule. The supreme importance of *causality*, subordinated to fashionable hoof-based therapies at hand, is the furthest thing from our minds. Impatience, like the neglect of causality, is arguably more harmful than the disease itself! Or so is my consummate opinion of the matter after 25 years in the field.

In contrast, an important cornerstone of lameness treatment in natural hoof care is recognizing that the hoof is basically a sound structure and seldom, if ever really, the root cause of serious lameness. The hooves are simply a repository for anti-holistic forces besieging the horse.

Thus, one of the cardinal rules of natural or holistic lameness treatment is this:

> The hoof cannot be forced to
> make the horse sound.

Problems in the hoof do not originate there, therefore they cannot be resolved there. Except only in the sense of temporary palliation. We must leave the hoof and all its dreaded

symptoms to find, confront, and dismantle the cause. This much, well within all our budgets and capability, will unleash the powerful healing forces of nature.

So, our destination in the treatment of lameness is crystal clear. Review the photos of the wild horse hooves in this *Guide* and hold those images in mind. Let nothing stand in your way to attain to the principles of this natural model. Accept no compromise and brush aside all protests to the contrary.

For the duration of this chapter, we can try to shed some important light on the issue of hoof lameness by pointing out the relationships between specific hoof ailments, real or imagined, and the known violations of natural hoof state and natural lifestyle that give rise to them. From there, it has been my and others' experience, treatment (or prevention) is simply a matter of acting consistently to reverse the practices which caused the lameness. And letting the hoof heal itself.

LAMINITIS (FOUNDER)

Laminitis is an inflammation and breakdown of the specialized tissues which hold the hoof capsule to the coffin bone within. When these attachments, called lamina, become sufficiently necrotic, the capsule breaks away from the bone, resulting in a stretched white line; the horse becomes lame and assumes the classic "founder stance" (Figure 16-1). If left untreated the bone may press downward into the sole resulting in "founder" — or in modern scientific vernacular, "coffin bone rotation."

Laminitis is virtually unknown in wild horse country. There is no reason for it to occur. Yet it occurs among hundreds of thousands of U.S. domestic horses each year, and probably millions worldwide. Most horse owners don't even know it's happening to their horses until it's too late.

Natural hoof care practitioners view laminitis as a life style issue rather than a specialized hoof-based problem. Diet, an unnatural one, is seen as the principal villain and battleground for change. The hooves are not the

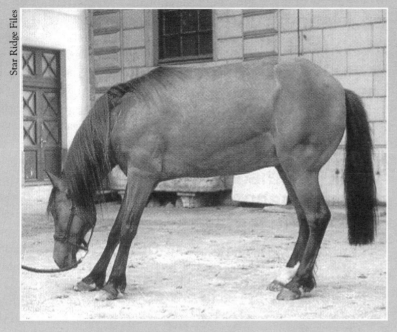

Star Ridge Files

FIGURE 16-1

FOUNDER STANCE

CLASSIC SIGNS

(*Left*) Founder stance during laminitis attack. When you see this, you can be pretty sure your horse has "got it."

(*Below*) Following the acute attack above, the coffin bone will begin to separate from the hoof wall. Slowly, the tell-tale "stretched" white line at the toe wall, marked by the dashed line, will emerge. If there's any doubt in your mind that your horse has foundered, the white line will let you know for sure.

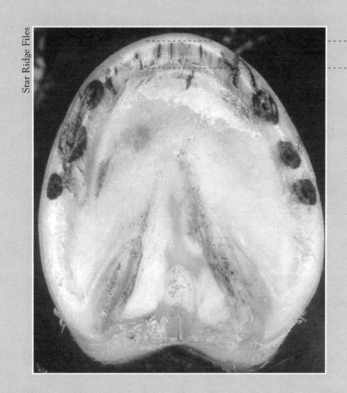

Star Ridge Files

problem. And nothing can be done at the hoof to effect a cure. What's happening down there, while indeed a glum affair in many cases (Figure 16-2), is a symptomatic smokescreen that can only blind and mislead the unwitting.

Beware of contemporary veterinary nonsense that proclaims barefooted horses are a prescription for laminitis! Beware too of the flipside farriery logic which will try to put or keep your horse in orthopedic shoes. These are founder traps that contrapose the very forces of nature necessary for healing.*

TREATMENT

Actual treatment is surprisingly simple, inexpensive, and straightforward. Some horses will sound out within three months, but most will require up to 9 months, or even more.

First, call your vet to confirm the lameness. He or she will probably prescribe pain medications — which I recommend. Next, remove the shoes (if the horse is shod) and provide a natural trim (re-trim at four week intervals). If your horse is in too much pain to offer his feet, wait for the pain medication to kick in and soak his feet in cool water. This can take a day or two.

Some professionals use a portable "sling" in laminitis cases to hoist the horse up off the ground, just enough that his front feet are barely touching the ground (Figure 16-3). So positioned, either front hoof can be worked without the horse having to bear his weight on the opposing front hoof. This is very helpful because the horse's center-of-gravity lies closer to his front feet, and relieving weight-bearing forces there does much to mitigate the horse's suffering during de-shoeing and trimming.

However you handle the hoof work, set about immediately — preferably even before doing the first trim — to naturalize the horse's lifeway. Laminitis cannot be treated at the hoof alone. Indeed, where horse owners, vets, and others run into serious problems treating laminitis is in not taking the holistic implications seriously. In other words, the hooves are perceived to be the central problem and there is a tendency to treat the symptoms without doing the essential detective work to find and remove the cause. Chronic laminitis is the result.

Because laminitis is so epidemic, and because the issues in the average horse owner's mind are so confused, I have written a book

*I have been confronted by various veterinary and farriery authorities who insist that through shoeing they have enabled the healing of laminitic horses. But I disagree. Healing occurs only if the root cause or causes of the laminitis have been eliminated. Shoeing simply exacerbates matters, and it is harder on some horses than others. In all instances, shoeing obstructs the mechanism and prevents wear — resulting in less than optimal circulation and long toes, the latter creating dangerous lever forces on the already stressed lamina.

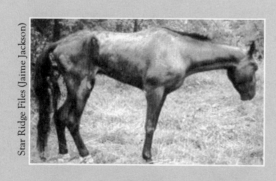

Star Ridge Files (Jaime Jackson)

FIGURE 16-2

HOOF SLOUGH

LAMINITIS WORST CASE SCENARIO

Worst case scenario of laminitis (other than euthanasia) is hoof slough. This terribly pathetic registered Quarter Horse, still in shoes and never given the holistic care he needed, eventually lost all his hooves. Please refer to my companion book, *Founder: Prevention and Cure the Natural Way*, to learn how to treat this and milder forms of laminitis. All stages of laminitis are healable with natural hoof care and post laminitic horses can be returned to riding with new hooves and completely sound.

FIGURE 16-3

LAMINITIS SLING

This innovative sling (see equis-ling@equinebiz.com) is handy for trimming laminitic horses as seen here. The horse is lifted by a series of integrated pulleys until the front feet scarcely touch the ground. Painful weight-bearing forces are thus reduced while the feet are trimmed.

specifically for treating and preventing laminitis the natural way, entitled, *Founder: Prevention and Cure the Natural Way.* It is available through the Resource section of this *Guide* or at many book stores and tack shops nationwide. If your horse is foundered, this book lays out a treatment program for you. It also will lead you to professional natural hoof care practitioners who can help you with specialized trimming procedures (*Overleaf*, "Founder Trim with Charles Hall"), life style changes, and customized booting that will be necessary to restore your horse to lasting soundness.

One final note, while founder is very serious and potentially life-threatening to your horse, please take refuge in the knowledge that it is also treatable no matter what its severity. I know that much has been written by vets, farriers, and others concerning its resistance to conventional treatment; but natural healing does not work according to conventional standards and expectations. Like natural hoof care versus conventional shoeing, it is an entirely different world with its own standards.

NAVICULAR (NAVICULAR SYNDROME)

Navicular, or navicular syndrome, refers to a chronic and crippling pain in the back of the hoof. For a variety of reasons, the deep digital flexor tendon is thought to put a levered death grip on the navicular bursa protecting the navicular bone, the navicular bone itself, and the interfacing length of the flexor tendon. The bursa, the bone, and the interfacing tendon, then become inflamed and are subject to damage. Obstruction of circulation is also thought to be part of the problem. Pain from hoof contraction (the result of shoeing) is also cited as a cause. There are probably other explanations.

Not surprisingly, navicular is unknown in wild horse country. Nor have I seen it among naturally trimmed, barefooted horses. In fact,

(Continued on page 222)

FOUNDER TRIM WITH CHARLES HALL

HEALING THROUGH TRIMMING THE NATURAL WAY

I have been asked countless times: how does one trim a foundered hoof? Or a "navicular" hoof? Or whatever. My answer is always the same: "The same as any hoof." And by that I mean very specifically a "natural trim." Why would I trim it otherwise? To make it less than natural than it already is? Indeed, it is the act of trimming the hoof naturally that sets in motion very important healing forces so vital — but not all-inclusive — to laminitis recovery. The hooves here, trimmed by Charles Hall (right), demonstrate the dramatic changes in the laminitic capsule that are possible when natural trimming is diligently brought to bear at approximately four week intervals over several months to a year's time. (Across, top) "The farrier before me just used a saw to cut the front of the hoof off," laments Charles. Eventually, the capsule was remodeled and the horse was restored to soundness. (Below) A similar protracted strategy of natural trimming saved the day for the horses below too.

Charles Hall
Tennessee
(See bio, Chapter 17)

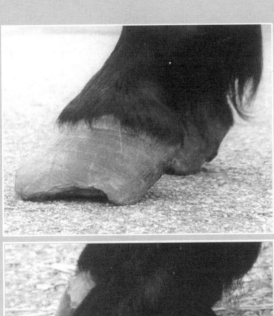

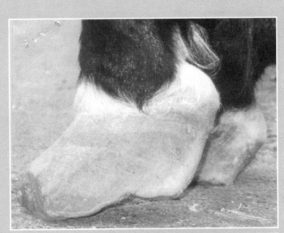

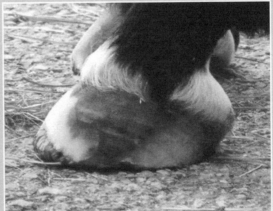

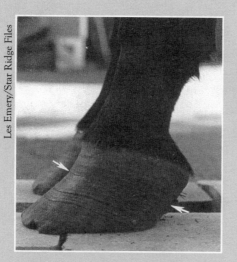

Les Emery/Star Ridge Files

FIGURE 16-4

"CLASSIC" NAVICULAR

This photo, taken from a shoeing text for treating navicular, reveals that the horse is simply suffering from laminitis, long toes, and long heals. The white arrows placed by the authors allegedly point out a "navicular waist" — a symptom caused by excruciating pain from "navicular." That "waist," however, is not a sign of suffering, but the hoof attempting to heal itself by growing a new wall at a higher and more natural angle of growth. This horse needed a new diet and natural trimming and he would have been fine.

(Continued from page 219)
let me say this, even at the risk of losing all credibility: there is no such thing as "navicular" at all. It is a myth (Figure 16-4). Often, it is simply improperly diagnosed laminitis. The rest of the time, it is aggravated ligament strain in and about the "navicular pulley system" of the hoof due to the deleterious effects of shoeing and unnatural trimming (Figure 16-5).

TREATMENT
Treatment is relatively straight forward: de-

shoe your horse, provide regular natural trims (four week intervals), let the horse move about at liberty barefoot, and give him time to heal. As soon as he stops limping, begin ground work (lunging) and check his progress. Fit him initially with hoof boots for riding, transitioning to barefoot riding as his hooves complete their adaptation to the environment. And please take heart, I am unaware of any "navicular" horse that has failed to heal in a genuine program of natural hoof care.

Pete Ramey/Georgia/Star Ridge Files

HORSE OWNERS GUIDE TO NATURAL HOOF CARE

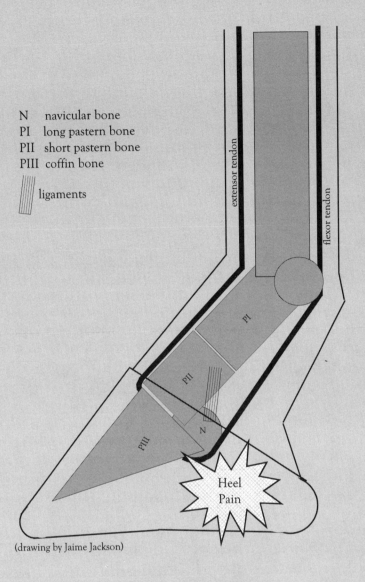

N   navicular bone
PI   long pastern bone
PII short pastern bone
PIII coffin bone

||| ligaments

extensor tendon

flexor tendon

PI

PII

PIII

N

Heel
Pain

(drawing by Jaime Jackson)

Figure 16-5 Navicular pulley system

This marvelous piece of structural engineering is designed to "receive" and "propel" body weight loading and unloading the horse's limb. The navicular bone plays a pivotal role, acting as a brace or fulcrum for the flexor tendon as it alternately stretches (loading) and contracts (unloading) during the hoof's support and flight phases. In effect, it is a tough and capable complex pulley system.

Podotrochleosis, the scientific name for navicular, refers to an alleged breaking down of this pulley. In fact, an array of support ligaments, adjoining and bolstering the navicular pulley, become stressed and inflamed like arthritis when a horse becomes "navicular." Understanding the natural function of the navicular pulley helps pave the way for a holistic cure. Physiologically correct "natural trimming" can help counter the ligament strain — the product of nothing more than hoof imbalance, shoeing, and in some instances unnatural riding practices.

FIGURE 16-6

HOOF CONTRACTION

MYTHS

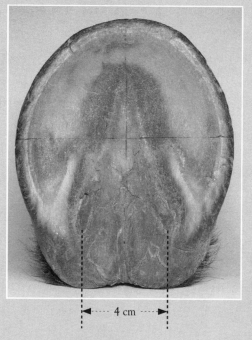

←---- 4 cm ----→

FIGURE 16-6A

HOOF CONTRACTION DEFINED

Conventional definitions of hoof contraction will have to be revisited and redefined. Wild horse hooves are contracted by such definitions. For example, the dotted lines over the hoof at left show the amount of space between the base of the heel buttresses. At 4 cm, it isn't much!

We've also learned (Chapter 2) that wild horses walk on the back of their heels, further challenging contemporary definitions of contracted hooves with run-under heels.

My observations of wild horse hooves suggest that our definitions of contraction — and no pun intended — are simply too narrow. Personally, I have retreated away from any preconceived set of axes which define contraction. Instead, I trim the hoof naturally and let barefootedness and the weight of the horse define the hoof.

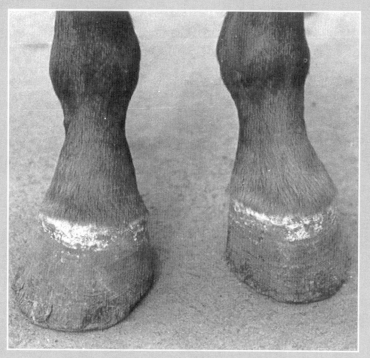

FIGURE 16-6B

HEEL CONTRACTION

Heel contraction per se is really a myth. The entire hoof is contracted — as seen in the far right hoof which is severely contracted. Although not as extreme as this pathological case, most hooves coming out of shoes will nevertheless be contracted throughout the entire hoof. Happily, all degrees of hoof contraction can be reversed through de-shoeing and natural hoof care.

HOOF CONTRACTION

As the term implies, a contracted hoof is one that has become too small. In other words, it is too narrow from side to side, or not long enough from front to back, or both.

My wild horse research demonstrates unequivocally that hoof contraction is not well understood here in the domestic horse world. By many of our conventional definitions — and there are many — wild horse hooves are considered contracted (Figure 16-6a,b)! Since these horses are robust and sound, such definitions are obviously not accurate and must be rethought out by those who profess them.

How do you know if your horse's hooves are truly contracted? Undoubtedly, they are contracted in some measure if they are shod. How much? There's only one way to find out: remove the shoes, measure the hooves, and remeasure them regularly as your horse advances into his natural hoof care program. When the hooves stop "spreading," they are de-contracted.

My experience has been that, on average, hooves spread approximately 1 cm (Hoof Width) following deshoeing. If you keep diligent records of your horse's hoof measurements, you can see exactly how contracted his feet were.

Is hoof contraction something to panic over? Absolutely not! Why get in a frenzy when all you have to do is remove the shoes and give your horse a natural trim?

Do you need to force the hooves apart by mechanical means (orthopedic shoeing) or aggressive trimming (e.g., ablating the bars and heel-buttresses?) No! The weight of the horse and barefoot movement is all that's needed. The hooves will de-contract as much as they need to, and at their own speed.

How soon will normal blood circulation be restored? It begins to restore immediately following de-shoeing. Just like releasing a tourniquet starts restoring normal blood flow. When the hooves are fully spread, blood circulation will be fully normal and optimal.

How long will it take your horse's hooves to de-contract? With natural trimming at four week intervals (I do not recommend trimming at shorter intervals than this), most hooves will be fully de-contracted within 6 months to a year.

What if your horse's feet get smaller after the shoes are removed? This happens occasionally. It simply means that his hooves were "flared" (see discussion below). Once the flare is removed or grown out, his hooves will probably be smaller. They were also probably contracted to a certain degree too. What this means is that the outer wall per se was flared, but everything else about the hoof was contracted. But as the flared hoof wall was removed (making the hoof smaller), weight upon the hoof (compressional forces) caused the hoof overall to become larger. Usually, there is more flare than contraction, so the latter is more difficult to detect. By using special hoof calipers (available in Star Ridge Publishing's Booter's Catalogue — contact SRP, see Resources) you can measure the diameter or circumference of the wall below the hairline. This measurement may increase with time, even though the base of the hoof wall is shrinking due to loss of flare.

Can you ride your horse if his hooves are contracted? Yes, ride him. Movement helps restore the hoof's natural size and elasticity.

TREATMENT

Contraction is easier and less time-consuming to treat than any other hoof problem. Simply remove the shoes, provide a natural trim, and wait patiently for Nature to spread the hooves.

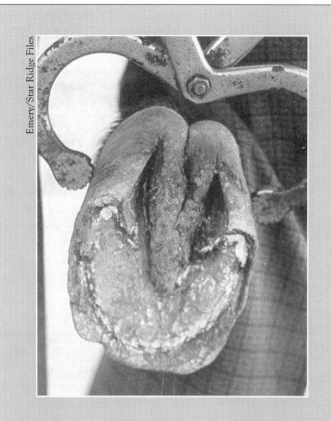

Emery/Star Ridge Files

FIGURE 16-7

RUN-UNDER HOOVES

Pathological expression of long toe/long-heeled, run-under hoof conformation. This hard-to-imagine hoof is a neglect case, but comparably abusive trimming methods can arrive at the same outrageous result. Note use of "hoof testers." Please don't do this to your horse. Testers harm the hoof and tell you nothing that common sense and 20/20 vision don't already tell you.

WALL FLARE

Wall flare is simply excessive hoof wall that grows outward due to excessive length and insufficient wear (Figure 9-2 and 9-3). Removing flare encourages healthy new growth in its place. This replacement growth will descend at a more natural angle.

TREATMENT

Wall flare may be removed by the practitioner either all at once or gradually. This is done with the nippers or rasp, or both. It does not harm the hoof wall to remove flare, provided the trimmer does not thin the wall to less than its normal and natural thickness. To avoid excessive wall thinning, flare may have to be removed over a period of two or more trims. In time wall flare is easily controlled by minor touch-ups with the rasp as needed (—refer to Figures 9-2 and 9-3).

RUN-UNDER/UNDER-SLUNG HEELS

The term "run-under heels" (or under-slung heels) is often heard in farrier and vet circles, and in recent years among horse owners too. It refers to the position of the heel-buttresses being too long and too far forward under the hoof, that is toward the toe wall (Figure 16-7). Hence, the heels are said to be "run under."

Generally, the condition arises because the heels have not been sufficiently shortened. The hoof's normal (and natural) angle of growth at the heels is sufficiently low that the ends of the heels (that is the ground bearing surface of the heel wall) are further forward than if the heels were shortened (and thus further back under the heel bulbs). Typically, such hooves appear very steep or high angled, although sometimes the toe wall is excessively long too.

But run-under heels also occur among wild horses. In fact, every wild horse hoof I have

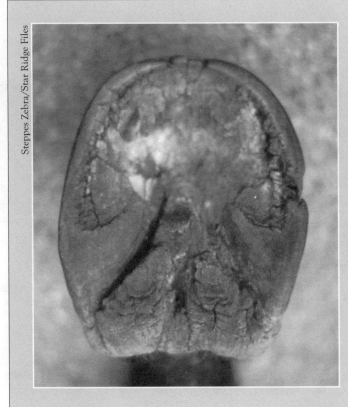

FIGURE 16-8

RUN-UNDER HEELS

Run-under heels are common in the wild among horses and, as seen in this photo, African zebras! Note also the folded-over bars: while this is not common in the wild, it does occur — even among wild horses. The bars, if insufficiently worn (due to lack of abrasion) will fold over, compress into the sole, and become part of the solar dome. With further wear, the bars will then thin out until they are completely worn back to a "stub", as seen in Figure 2-8. This is an obvious adaptive defense mechanism of the hoof to circumvent dangerous lever forces associated with excessive heel length and severe mediolateral and anteroposterior capsule imbalance.

ever examined has had run-under heels! It can be seen in the wild hoof photos in this *Guide*, and in the wild zebra hoof in the accompanying photograph in Figure 16-8.

The difference is that the heels in naturally worn hooves are (usually — not always) short rather than long, and the horse (zebra) walks on the back of his heels instead of the ends! The only explanation I can offer is that in the wild the back of the heels rotate over so that the horse is walking actively on the entire heel-buttress structure, ends and back! In this way, "long heels" are apparently avoided and yet the heel-buttresses are positioned wherever they are most needed to provide an effective, balanced, and broad base of support with optimal biomechanical advantage and little opportunity for wall breakage.

Pathology aside, this is a very complex growth/wear dynamic in naturally worn hooves, and one I am addressing currently with other natural hoof care practitioners. I'll address the subject further in the last chapter

of this *Guide*.

TREATMENT

For run-under heels resulting from excessive growth in the absence of insufficient natural wear, correction is very simple. Perform a natural trim, making sure the heels are lowered as described in Chapter 8 and in my companion video.

I caution against trying in some manner to "force" run-under heels on the hoof "to make it more natural." Don't force anything. The natural mechanism for this has not yet been investigated or demonstrated. All we know at this point in time is that it occurs as a result of extraordinary compressional (weight bearing) forces and much, much natural movement. From a biomechanical standpoint, natural hoof care practitioners accomplish the same effect by simple shortening of the heel-buttresses.

FIGURE 16-9

LONG TOE/RUN-UNDER HEELS

. . . can be unnatural as depicted here in this Tennessee Walking Horse shoe job. Folks, please don't do this to your horses! If you are, please refer to my Resource section and find your way to the horse boots. I'm designing a new boot which will enable you to trim your horse naturally and at the same time give you the temporary "lift" and "action" needed in your competitions which are afforded by the shoeing method seen here.

LONG TOE/LOW HEELS

The term "long toe/low heels" simply means that the hoof has a relatively long toe with short heels. This is in some quarters of the horse world a prescribed way of trimming (and shoeing) the feet in order to compel the horse to move in a more animated way (Figure 16-9). The condition also arises from just plain lousy trimming skills, or worse, chronic neglect.

So, if you trim your horse's feet with short heels (natural) and long toes (unnatural), you get a horse with "long toe/short heel" hoof conformation. The argument against trimming hooves this way, besides being unnatural, is that the long toe creates lever forces that can cause the horse to fatigue and cause damage to the hoof capsule. Toe wall splits, quarter cracks, laminar stress, tendon and ligament strain ("navicular syndrome"), and gait obstruction are often cited in the veterinary literature. Long toes will also exacerbate lamini-

tis. They can also create a rather weird low slung toe wall; these are a formidable challenge to correct, and you'll probably need a professional to aid you in this work.

TREATMENT

Simply shorten the toe, dress the outer wall to remove flare, and render a generous mustang roll. Trim at four week intervals.

For slippered and low slung toes treatment will require that the toe be shortened as much as possible and gradually "backed up." This is done with rasp and nipper, and may require the experience of a professional if you lack confidence and a real sense of what's needed. Eventually, under this trimming pressure, the white line at the toe will "migrate" back to where it belongs [see Discussion: "Restoring a Runaway Hoof" (*facing page*)]. You can't force this change, it must come with time. Fortunately, it is completely treatable and you can ride your horse at any time without causing him or his feet harm.

SCHEMATIC: RESTORING A RUNAWAY HOOF

UNDER SLUNG HOOVES

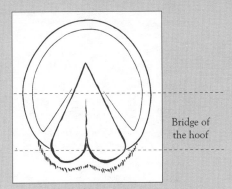

Bridge of
the hoof

These are roughly the trimming sequences I use to restore a forward migrated runaway hoof — otherwise known as a long toe/run-under heeled foot. The actual time frame is relative; it may take longer than two or three trims to effect the same changes, depending on the individual horse and his feet. Be flexible!

In effect, we are dragging the long toe back under the horse, shortening it, and enabling it to grow at a steeper angle. We do this by building in the "bridge" of the hoof, namely the heel-buttresses (heel wall and bars). The buttresses are allowed temporarily to grow longer and thicker.

Once the toe has been brought back in, reduce the buttresses if the heels seem excessively long. On the other hand, if the hoof is propped up at a nice angle (review angle ranges in Chapter 2 and Chapter 9), leave the heels longer. The runway hoof could have gotten that way because the toe angle was simply too low.

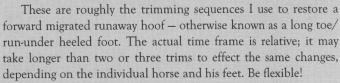

The toe is too long and the toe angle is too low. Moreover, the heels are run under.

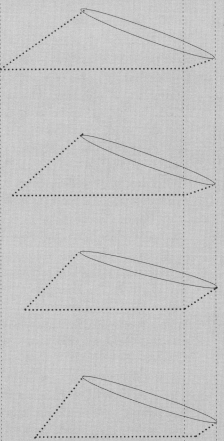

First trim
START: Shorten the toe wall as much as you can, but don't thin the outer wall —called snubbing the toe (Figure 9-6). Don't shorten the heels at this stage.
RESULT: The toe is short, the angle is somewhat higher. Heels are still too low and too far under the horse.

Second trim (Four weeks)
START: The heels have grown, now let them be; the toe is longer but more "under the hairline" — go ahead and shorten it; the toe angle is unchanged before trim.
RESULT: Following trim, the toe is shorter, the angle is definitely higher. Heels are longer but about same position under the horse.

Third trim (Eight weeks)
START: The heels have grown again, now shorten them; the toe is longer than at second trim but has grown still more "under the hairline" — go ahead and shorten it; the toe angle is unchanged before trim.
RESULT: The toe is shorter (as short as it was following second trim), the toe angle is definitely higher now after trim. Heels are shorter but further back where they belong, and there has been no drop in toe angle.

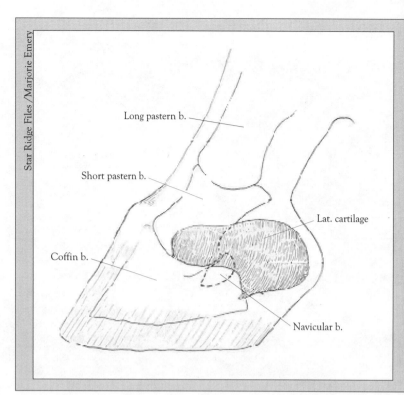

Star Ridge Files / Marjorie Emery

Long pastern b.

Short pastern b.

Lat. cartilage

Coffin b.

Navicular b.

FIGURE 16-10

SIDEBONE

Grayed area marks cartilage. Upper border of cartilage undergoes calcification known as sidebone. But there is no pain associated with this natural bone formation, no doubt due to normal stress of the cartilage. Hoof imbalance and unnatural riding practices however may cause pain at the cartilage attachments to the bone. Natural hoof care and natural movement will remedy the problem.

SIDEBONE

Ossification of the cartilages is called sidebone (Figure 16-10). There is no evidence in my opinion that sidebone is anything but perfectly natural. Nor is there pain associated with it according to Dutch researchers Verschooten et al., and I quote — "Finally no treatment for the ossification is possible and no shoe of whatever shape is necessary to relieve the 'pain' of sidebones, which is localized in the brain of men!"* Nor does sidebone impair the hoof mechanism. [Verschooten]

TREATMENT

There is no treatment, because there is nothing to treat. Like navicular syndrome, sidebone is another mythical malady whose pain should be attributed to hoof imbalance. Simply trim your horse naturally, ride him naturally, and forget about it. Nature will heal all!

1995 Bluegrass Laminitis Symposium

Finally no treatment for the ossification is possible and no shoe of whatever shape is necessary to relieve the 'pain' of sidebones, which is localized in the brain of men!

WHITE LINE DISEASE

Once more, at the risk of losing credibility, I have grave doubts that there really is such a thing as White Line Disease (WLD). "WLD" is believed to be the work of opportunistic pathogens — fungi, bacteria, and possibly viruses — which purportedly invade, devour, and destroy the laminar junction bonding the capsule to the coffin bone. In its advanced stages WLD does appear to be a pretty frightening sight (Figure 16-11). It is now thought to be epidemic in domestic horse populations, particularly shod horses, but among barefoot horses too.

But I have yet to see an actual case of WLD that in fact isn't simply a laminitic hoof. So far as I'm concerned, they are the same thing, and successful treatment of WLD is no different than treating a laminitic

Star Ridge Files

FIGURE 16-11

WHITE LINE DISEASE

White line disease (WLD), like laminitis, is a frightful and destructive malady of the hoof — as can be seen in this advanced case. Yet the hoof is not really the problem. Like laminitis, WLD is a holistic issue and must be resolved outside the hoof to effect a lasting healing.

hoof.

It doesn't surprise me that veterinary researchers are able to culture a range of invasive bacteria and fungi, which they attribute this condition to. Indeed, a chronically laminitic hoof is a breeding ground for these kinds of pathogens. Why wouldn't it be? Regardless, in every case of WLD I've investigated, I've found all the ingredients necessary for laminitis. Clean up the conditions that cause laminitis, and WLD mysteriously disappears every time. The problem, as stated earlier in this chapter, is that most horse owners, farriers, and vets — and veterinary researchers too — in my opinion don't understand the whole laminitis picture.

But in wild horse country, the picture is very clear. This mythical condition, like the real culprit masquerading among domestic horses in its name, is not seen in wild horse populations. The arid environment of wild horse country, which is certainly not conducive to aerobic pathogens of WLD, and the all-important "founder free" diet of the wild horse, do not provide the necessary foothold.

For these reasons, natural hoof care practi-

tioners try to ignore the hysteria and pretzel logic characterizing the WLD quagmire, and get on with the job that needs to be done to clean up the actual underlying issues. Education, diet and environment are the main battlegrounds; indeed, unless these issues are confronted and solved, there is little we can do at the hoof except grimace. Cleaning and soaking severely infected hooves with disinfectants should be used only as an adjunct to natural care changes — not as a substitute.

TREATMENT

Rush your horse into natural hoof care, feed your horse naturally, and naturalize his lifestyle and habitat as much as possible. Like laminitis, WLD can then barely hang on. What does this mean, practically speaking?

Follow the same healing plan laid out for laminitic horses detailed in my founder book (see Resources). If your horse has serious WLD, then relegate the hoof work to a professional natural hoof care practitioner who can aggressively remove infected horn, balance the feet, and aid you in applying palliative measures (hoof soaks and tincture of liquid bee

Les Emery/Star Ridge Files

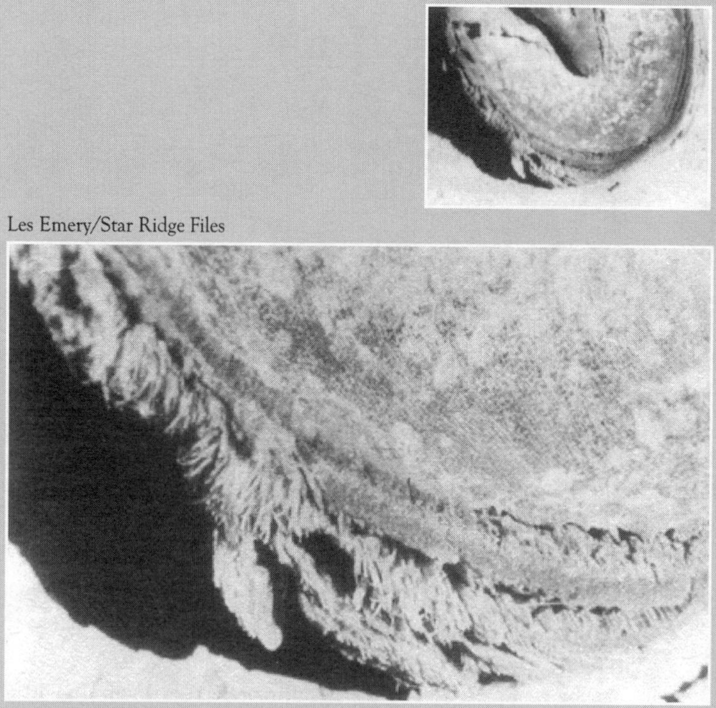

FIGURE 16-12

HORN RAVEL

This hoof has fallen apart for two reasons: the horse was stalled constantly in his own wastes and the hooves, while barefooted, were not properly trimmed. What is one obvious step missing in the trimming?

propolis – and fungicides if deemed necessary too). Movement is also important to healing. So boot up and ride your horse liberally!

POOR QUALITY HORN

I can't recall in 25 years seeing poor quality horn which couldn't be attributed to either lousy trimming methods or excessive growth (Figure 16-12). Of course, the deleterious effects of shoeing are not included in this discussion because by definition, shoeing creates weak hooves.

There is some concern too that nutrition plays an important role in horn quality. I think here only extreme neglect is at issue, meaning the horse is being deprived of feed basics. Of much greater concern, however, is over-feeding, and feeding things that aren't natural for the horse's digestive system.

And as for the adverse effects of moisture, or lack of, the hoof appears naturally capable of adapting to both extremes within limits. In the wild, horses stand in the water they drink

every day; this lasts for 10 to 20 minutes. During summer and much of fall and winter, their hooves are subject to arid conditions that border on a laboratory desiccator. Yet they do fine. In the middle of winter and early spring, their high desert rangelands can become muddy bogs for weeks on end; still the hooves adapt. Therefore, it would appear, overall, that the hoof has selected for daily brief soaks in a principally dry biome but with seasonal periods of rain and snow. Boarding a horse year round in constant mud, or upon perpetual dry ground with no chance for hoof soaks, may be an invitation to hoof breakdown and predation by opportunistic pathogens.

There are many dietary hoof nutrition supplements on the market. As these are feed concentrates, I recommend avoiding them – in my opinion, they are founder traps. Hoof dressings or "conditioners" are also abundant and should not be used as a substitute for natural boarding practices. See the Resource section for one that I use on the outer wall only following trimming – as a replacement for lost perioplic horn.

TREATMENT

Four week intervals of natural trims, a hay based diet, and lots of movement will remedy 95 percent of all horn quality issues. As to moisture, short of moving your horse to wild horse country, simply provide him with dry ground (e.g., under a covered shed) and a muddy watering site (e.g., overflowing water trough). I see no harm in hoof dressings which do not block perspiration or weaken the capsule, providing they are used only to replace periople following rasping of the outer wall (see Resources for my recommendations).

THIN, MUSHY, BRUISED AND ABSCESSED SOLES

The sole is not naturally thin and weak, but thick and firm so that it may protect the coffin bone and other sensitive structures within the capsule, and yet flexible enough that it may serve the hoof mechanism. The soles are rendered weak and unnatural in several different ways.

Shoeing weakens and harms the sole in many ways. It does this by preventing natural wear, which hardens the sole, and therefore puts the "soft sole" at risk of bruising by concussional forces. Shoes, especially those with bars, pads, and clips, obstruct the hoof mechanism, and can cause bruising of the solar corium by the descending coffin bone. (Review Chapter 3 for related discussion concerning impact of shoeing on the mechanism.)

Unnatural trimming weakens the sole too. Hoof walls that are left too long, or which are not mediolaterally balanced, stress and weaken the sole just like shoes. Soles that are trimmed too thin with the hoof knife lead to bruising and abscessing. Unnaturally over-trimmed soles can leave horses perpetually sore for months and years.

Artificial horn conditioners or plastic resins purportedly formulated to "harden" weak soles and fill holes (and wall cracks) respectively are also problematic. These can compromise the native flexibility of the sole, obstruct the release of moisture from the capsule (perspiration), or seal in infectious materials which cause abscessing.

"Dropped Soles" from founder is also an issue, and the cause here is diet. When diet is overlooked, laminitis can cause the sole to descend and flatten out, not only bruising the sole and making it vulnerable to infection but leaving the horse in great pain with each step.

If the above isn't enough, there is also the problem of close confinement – horses standing in their own waste. Or horses compelled to live on boggy ground with no relief from the constant moisture (Figure 16-12).

Fortunately, weak soles and complications from this condition are easily remedied through natural hoof care and common sense horse management.

TREATMENT

First, remove shoes if your horse is shod. If the hooves are abscessed, then de-shoeing, regular natural trims at four week intervals, and daily hoof soaks (50 percent vinegar in water) will bring about a natural healing. Tincture of propolis (see Resources) will also help. Your veterinarian may prescribe antibiotics if the hoof has become seriously infected. Until the hooves have healed, I recommend that you defer the necessary hoof work to a professional natural hoof care practitioner. Unless your horse is limping, I wouldn't discourage you from riding him. But use hoof boots until the sole is entirely hardened off and completely pain free.

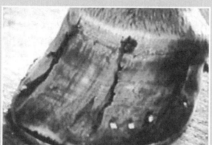

European Farriers Journal

FIGURE 16-13

WALL SPLITS

There are many kinds of hoof wall cracks, some due to hoof imbalance, some a result of laminitis and WLD, others from trauma injuries to the coronet, and of course from shoeing itself (e.g., over-nailing). But whatever their cause, the way to eliminate the cracking and restore the hoof is through natural trimming and appropriate natural lifeway changes. Wall cracks like those seen here should be handled by a professional natural hoof care practitioner. Moreover, if your trimming method suddenly incurs cracking, even hairline, it's time to get professional help. This person can help review your skills and management practices and get you back on track.

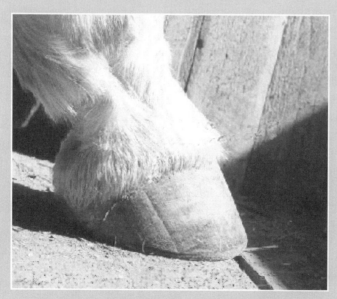

FIGURE 16-14

WALL SPLITS

Some wall cracks are caused by trauma wounds to the coronary band. When this happens a "scar" seam results below the injury site (left). The seams never go away and cause the horse no discomfort. Nor is the hoof capsule rendered weak; in fact, I have seen these seams in wild horse hooves and the horses were in no way incapacitated.

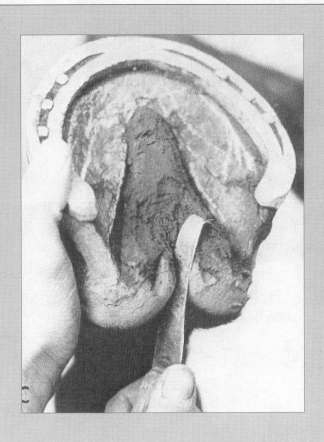

FIGURE 16-15

THRUSH

Advanced thrush in frog of shod
hoof. Barefootedness and natural
trimming are no guarantees that
thrush won't infect your horse's
feet. Lifestyle issues may be over-
riding. To effect a natural healing, alter your horse's diet and
living quarters to resemble wild
horse country. Read my companion book, *Founder: Prevention and
Cure the Natural Way* to learn
how to do this. Thrush will then
gradually abate with regular natural trims at four week intervals.

WALL CRACKS

There's nothing more disconcerting to hoof
care practitioners than the sudden appearance
of cracks or splits in the hoof wall. There are
many causes of wall cracking (Figure 16-13),
but all can be healed through natural trimming
and adjustments in the horse's lifestyle.

Most wall splitting can be completely healed
with no visible traces of the original fracture.
Others, like trauma injuries to the coronet,
may leave a permanent scar or "seam" (Figure
16-14). The latter is not painful to the horse
and in no way restricts or obstructs the horse's
movement or incapacitates him for riding's
sake.

TREATMENT
Most minor cracks will clear up over time
through natural trims and a well-rendered mustang roll. If your horse's foot has very serious
cracks, defer your trimming to a professional
natural hoof care practitioner.

THRUSH

All horse owners are familiar with thrush,
the affliction being that common. Therefore I
won't labor the issue here, except to say that
thrush does not occur in wild horse hooves
and so there is no reason for it to occur among
domestic horses either. Natural hoof care, barefootedness, and natural boarding will cure any
horse of thrush.

TREATMENT
As stated, follow previous protocols for
natural hoof care and lifestyle management
and thrush will eventually yield. Try using tincture of bee propolis (see Resources) to expedite
natural healing. If the condition is very advanced (Figure 16-15), yield your work temporarily to a professional natural hoof care practitioner until the matter is brought back under
control.

FIGURE 16-16

COFFIN BONE INTEGRITY

I x-rayed a set of hooves removed from a healthy wild horse that died during a BLM gather. To my surprise, I discovered bone loss at the tip of the coffin bone. But only on the front feet *(bottom)*, and, at that, bilaterally. The hind were "normal" *(top)*. Why the loss of bone if it is not associated with lameness — as some veterinary authorities claim?

Star Ridge Files

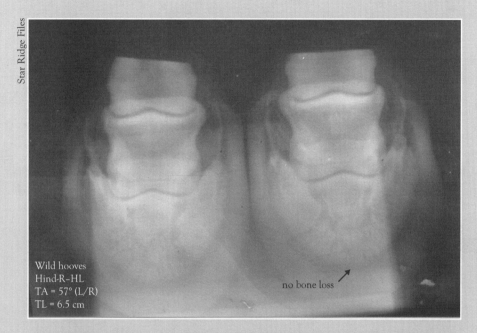

Wild hooves
Hind-R–HL
TA = 57° (L/R)
TL = 6.5 cm

no bone loss

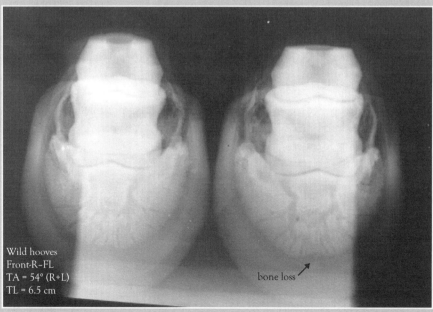

Wild hooves
Front-R–FL
TA = 54° (R+L)
TL = 6.5 cm

bone loss

INTERFERENCE

Interference refers to a disruption or obstruction of the horse's natural gaits. This can happen naturally from an accidental slip, or unnaturally from hoof imbalance and unnatural horsemanship. Whichever the case, one limb "interferes" with or obstructs the movement of another; commonly, the hooves collide with each other or with the lower legs. Damage to the horse's legs or hooves can result.

There are many variations of interference depending on the peculiarities of the unbalanced hoof. Conventionally, they are identified by different names among farriers; for example: *forging*, the toe of the hind foot hitting the sole of the forefoot on the same side; *overreaching*, the toe of the hind foot catching the heel of the forefoot on the same side; and *interfering*, or "clipping," the hitting of opposite hooves.

The rise of "corrective shoeing" in modern times is due in part to interference problems. The farriery and veterinary literature is replete with theories, opinions, and methods to deal with interference. This is understandable since horseshoeing, according to natural hoof theory, unbalances the hoof. But the adverse effects of unnatural riding habits cannot be overlooked either.

TREATMENT

Assuming one's approach to equitation is assessed and found to be reasonably natural, then giving your horse natural trims at four week intervals should be all that's necessary to correct any form of interference.

COFFIN BONE INTEGRITY

I decided to add this issue if only to combat a widely held perception that demineralization or loss of bone mass on the periphery of the coffin bone is pathological and unnatural. Yet I have direct evidence from the wild, shown in Figure 16-16, that shows that the absence of bone mass where it is "supposed" to be present can be natural after all. The radiographs demonstrated demineralization in both front hooves. The hind hooves had no such bone loss. The question is why? Well, I have no explanation. Clearly, this is another area in need of research.

SUMMARY

In this chapter, I've covered some of the foremost lameness issues involving the horse's feet. The forces of domestication that bring horses to a state of lameness, and even premature death, are vast and as varied as the practices of horse owners who create them. Happily, the wild horse model provides a way out. A way to see what's natural and healthy with no human bias to get in the way. The decision is ours. We can keep on doing things that harm our horses. Or we can change.

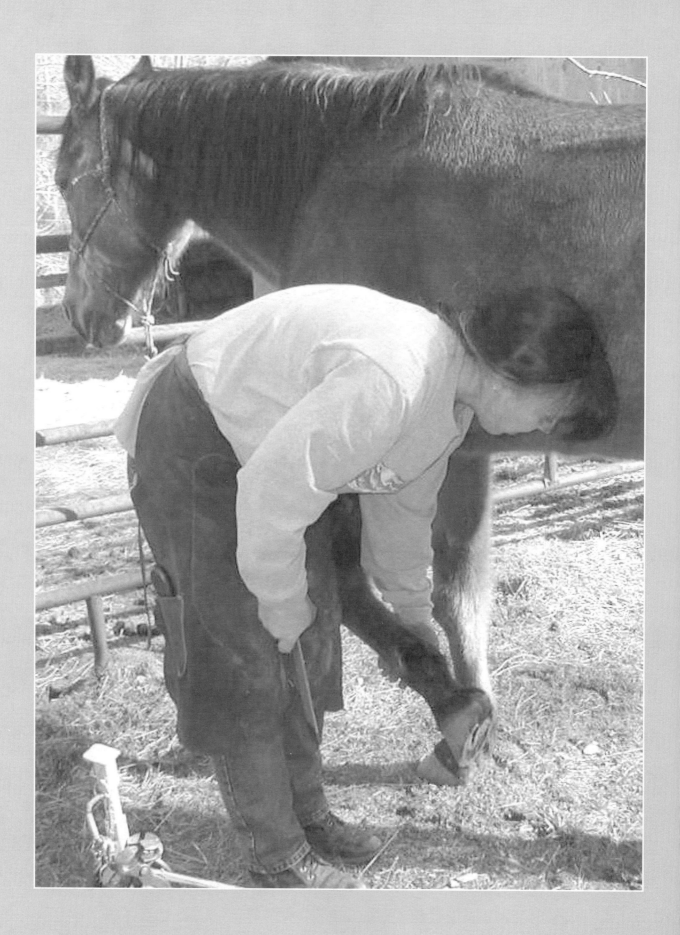

CHAPTER SEVENTEEN

NATURAL HOOF CARE

PRACTITIONERS

"Never doubt that a small group of thoughtful, committed citizens can change the world. Indeed, it's the only thing that ever has." Margaret Mead

The "natural hoof care" movement can probably trace its modern roots to the first edition of this *Guide* (1998), if not even further back to the publication of *The Natural Horse* (1992). If I were to venture a guess as to the total number of de-shod, barefooted, and booted horses this book has influenced in the U.S. today, I would put that figure in excess of ten thousand horses.

But that figure is growing daily. More and more horse owners are making the jump to natural hoof care. It is a trend based on a powerful, grass roots movement involving thousands of horse owners who are sharing the good news with each other. They have gone around resistant shoers and vets. Many have learned to do the work themselves.

Ironically, and perhaps much to the chagrin of fixed-shoeing proponents, the natural hoof care movement has actually been pioneered by forward-thinking farriers and horse owners. Professionals and amateurs who have decided for themselves that "going natural" isn't such a bad thing after all, in spite of indus-try protests to the contrary.

At the last minute before going to press, I decided to add in this chapter. It's a short list of biographies of just a few men and women in the growing ranks of natural hoof care practitioners. Many have one thing in common: they, like myself, formerly shod horses. All are also horse owners; therefore, each has felt personally the responsibility of their actions. Why do something to your horse if you *really* felt it were harmful?

These are, as I think of them, "brave hearts" — pioneers who have discovered against great odds the ancient roots of the horse in the form of a powerful "natural hoof" paradigm for modern hoof care. They all know from first hand experience what the actual effects of shoeing are on the horse's feet, locomotion, and health. They don't need "experts" to tell them anything about it because they are the experts. Some, like myself, have been working the hoof for over a quarter century; others half that and less.

We all know what it means when we pull

the shoe off a hoof with a quarter crack or with laminitis or "navicular." And then, contrary to every "accepted" protocol of farriery and veterinary science, let the horse go bare-footed in order to heal the hoof malady. We're fully aware of the farrier's and vet's protests, ringing in our ears or our clients'. We've all been through it.

But the "conventions" of modern scientific farriery and veterinary hoof care are dead wrong. And we know that too. The natural hoof is intended for the horse. It is not a pariah to be scoffed and relegated to wild horse country. It is part of the future. Indeed, it is destined to become the mainstream standard.

(*Across and overleaves*) Interviews with natural hoof care practitioners.

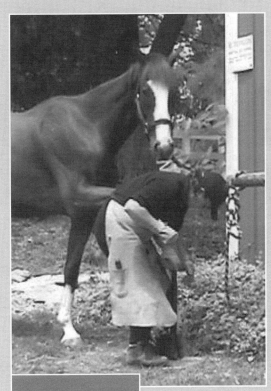

Derry McCormick
Missouri

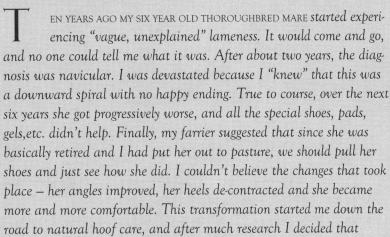

TEN YEARS AGO MY SIX YEAR OLD THOROUGHBRED MARE *started experiencing "vague, unexplained" lameness. It would come and go, and no one could tell me what it was. After about two years, the diagnosis was navicular. I was devastated because I "knew" that this was a downward spiral with no happy ending. True to course, over the next six years she got progressively worse, and all the special shoes, pads, gels,etc. didn't help. Finally, my farrier suggested that since she was basically retired and I had put her out to pasture, we should pull her shoes and just see how she did. I couldn't believe the changes that took place – her angles improved, her heels de-contracted and she became more and more comfortable. This transformation started me down the road to natural hoof care, and after much research I decided that natural hoof care based on the wild horse model made the most sense to me. I applied for certification with the American Association of Natural Hoof Care Practitioners so I could learn to trim and help my own and other horses. I am happy to say that today, while her feet are still remodeling after so many years of dysfunction and deformation, my mare runs around like a two year old again and continues to improve. It is fair to say that had I not found Jaime Jackson's works and the AANHCP, she might not be here today. Accordingly, both my horses are now barefoot, and I am dedicated to helping spread knowledge and understanding about natural and holistic hoof and horse care. I am honored to be a part of the AANHCP, an organization that is striving through research, education and field work to bring the domestic horse into harmony with its environment and human companions in order to live a healthy, happy and pain-free life as nature intended.*

(*Right*) Debbie with her mustang, "Teja".

Debbie Dutra
California

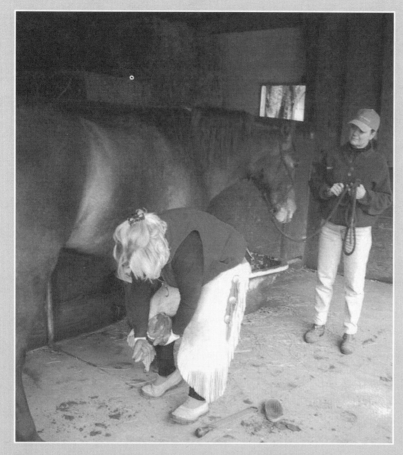

IGOT STARTED WITH NATURAL HOOF CARE *many years ago on my own horses. They never wore shoes and I could ride them anywhere in the Sierra Nevada mountain range. I didn't know much about hoof care at that time, but then I stumbled upon Jaime Jackson's books. This was a major breakthrough in my education in trimming. It was from these books that I taught myself how to care for my horses' feet. After years of trial and error I decided to give back to the horse! I started trimming as my profession. My main focus is to teach others how to trim their own horses. I conduct trimming workshops and I'm in the process of writing my own "how to trim" book. I hope to open a hoof care learning center, which will include organized trips to watch and learn from the wild horses here in Nevada. I realize I have only scratched the surface in all there is to learn about hoof care, but with each horse I trim, I become more enlightened. We all need to become more aware of our care for our horses' health, which is what I try to promote and teach. As with everything we do with our horses, support and information is a big part of how successful we will be. To all my students who are now trimming on their own, congratulations! Horse owners can and do successfully trim their own horses. I also teach natural horsemanship-starting colts and teaching people to get handy with their horses. This includes handling of their feet. The combination of natural trimming and horsemanship makes for a great outcome.*

A S A FARRIER, I STARTED LATER *in life than most pursuing my love for horses into a career. In the past 7 years as a professional farrier, I have always questioned the application of shoes to the horse's hoof. As I searched for answers, a client informed me of a new book,* THE HORSE OWNERS GUIDE TO NATURAL HOOF CARE, *by Jaime Jackson. I ordered the book and was truly amazed at the format that was presented towards horses and their hoof management. I discussed this information about barefoot horses with several of my clients and one client in particular, Theresa Brummett, agreed to remove all four shoes and begin the regimen towards being barefooted.*

Steve Dick
Florida

The transition was quite impressive as the hoof capsule began to change. Theresa and her 18-year old Thoroughbred "Cynch One" eventually earned all of her required Dressage scores and was awarded her Silver Medal from the United States Dressage Federation for their achievements at Fourth Level and Prix St. George. All while barefoot. Needless to say, the owner was ecstatic. As a professional, I have always tried to educate my clients about their horses and products that may help with proper management. I cannot express enough how important barefoot horses and their return to a natural environment is for a healthy horse. After 6 months of trimming the natural way and becoming a Certified Horse Boot Specialist, I am convinced that I will have a lot of rusty shoes to use for something other than placing them on the bottom of a horse's hoof.

Richard Drewry
Arkansas

M Y INTEREST IN NATURAL HOOF CARE *and management came about initially because of a hoof problem that just couldn't be resolved while the mare was in shoes. After about a year of trying to solve the hoof's problem with different shoeing techniques, I consulted Jaime Jackson, natural hoof care specialist, for his advice and assistance. The first thing he did was de-shoe this mare, perform a natural trim and then fit her with Swiss boots. This mare's hoof recovery to complete soundness was amazing. In addition, her new boots provided her with the footing she needed to out perform all my other horses, whether on pavement during a parade or on the roughest rocky trails the Buffalo River had to offer. I was sold. Jaime helped me pull the shoes from my other 5 horses, give them a natural trim and boot them as well. With Jaime's help and patient instruction, I have learned to trim my horses' hooves the right way - mimicking the natural hoof! The combination of the Swiss Boots allowing me to go shoeless, and the natural trim's creating conditions for healthier hooves has significantly reduced my costs associated with hoof care and management. And to me, one of the most significant advantages of this system is that I am always ready to ride! No more lost shoes just before the ride. No more pulling a shoe off getting into, or out of, the trailer. No more throwing a shoe on the trail and worrying all the way back to camp. I just "boot'n go"! This system of natural trimming and booting has worked so well for me that I just have to share it with others. That's why I have become a certified practitioner in Jaime's new Horse Boot Specialist Program.*

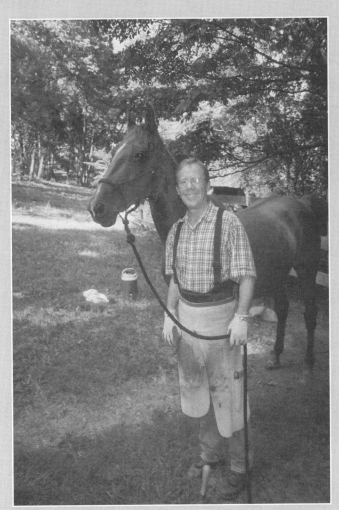

Kel Manning
Tennessee

My wife, Sharon, and I have owned horses for many years. They have always been a big part of our lives. We have learned a lot and we have also made many mistakes, including keeping our horses shod for about ten months every year. My introduction to keeping horses barefoot began when Sharon said, with conviction, "I do not want shoes on our horses anymore." Therefore, it seemed to me that pulling our horses' shoes was a good idea. We removed their shoes and had our farrier give them a pasture trim until we heard Jaime Jackson discussing the idea of keeping horses barefoot on Rick Lamb's radio show. I bought Jaime's book, "Horse Owner's Guide to Natural Hoof Care" and the companion video. They were the beginning of my introduction to the natural trim and natural hoof care, and I began trimming my horses based on the guidelines in the book and video. I gained experience and also made mistakes. I found help, attended clinics and continued to read everything I could find about trimming horses to go barefoot. I began to have some success and started trimming friends' horses. I had never expected to be one to promote the idea of keeping horses barefoot, but during this process I became dedicated to the concept of keeping horses barefoot rather than shod. When the American Association of Natural Hoof Care Practitioners (AANHCP) was formed I completed the membership application and was accepted into the organization's training and certification program, and I started a new career that I had never envisioned. It has become a personally satisfying career that is reinforced in a very big way with every barefoot hoof that begins to return to a healthy condition and conform to its natural shape. I frequently walk away from a client's barn with a smile on my face and a deep feeling of gratitude to be part of an organization that is committed to enhancing the lives of our domestic horses instead of treating them as commodities. I believe all horses understand the difference.

Charles and
Janice Hall
Tennessee

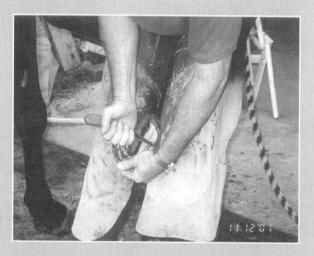

F OUNDER IS VERY COMMON *in the Tennessee Valley where I live. After trying different types of shoes on the two foundered
horses that I was asked to work on, I found that
none of them were working. Both horses never got
any better. Their hooves became convex, and in
the end the owners decided to put the horses
down. The thought of not being able to help those horses kept me awake at night, and was always on
my mind. Shortly after that, I was introduced to information about the Natural Trim including the
concepts of treating founder without shoes. I was fascinated and inspired and I decided to give it a try.
The next case of founder I was called on was a big, red Tennessee Walker with the hoof capsule sepa-
rating from the coronary band. I pulled the shoes, applied a natural trim and today he is back to the
trail horse that he was before the founder, with gorgeous and functional feet. I later began offering the
option of hoof boots to my clientele as an option to bridge the transition from shoes to barefoot. Fitting
Swiss Boots gets the horse owner back in the saddle during the transition period once I have pulled the
shoes. They are happy and their horses are on the road to recovery from years of shoeing. Being a bare-
foot/natural/hoofboot practitioner allows me to help horses in more ways than shoes will. I cannot begin to describe the joy that comes to me when I see the changes in their hooves, and knowing that I can
now help horses with laminitis, navicular, convex hooves, under-run and contracted heels. I have been a
horse owner since 1979. I cannot imagine walking out the door and not seeing my horses in the pasture. From 1983 to 1998 I managed my own boarding stables in North Carolina. I started my appren-
ticeship in farrier work in 1997 through early 1998. I received my diploma from Common Sense
Horseshoeing School in 1997. I moved to the Tennessee Valley in 1998 and attended Auburn Horseshoeing School (Alabama), completing the course with my Journeyman 1 Certification. I continue my
education with my main concern being the horse and his soundness. My wife Janice accompanies me
every day; I could not have done this without her.*

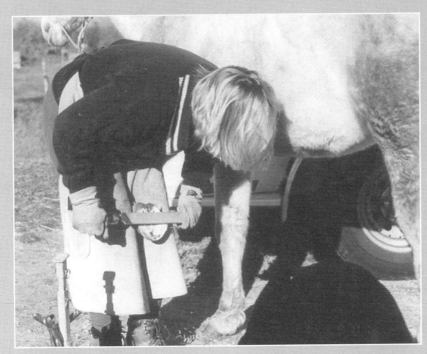

(Left) Ruth and "Flip"; (below) with "Bud".

Ruth Green
Michigan

I ORIGINALLY STARTED GOING BAREFOOT *after a shod horse lost traction and fell on me, breaking my leg. After four months on crutches, I decided no horse of mine would ever wear shoes again. I had already been doing my own trimming for six months, when I discovered Jaime's work. I was so delighted to a) find help with what I was already doing, and b) learn that what I was doing for my own health was also in the horse's best interest. I took Jaime's horse owner's clinic in November of 1999 and have never looked back. The most important part of trimming for others is the ability to help those with "incurable" problems. Several foundered horses have healed with this trimming. One of them is the gelding whose hoof I'm working on in the photo (top). He had 18 degrees of "rotation," now he's back barrel racing. And winning. I'm so pleased to be able to help. I very much enjoy teaching others to trim their own horses and returning to find they have done a great job!*

WHEN I ENROLLED IN FARRIER SCHOOL *five years ago, I began to study past and present hoof research. As I continue to follow current research, the studies I have seen on "the natural hoof" provide evidence of what I find in my practice: the well-balanced bare hoof is physiologically able to support the horse, without hoof capsule distortion, in a wide variety of conditions. For the past two years in my farrier business I have specialized in working on barefoot horses. I have clients with barefoot performance horses competing successfully in diverse sports. However because I do believe some horses need shoes to do the jobs that humans ask of them, I am supportive of my clients who choose to keep horses shod for part of the year. But the maximum potential for enhanced soundness comes from maintaining perpetual balance in the horse's hoofs, which in my experience is achieved most effectively by keeping horses barefoot. I have found that a team approach produces high success rates for determining the ideal balance and trim for each horse. The team consists of a veterinarian practicing integrative medicine, a properly trained farrier, and a dedicated horse owner. Together we provide each horse with customized hoof care for optimum soundness.*

Lisa Simons
Colorado

Jaime Jackson
Arkansas

I'VE BEEN A PROFESSIONAL HOOF CARE PROVIDER *for most of my adult life. In the past 10 years, I've gone "natural" – no shoes, just natural trimming and booting. I do this now because my wild horse research and 25 years of experience has taught me that it's the thing to do. It's good for the horse's feet and overall health, it's good for the horse owner who wants what's best for the horse, and, to be perfectly honest, it's been good for my back! Today, an important part of my work is spreading the "barefoot" word to horse owners, professional hoof care practitioners, vets, and anyone who will listen. And by barefoot I mean "natural." My barefoot model is the wild horse hoof. It's totally natural, sound, and adaptable to all domestic horses. I would encourage all professional farriers or horse owners with latent talents and desire for doing this kind of work to join me and many others in this exciting new hoof care frontier. I recommend getting educated, trained, and becoming a certified practitioner in our new organization – the American Association of Natural Hoof Care Practitioners.*

I OFTEN TRAVEL WITH MY MOM (*facing page*) *when she trims horses and I have seen how it helps them get so much better when the shoes are off and the feet are trimmed naturally. I love horses and I would always want to do what's best for them, so I want to follow in her footsteps and learn to do a natural trim. Perhaps I will make a career of it, or perhaps I will only trim on the side. Either way I plan to become as skilled as possible and help as many horses as I can . . .*

Jessi Sullivan
Georgia

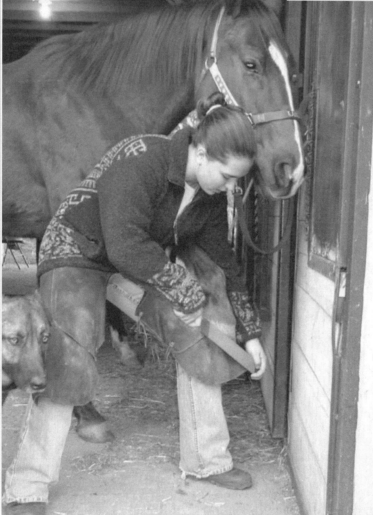

. . . I would like to help spread the news about barefoot horses, how much they benefit from a natural lifestyle and not having shoes. I want people to know about the wild horses and what they have given us. Hopefully, I will be able to encourage other young people to start off right in the way they think about and interact with horses. Maybe, in my lifetime, unnatural practices with horses (especially shoeing) will be just a memory . . . something that was done in "the olden days."

Cindy "Hawk" Sullivan
Georgia

URING MY 30-PLUS YEARS OF HORSE KEEPING, *I had trimmed my own horses and occasionally those of others based on the standards taught to me by farriers when I was a teen. My interest in a truly natural trim began in 1998 when I adopted my first mustang from BLM. I was amazed and fascinated by his feet - healthy, strong and completely sound without the "benefit" of human assistance. Why were his feet so perfect? Could domestic horses have such feet? Thus began my search for answers- a search that would land me squarely in the path of the emerging barefoot movement. After a great deal of study, I began trimming professionally and working to teach others about high performance barefootedness – that it is not only possible, but the only natural way to achieve lasting soundness for any horse. As I expand my hoof care practice, my focus is to support the growth of the American Association of Natural Hoof Care Practitioners – an organization with a membership that has an intimate understanding of and profound respect for the wild horse model. I am dedicated to holding up the model for others to see, to learn from and to embrace.*

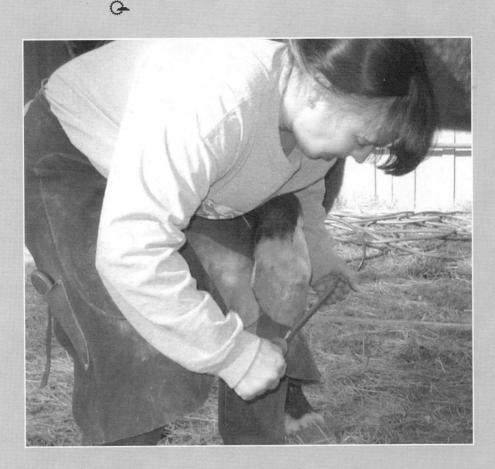

I CAME TO BAREFOOT HOOF CARE BECAUSE *I wanted to trim my own horses' feet, and the horse-shoes were just in the way. Later on I learned how good it is for their health to go barefoot, and added outdoor living to the picture. I got "hooked" on trimming. It's satisfying and powerful to trim a hoof and make it feel better. It deepened the personal connection with my horses. Now they let me trim out in the woods while they munch hay. I began showing friends how to go barefoot and how to trim, and the work has spread from there. My website, "Barefoot for Soundness," at www.barefoothorse.com tells about going barefoot. I try to make it clear to horse owners how much there is to gain, as well as how to make barefoot work well for their horses.*

Marjorie Smith
Rhode Island

Me and John. John is a 10 year old Saddlebred gelding.

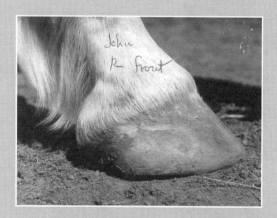

John's right front: side view and front views.

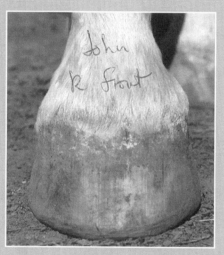

Pete Ramey (Georgia)

I BORROWED A COPY OF JAIME'S HOG IN '99 in hopes of improving my horseshoeing. What I read blew me away. I didn't have to take Jaime's word for any of it. I knew it was the truth. At the time, I was running a trail riding facility in the mountains of North Georgia. The trails were steep and rocky, and riders canter and jump on most rides. In a moment of inspiration, I pulled the shoes off all 29 of the horses and "went natural." This has been wonderful. I soon found out I could get more out of the barefoot horses than I could when they were shod, and there were far less injuries and stone bruises. Soon, I was buying foundered horses from the killer pens and helping friends' horses. Quite by accident I wound up in the hoof business. These days, I am maintaining hundreds of horses full time. I have seen natural hoof care work for all breeds, and almost every hoof disorder you could think of. I've learned a lot along the way, but I've only scratched the tip of the iceberg. The biggest problems I see now is that there are not enough competent hoof professionals to keep up with the nationwide demand. Mountains of confusing information have been put out there as well as invasive trimming methods that do not produce sound, barefoot horses. It is hard for a newcomer or a progressive farrier to go straight to the methods that work, without taking detours into the methods that sore horses. For this reason, I've joined others in forming the American Association of Natural Hoof Care Practitioners and creating a comprehensive training and certification program.

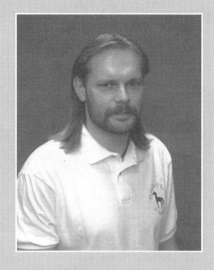

I'M A NATIVE OF RUSSELLVILLE, Arkansas. *Before I met Jaime, I had taken a B.S. degree in agricultural studies and later became a professional farrier, working closely with a Dr. Howard Mitchell, a holistic equine veterinarian, in Oklahoma. Dr. Mitchell discovered the natural hoof care movement on the internet and asked me to visit Jaime to learn more about it. The result - to make a long story short - was that I have become a full time advocate and practitioner of "natural hoof care" - assisting horses to be ridden barefoot or in some instances with hoof boots. I told Dr. Mitchell that at long last, I've found something I can wholeheartedly believe in, and I've happily abandoned my "shoeing bag of tricks" for a program that works every time and is in the best interest of all horses. My wife Tammie, also a lifelong horse owner, shares my enthusiasm and together we have put together a national natural hoof care clinic program, which is described on our website, www.naturalhoof.com I am planning to become a certified practitioner with the American Association of Natural Hoof Care Practitioners and will dedicate my professional life to the promotion of its goals.*

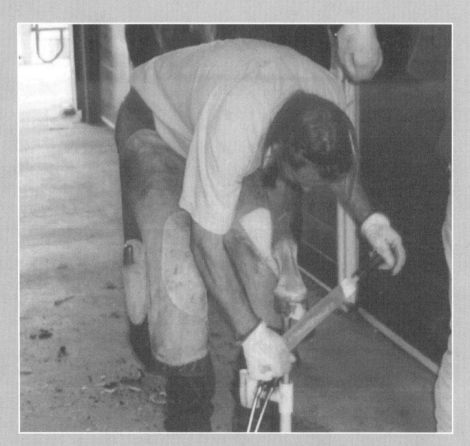

IN MY 26 YEARS OF FARRIERY, *I was constantly searching for a deeper understanding of horses and the desire to help them – which led me to working with Linda Tellington-Jones, a host of holistic veterinarians and practitioners in Europe, eventually culminating in the development of a handful of holistic vet practices and educational programs here in Colorado. Through these experiences I began to understand the more non-obvious function of the hoof and its overall importance in the physical and energetic or electromagnetic balance of the animal. In my current practice, I and my partner are applying basic, non-invasive holistic measures to help re-ground the horse, reestablishing the hoof-earth connection and are re-educating our clients and local veterinarians. Our efforts over the centuries to improve on nature's design have brought us a host of troubles . . . realizing this, we encourage, support and add our efforts to a return to a more Nature-based way of stewarding the horse. Trimming the hooves to restore natural function makes innate sense to me. I was beginning to see disturbing changes in the hooves that I had been caring for long term. In some cases, I was frustrated after running through all the conventional corrective and pathological shoeing formulas for navicular, laminitis, etc., with little to no positive change. I really have come to believe that when something drops into my lap, it's a sign or message that a change in technique, attitude or belief is up for me. When I learned about the natural trim and put it into practice, I began to see real healing take place in so many non-responsive cases. I was sold on it!*

Eryn Wolfwalker
Colorado

WILD VS. DOMESTIC: A UNIQUE CROSSROADS IN THE MONGOLIAN OUTBACK

This extraordinary photo of a semi-feral Mongolian horse has captured an important glimpse of sound, naturally worn hooves among the herds of modern semi-nomadic tribal peoples who know nothing of modern hoof care — and who could care less. The hooves seen here, with thick, rock hard soles, prominent heel-buttresses and bars, are in a crossroads between the horse's uncompromised natural world as seen in the mustang of the west, and the simple but demanding needs of horsed peoples there in the wildest reaches of domestication. This unique intersection of wild and domestic represents an important research sector in the natural hoof care movement. (*Star Ridge Files*)

CHAPTER EIGHTEEN

THE NATURAL MODEL:

WHAT WE DON'T KNOW

What is there to be learned? We have just touched the tip of the iceberg. Are these tough, well-shaped feet a reflection of environment or genetics or a combination of both? Ric Redden, DVM (The Wild Horse's Foot, 2001 Bluegrass Laminitis Symposium)

Anyone at the cutting edge of the natural hoof care movement sooner or later discovers that the more we learn, the more we become aware of just how much we don't really know. This uncanny paradox confronts all pioneers seeking deeper and more profound understandings of nature. Albert Einstein conveyed as much in his symbolic "Circles of Knowledge," which I've adapted in Figure 18-1. Let's think about them for a minute.

The gray area within the small circle represents our consummate knowledge in life. The circumference of the small circle represents our awareness of what we do not know. Now, as we learn more in life, our circle of knowledge increases; but now we are confronted with the fact that there is even more that we don't know. Paradoxically, the more we learn, the more we are cognizant of how much *more* we don't know.

So it is true as we look closer at the natural hoof model. It is infinitely complex. The closer we look at it, the more questions it raises. Thinking about the thousand or so wild horse hooves I studied years ago, I realize now that the most important thing they ever taught me was how to look at things in a balanced way. Although there was endless variation in hoof form, the result was not chaos. Measurement data could be sorted and organized to reveal trends, averages, and other statistical information. Intuitively, I knew that the Laws of

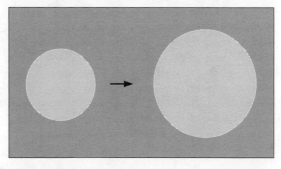

Figure 18-1   EINSTEIN'S CIRCLES OF KNOWLEDGE

Nature were being expressed by the hooves. The struggle was in deciphering them, gaining knowledge while being cognizant of the vast and increasing body of information lying beyond my sphere of knowledge.

As much as I know today, twenty years later, I'm still painfully aware of how much more I don't know. But really want to know! I'm not talking about mysterious other-worldly stuff in the deep interior of the hoof "spirit." I mean practical information that we natural hoof care practitioners should know if we are to provide better hoof care for horses in our charge.

So, I've included this chapter to help pave the way toward future research. I believe in getting new ideas out there. If we don't bother, then their potential value may never come to light and our circles of knowledge will stagnate. The following areas of inquiry have been on my mind since my earliest encounters with the wild hoof. They are complex and we cannot, aside from sheer speculation, extrapolate definitive answers for them directly from domestic horse populations. I've discussed them with other professional practitioners, and we all agree — the time has come to return to wild horse country.

POSITION OF P3 IN HOOF CAPSULE

There have been countless claims and counterclaims by farriery and veterinary authorities about the "correct" anatomical position of the coffin bone (P3) in the "balanced" hoof capsule. I've made a few myself!

For example, in the radiograph in Figure 18-2, it would appear that the base of the coffin bone aligns parallel with the ground. While this may be true, more research is needed to prove or disprove the statement. In other words, if true, does it apply to all hooves? Front and hind hooves? If not, than what variation is there? And just as important, to what criteria (toe angle, leg and body conformation, etc.) can we correlate this information?

We need clear answers. Not only for balancing the hooves of domestic horses, but in the treatment of lameness. The way to do this is to drag radiographic equipment into the BLM holding stations following a gather and take some x-rays. Simple enough!

SHORTNESS OF HOOF CAPSULE

This is a big one with me and any person of sound mind who has witnessed a 2½ inch toe wall on a 1400 pound wild stallion! The great mystery is not in the shortness of the toe wall (i.e., Toe Length) per se, because we know the relationship of the dorsal wall of P3 to the toe wall of the capsule (Figure 18-3) — P3 seems to "dwell" higher in the hoof capsule of wild hooves than domestic hooves. But rather,

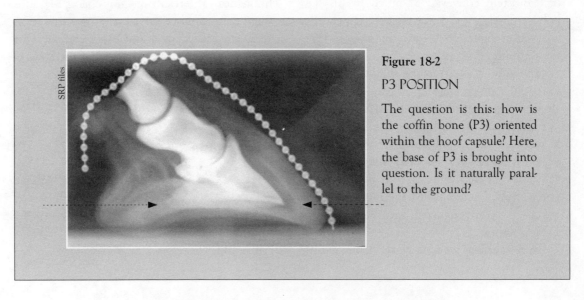

SRP files

Figure 18-2

P3 POSITION

The question is this: how is the coffin bone (P3) oriented within the hoof capsule? Here, the base of P3 is brought into question. Is it naturally parallel to the ground?

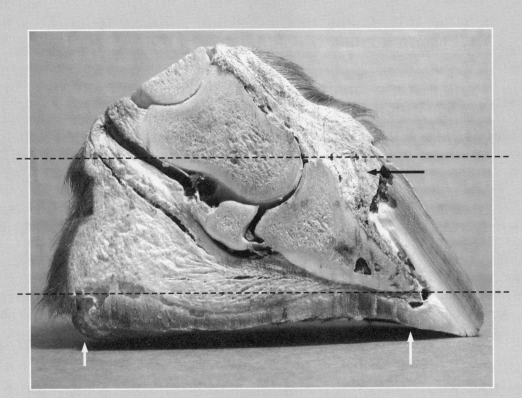

Figure 18-3 RELATIONSHIP OF P3 TO HOOF CAPSULE/TL

Dashed lines frame the solar margin (below) and extensor process (above) of coffin bone (P3) in this unique cross-section of a wild horse hoof. My opinion is that P3 occupies a higher position in the capsule than is seen in domestic horse hooves. Black arrow points to extraordinary mass of soft tissue surrounding apex of P3 — has Nature provided for this cushioning through some obscure activation mechanism? [TL = 2.5 inches; TA = 57°; 12 yr. mare]

how does it happen exactly?

To answer this question, our research will require that we introduce horses into the wild and evaluate the hooves as they transform over time. X-rays and 3-dimensional images will be needed, and the hooves will have to be measured and evaluated at very close intervals — possibly once a week. This can be done, but we will need access to BLM Herd Management Areas (HMA's) to conduct the research.

From the standpoint of natural hoof care, this information is important because we simply do not understand the mechanisms that drive P3 into its elevated natural position. Certainly it is obvious that the higher the orientation of P3, the shorter the capsule can be. I can only speculate that natural wear, particularly the compressional (weight bearing) force has a lot to do with it. But we don't know how we can adapt our trimming strategies to help

or even stimulate the transformation without rendering the solar dome hypersensitive. In 20 years, I have not been able to figure it out using domestic horses for observation.

FROG THROUGH THE SOLAR DOME

One of the most extraordinary characteristics of the natural hoof from the wild is how advanced the frog is across the solar dome, front to back. This can also be seen in the hoof cross-section in Figure 18-3. Note the rear white arrow marks the frog's central sulcus junction with the hairline, the fore white arrow the point-of-frog. Rarely does one see the frog advanced this far in domestic hooves. Why?

Part of the reason clearly is explained by the descending of the heel-buttresses — discussed in the next section. The frog is "cast" forward by this equally unique configuration of the buttresses. But even in my own trimming, which can put the heel bulbs in close proximity of the ground, the point-of-frog does not advance to the degree I see in wild hooves.

This will be a great one to investigate and we will all learn much, much useful information about the dynamics of frog adaptation. Perhaps more than anything, we will learn more completely how the frog fulfills its mission in the hoof mechanism. The shape and mass of the frog, being mutable, can impinge or enhance the frog's role as hinge in the solar dome. We must lead domestic hooves through the pipeline into wild horse country and assess the transformation of this most critical structure.

ROTATED HEEL-BUTTRESSES

Of all the perplexing features of the naturally shaped hoof, the one that seems to baffle every hoof care practitioner the most — not to mention that this characteristic also breaks all the rules of "modern" hoof care science — is what I call "rotated heel-buttress" (I'm sure the descriptive name will change as we study it more closely, but for now it will suffice here.).

Most of us who work the hooves professionally would like to think that the (horn tubular) ends of the heel wall do all the weight bearing at the buttresses. But nothing could be further than the truth in the wild horse hoof!

The wild ones literally walk on the "back" of their heel buttress — along with their ends. By every definition of conventional hoof care science, this would mean that naturally shaped hooves are "run under". So be it, if that's what is natural.

While I personally accept this unique conformation of naturally worn hooves, what I cannot figure out is how it happens exactly. Nothing new! It simply means we must run more domestic horses through the HMA pipeline to see how it occurs. I've been unable to affect a comparable rotation in domestic horses — close, but not exactly the same.

There is some credible evidence that this particular "heel bulbs down" trait is a built in natural defense mechanism against navicular syndrome — or more accurately, pain in the back of the hoof due to imbalance. Natural hoof care practitioners know from experience that reducing long heels to what are short heels by industry standards, will eliminate this pain (Figure 18-4). This is incentive enough to see exactly how nature intended the rotation to occur.

HOOF SYMMETRY AND ASYMMETRY

Thinking of the many intriguing aspects of the naturally worn hoof, another one that has really baffled me is what I call the asymmetric configuration of hind hooves. It's almost im-

(Continued on page 263)

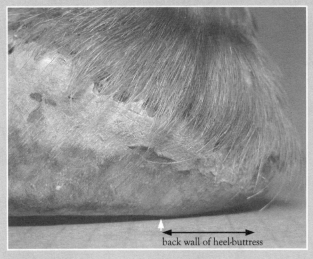

back wall of heel-buttress

Figure 18-4

ROTATED HEEL-BUTTRESS

This is an interesting contrast of well-shod hoof with long heels (thought to be a cure for navicular) with low heeled wild hoof in lateral view showing rotated heel-buttress. The hairline of shod hoof is a good 3-plus inches off the ground — the wild hoof's is within a centimeter. The vertical white arrow marks the location of the seat-of-corn; a full 1¼ inches (3.5 cm) of buttress "back wall" is in direct weight bearing position!

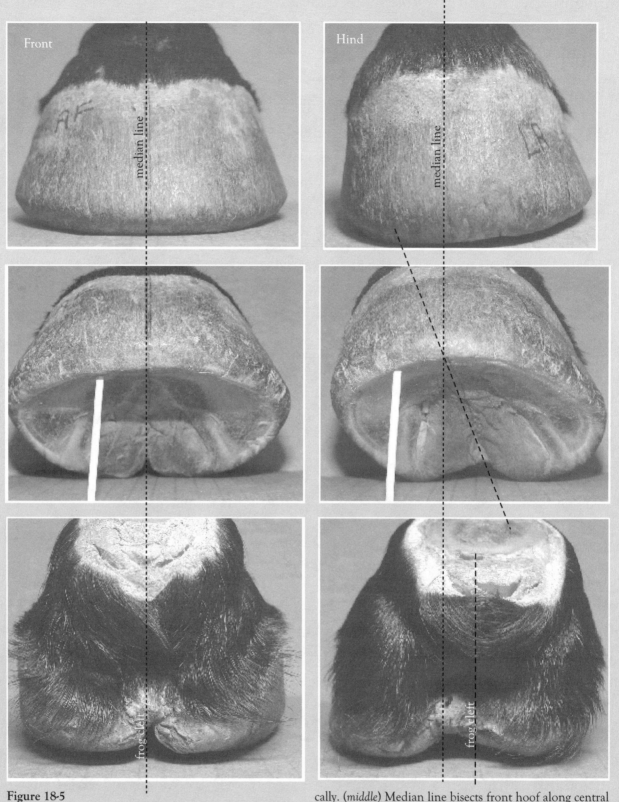

Figure 18-5

ASYMMETRY IN HIND HOOF CAPSULE

Vertical dotted-line marks median line of hoof capsule, front and hind hooves viewed from the front. (*top*) Median line bisects front symmetrically, hind asymmetri- cally. (*middle*) Median line bisects front hoof along central frog sulcus, but asymmetrically intersects frog sulcus of hind hoof. (*bottom*) Median line bisects posterior view of front hoof, asymmetrically divides hind. Note, however, that median line bisects P1 (pastern bone) of both front and hind hooves.

possible for me to describe here, but I'll attempt it.

Refer to Figure 18-5. Notice how the dotted median line bisects every profile of the "symmetrically" shaped *front* hoof. Now, look at the corresponding profiles of the hind hoof: anything but symmetrical — except the volar profile, which is bisected symmetrically (Figure 2-6). Why? In my book, *The Natural Horse*, I speculated that it must have something to do with lateral thrust? In other words, how the hind hoof lifts and propels body weight to the left or right as the horse turns.

This is important because it tells us that trimming strategies which aim to either render asymmetric hooves symmetric, or vice versa, are contraposing underlying natural growth patterns. Let me elaborate here in case you are a farrier reading this.

As a former farrier, I have seen this in shoeing, where it is commonly believed that the medial branch of the shoe (front or hind) must be narrowed to prevent interfering or to conform to the hoof which is seductively asymmetric in its anterior profile yet is, paradoxically, symmetrical across its volar plane. As more and more farriers enter the natural hoof care movement, we need clear evidence from the field to convince them to take another look at how they are dressing hooves for "symmetrical and asymmetrical balance." Equally important is that future boot manufacturers don't make the same mistake, and as I reflect on the numerous (including many European) models out there now, all have failed to incorporate this important dimension of the naturally configured hoof capsule.

HEEL CONFORMATION

I mentioned in Chapter 16 ("Hoof Contraction") that many, perhaps most, naturally shaped hooves are "contracted" by most industry standards and definitions. At one time I stood firmly behind some of those definitions, but after entering wild horse country and seeing nature's grand plan for the heels of the hoof, I was forced to recant my former opinions. We must all do the same in view of the facts.

The fact is that the proximity of the "backside" of the heel-buttresses to each other in many wild horse hooves borders on approximating "egg bar" shoes! But this may be an illusion since it is exceedingly difficult to differentiate wall horn from frog horn due to the planished finish of heavily worn wild hooves.

(Continued on page 264)

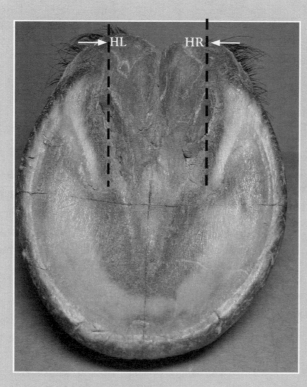

Figure 18-6

HEEL CONFORMATION

(*left*) Dotted lines and arrows mark base of posterior bend of heel-buttresses. Note that these edges are on the back side wall of the buttresses, not the distal ends of the tubular horn. Also of interest is that the heel bulbs themselves are heavily compressed and virtually "disappear" into the wall/frog horn "blend". [Right Front: HW = 10.2 cm; HL across to HR = 30 cm]

Figure 18-6 provides a close up view of exactly what I'm talking about. Not all wild horse hooves are this close together, though, and we must remember that variation is an important lesson from the wild. No doubt the "close heel" conformation expresses itself as a variant adaptation to the environment of the home range. But what influence the horse's conformation has on this adaptation is completely unknown at this time. There's only one way to find out — put horses through the HMA pipeline and observe.

What a wealth of important and useful information could be harvested from a thorough and comprehensive study of heel conformations in the wild.

ACTIVE AND PASSIVE WEAR

The issue of active and passive wear around the hoof wall of the capsule is something I discussed at length in Chapter 2. There and in Chapter 8 I advised that the hoof care practitioner initiate a "work plate" approach to balancing the hooves: putting both heel-buttresses and the entire toe wall in a single plane. Out of that plane, of course, emerges active and passive support points along the hoof wall.

The problem, of course, is in learning to distinguish those support points which are natural from those that are not. The latter can include among other possibilities: the effects of lameness, our rasps, and riding styles. Lost or buried in the jumble of competing forces vying to shape the capsule are the deeper forces of the horse's own true identity that we suppress.

By driving domestic horses through the HMA pipeline we can observe changes in the support profile of the capsule and correlate the changes to such things as body weight, conformation, locomotive style, hoof size and proportion, and even diet. In so doing, we can predict how hooves in domestication are compensating for unnatural forces. We may even be able to change our habits (e.g., trimming methods) to reverse some of these forces. And here, I have those particularly in mind which can be attributed to causing lameness.

I predict that studies of wear patterns will be the most difficult to catalogue, interpret, and apply. Yet, the body of knowledge gained would be worth every bit of the challenge.

LAMENESS

This study is probably the most exciting in the minds of natural hoof care practitioners I've talked with. In short, and I will be disproportionately brief, what will be involved here is taking lame domestic horses, "banding" them with viable herds in the HMAs and observing the healing forces of nature at work.

Obviously, watching the hooves transform will be of keen interest. But so will other related phenomena: changes in the horse's musculature (e.g., his back), changes in locomotive habits, his temperament and attitude towards other horses, and so forth. In the holistic realm of lameness treatment, anything and everything that effects the horse's life is of paramount important.

DIET

This is another intriguing, if not critical, topic and the subject of great interest among natural hoof care practitioners. It can be summarized in a single question, "Given that wild horses in viable HMA's are so healthy, what are they eating?" There has been some speculation based on field observations, including my own, that the wild ones aren't just eating to fill their bellies. They may also be seeking out — perhaps consciously, perhaps unconsciously — certain flora and rock minerals for medicinal purposes. Whatever the reason, no one really knows exactly what they're up to because nothing has been investigated systematically and reported. It's a wide open field.

One dietary area of intense interest among natural hoof care advocates concerns laminitis. What is it about the wild horse diet that ren-

ders their population so "founder free"? Is it something they are eating, or, perhaps something they are not eating? Or is it in how they are eating? I believe the answer can be found in wild horse country.

Ironically, the dietary landscape of wild horse country more closely resembles a barren moonscape than a land of cornucopia (Figure 18-7). Yet the horses proliferate with seemingly nothing to eat. Why? And, again, what are the implications for dietary based lamenesses such as laminitis and WLD?

Conceivably, we could identify the bulk grasses and browse the wild ones frequent, and make recommendations for commercial harvests on private — or leased public — lands (which could help in the fight against ecological overgrazing by livestock). A new generation of founder-free hays could be unleashed. Commercial feed companies such as Ralston-Purina could lend a hand by helping to evaluate other carbohydrates, proteins, and minerals that wild horses consume, thereby producing bona fide founder-free feed supplements.

These are ideas of course, but who knows where they may lead to one day.

DENTAL HYGIENE

I wrote in *The Natural Horse* years ago that wild horse country has no veterinarian making the rounds floating teeth! Neither are there horses out there falling over each other and dying from dental complications. Actually, I know the answer to this one, but it's worth a formal research project to strike broader interest from our veterinary community.

THE DOUBLE-BACK

Xenophon in 500 BC was I believe the first person to describe the "double back" — a little known anatomical trait of healthy, sound horses that one sees everywhere in wild horse populations, and practically never among domestic horses. That this astute observer and icon of natural horsemanship thought enough

Star Ridge files

Figure 18-7

DIETARY LANDSCAPE OF WILD HORSE COUNTRY

I was staggered when I came upon this fence line in wild horse country years ago. This is an official government "riparian area" — a section of land fenced off from all livestock, including wild horses, for ecological study purposes. Based on what I had seen and heard, I always thought Nevada and other high desert biomes of the American West were "wastelands." In fact, they are rich grasslands. But with millions of cattle, sheep, and goats (there are less than 40,000 wild horses in all of wild horse country) grazing the 200 or so million acres of stressed public lands, well, look for yourself. It is a national disgrace. In spite of this, there are important lessons in this for natural hoof care practitioners. One lesson concerns a dark symbiosis between wild horses and livestock: why do wild horses do so well on lands over-grazed by livestock? Many questions are raised, and answers could lead to a badly needed dietary revolution for a very laminitic domestic horse population.

of its importance to bring the matter up for future generations of equestrians, earns him my high regard.

The "double-back" is a physical characteristic wherein the longitudinal muscles that parallel the horse's spine rise up even with or above the interjacent spine. This muscular configuration occurs in sound, healthy horses that move naturally most of the time — like our wild horses (Figure 18-8). Without badly fitting saddles and unbalanced riders hampering them, their backs rise fully and increase in mass — like one of Arnold Schwarzenegger's flexed biceps — under pressure from the horse's hyper-extending joints of propulsion.

Xenophon noted that the double-back was a sign of correct training and that it was more comfortable to ride than horse's with unnatural backs with protruding spines and withers. But the ancient Greeks, of course, rode bareback — the saddle was yet centuries away. I would raise the question, logically I think, do our "modern" saddling systems obstruct the free-flowing natural movement of the horse, and thus the full, natural development of his back?

There is evidence for this thesis, most notably in the saddling research and rehabilitation work of Lesley Ann Taylor and Carol Brett of England. They have written:

> One common symptom of saddle damage is the horse that is described as having 'high narrow withers'. It has long been accepted by the equestrian world that certain horses have this as a natural conformation . . . [but] it is usually a lack of natural, healthy muscle below and to the rear of the withers that makes them and the shoulder blades appear more prominent than they should be. This lack of muscle mass is often caused by the pressures of a saddle fitted or used in a way that does not allow normal movement and blood flow in this area. There are

The Natural Horse/Jaime Jackson

Figure 18-8 DOUBLE-BACKS IN THE WILD

One of the most conspicuous characteristics of wild horses themselves is their "backs." These battling monarchs exemplify the trait: well-rounded, muscular backs. Xenophon referred to this as the "double-back," and considered it a product of sound training. But the ancient Greeks did not use saddles. The trait is not common among domestic horses today. Could it be that our saddling systems inhibit the development of sound, muscular "double-backs"? To answer this question definitively, I propose that we send weak-backed horses through the "pipeline" into wild horse country and study the rehabilitative changes. I think we will be shocked by what we learn.

Balance International/Star Ridge Files

Figure 18-9

REHABILITATED BACK

(*Top*) Conspicuous withers and pronounced backbone are evident in this photo of "Orlando," a 7 year old Belgian Warmblood. (*Bottom*) The same horse, one year later, with rehabilitated "double-back" in the aftermath of Balance International's revolutionary padding and saddling system. The "hollow" at the wither is completely filled in with muscle mass (upward arrow) and the protruding spine is now "rounded" by muscle mass too (downward arrow). The same mechanically obstructive forces that damaged this horse's back — improper padding and saddling — also obstruct the hoof mechanism. Can you explain why? [The dotted lines provide an important clue.]

so many horses who have this 'compromised' shape to some degree or another, that it is considered normal.

Having seen that the backs of wild horses are often extraordinary in comparison to their domestic counterparts, I think it's an issue worth investigating. I have talked at length with Taylor and Brett about the impact of unnaturally fitted saddles on the action of the semi-flexor joints (major joints of propulsion), and we agree that obstruction is probably a big issue Figure 18-9). Not only are the horse's back, joints, and gaits, at stake, so are the hooves.

I propose that we run "normal" backed domestic horses through the pipeline into wild horse country and observe the changes in their backs, movement, and hooves.

SUMMARY

The preceding detailed descriptions of needed wild horse hoof research only scratch the surface of what is possible. The suggestions are based on my admittedly limited understanding of nature's profoundly complex natural hoof. But the information learned would nevertheless go very far in helping those of us who are practitioners wanting to improve the quality of genuine natural hoof care.

Should these and other related research projects ever come to pass, I would suggest great caution in how we interpret and apply the knowledge. Our expanding Circles of Knowledge should not be reckless endeavors to force what is "wild" on the "domestic" realm. Indeed, the wild hoof model has been engineered by the great and powerful forces of natural living. Most domestic horses still do not have that opportunity, being caged as most still are today.

The wild model is not a blueprint to reconstruct the domestic hoof with, as many have learned mistakenly the hard way. To the contrary, it is a filter through which the Laws of Nature have passed. The wild hooves in the color plates at the center of this *Guide* illustrate this perfectly. They are unique and applicable only to the horse who once wore them. They apply therefore only to that horse: the angles, the toe lengths, the hairlines, everything.

The challenge is to read the Laws of Nature through them, and through every set of hooves that come to us from the wild — or from the domestic realm for that matter. There is no prescription for any hoof anywhere, except from the animal himself. The health and soundness of the animal will be proven when, and only when, we have applied our "lessons from the wild" successfully to the hooves. So that the Laws of Nature pass through them in ways that the wild ones have shown us to be true.

EPILOGUE

"Study Nature, love Nature, stay close to Nature. It will never fail you."
Frank Lloyd Wright

Several of my closest associates in the natural hoof care movement have requested that I reflect upon my 20 year long quest to bring Nature's most perfect model for the horse's foot before the horse using community. How does one answer such a calling? Along similar lines, I believe Johann Sebastian Bach tersely summed up his life work in three simple words, "I've worked hard." And that's about my sentiment. But whereas Herr Sebastian breathtakingly codified the old Baroque musical forms into a new outlook and system of viable contrapuntal methodology for musicians, paving the way for the brilliance of the Classical epoch that followed (I am an appreciative classical guitarist), I am practically in despair that I and others who have joined me have failed to reach even a small fraction of the horse using community with our equally important innovations. With my own eyes I have witnessed generations of horses trample the earth with vexed hooves and lifeways that reveal not a single influence of my life's work. What is one to conclude? Either it doesn't matter, the message being

mired in indifference or idiosyncratic resistance, or given the vast landscape of horsemen and horsewomen, it simply hasn't been heard or presented in such palatable form that it may be consumed. Assuming the latter, then I must raise the question – which is more important: leading a quiet life of practitioner with limited peregrination and influence, or fighting in the worldly trenches as a wordsmith and organizer? I have actually coined an expression if not an omen within my closest circle of trench soldiers, "The pen is mightier than the rasp."

But, as the last chapter of this *Guide* reveals, the necessary work of discovery in the field, so important to establishing our full "classical" roots in a parallel Bachian sense, is not even partially fulfilled. A lifetime of endeavor still lays there waiting. So, I feel an immense tension within what I have become through uncalculated evolution: practitioner versus researcher versus teacher spreading the word. Indeed, in what must have been a grand personal delusion, I once thought of myself as a simple hoof man, not a broker for some higher ideal, not in my wildest imagination.

On the other hand, progress has been measurable in unanticipated ways. Whereas "mustang" was once a dirty word among many horse owners — a client once said to me 20 years ago, "I don't want a 'wild hoof' on my horse" — thousands of horse owners are now keenly interested in what the animal has to offer them. Tens of thousands of mustangs have been adopted from the government since the early 1980's and have adapted well to domestic life with their happy owners. Lisa Dine's new book (2001), *the American Mustang Guidebook* (available through the SRP catalogue or website — see Resources), tells horse owners how they can find, observe, and adopt wild horses right off their HMA's. Researchers such as Bowker, Page, and Redden, have finally entered wild horse country — not to experiment with the latest sterilization chemicals, but to study their hooves, bone structure, and behavior. Countless wild horse organizations have sprung up everywhere, where before I could count less than half a dozen. Movies about wild horses abound, including Ginger Kathryn and Marty Stoffer's remarkable *Year of the Mustang*, which I show in my private seminars and classes. On the hoof care front, the "natural trim," the "the mustang roll," and "wild horse hooves" can be read about in nearly every horse journal or magazine whose editor is not totally asleep at the wheel. Web sites and clinics and seminars touting the benefits of natural trimming based on the wild horse trim are inescapable. Indeed, much has happened. And 20 years ago, not a single word about any of this could be found anywhere. It is all new.

With the publication of this newly revised and expanded *Guide*, I am confident that the message and calling of nature's grand plan for the horse's foot — and lifeway, lest we forget the bigger picture — will reach new audiences and inspire further interest. I plan to continue to push the message hard everywhere. And I am grateful that I won't be alone in this effort. Each day, horse owners, vets, and even farriers are coming to appreciate the potential of the new hoof care paradigm. And from their ranks has emerged a dedicated army of caring individuals who have tested the waters and are determined to see that others test them too. After all, it's for the horses. And what could be more important? — JJ

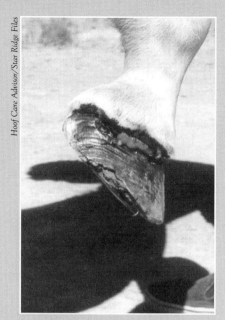

(*Top*) Hoof oozes blood and wound serum from coronet. (*Middle*) Abscessing hoof prolapses at swollen coronet and literally collapses over medial (inside) hoof wall. (*Bottom*) Following de-shoeing and natural hoof care intervention, hoof capsule slow begins to generate new wall in anticipation of healing.

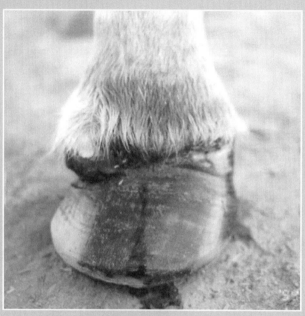

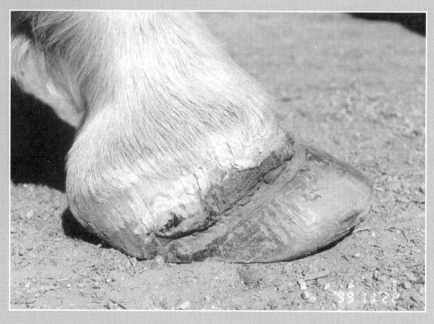

TROUBLESHOOTING

"Always do right. It will gratify some people and astonish the rest." Mark Twain

"If we believe absurdities, we will commit atrocities." Voltaire

Most problems at the hoof can be negotiated and resolved by simply restoring the hoof's vital and natural form while respecting its unique variations so inherent in any individual subject. Beyond this intervention, there isn't really anything we can do to the hoof per se, except to invite other problems from tampering with what when left alone is a perfect system. Of course, anything done to the hoof must always *always* be factored against the myriad possibilities of unnatural forces stemming from unnatural horse care practices beyond the hoof itself. This is the holistic focus I've emphasized everywhere throughout this *Guide*.

Nevertheless, in navigating the hoof inward and outward with our tools towards its mysterious and sometimes elusive natural form, we can and often do go too far. Normally, I would ignore this extreme altogether, being reassured that the indiscretions of the novice will be self-corrected through the forces of conscience and common sense when the hoof bleeds or goes astray. But it has been my observation in recent years that in the burgeoning barefoot trim movement, there are those who are not only undaunted by the prospect of "clear cutting" the hoof to the bloody nub, they openly advocate it.

On principle I am an opponent of surgically invasive procedures, at least if natural healing pathways truly render them obsolete. If not, then I will stand behind our veterinary community as the only legal and authorized body of professionals to open the hoof in the ablative sense. Surgery is not the providence of unlicensed veterinary practitioners. Or shouldn't be in the moral and ethical sense.

Regrettably, the veterinary community has failed to address hoof care standards in the

(*Across*) In the wake of the notorious and completely uncalled for "Coronary Groove" — a vogue veterinary trimming procedure that carries extraordinary risks for the laminitic horse. Natural hoof care is the humane alternative.

U.S. Indeed, virtually anyone can do anything they wish to the horse's feet, with the provisions that the horse owner concurs and grants permission, and the practitioner has not misrepresented him or herself as a licensed veterinarian when in fact they are not. If these red lines are not trespassed, it is an open door on the horse's foot. State prosecuting attorneys — the only legal entities able to prosecute abuses at the hoof — will do nothing because there is no clear mandate specified in any state statue in the U.S. The horse, at least at the level of his feet, is today as vulnerable to abuse as children were in 19th Century U.S. at the hands of industrialists before child labor laws were enacted to compel their safety and extraction to public education.

The excesses of mechanically obstructive horseshoeing, pastern soring, and other barbaric miscreations of modern horse stewardship have been taken up in some measure by the Horse Protection Act of the 1970's. But beneath the shoes, pads, and mustard packs lays the bare hoof — a still uncharted territory where, as I've stated, anything goes. Natural hoof care — genuine natural hoof care — attempts to redefine the vacuum and correct the witting and unwitting abuses.

Surprisingly, the traditional farrier community has little or nothing to say about this pedal landscape. Except to flatten it sufficiently that the shoe, pads, etc., can be applied and held for the traditional 8 week abeyance. The veterinary community, as intimated above, has even less to say and generally yields to the hoof care practitioner except in matters of surgical or chemotherapeutic intervention. As a result, it is the natural hoof care movement that has in recent years single-handedly electrically charged the debate over how in very specific terms the hoof should be remodeled against the forces of domestication.

Thus, and I suppose it is inevitable, the debate has occurred principally within the ranks of natural, and not so natural, hoof care practitioners, along with increasing numbers of horse owners, who themselves have joined the ranks of trimmers. This Troubleshooting appendix addresses some of the more egregious differences that have emerged in the debate. What follows are my personal and professional assessments, or if you prefer, indictments of what I consider to be serious infringements of bona fide natural hoof care. These practices are excesses — extremes to be avoided at all costs. Indeed, while a natural trim is a barefoot trim, it is not axiomatic that all barefoot trims are natural trims.

If you find yourself doing them from ignorance I am confident you will retreat at once and resume the natural pathway that awaits you. If you are conducting them systematically from design, I would ask you to reconsider the counter arguments I've proposed. Whatever your decision, this section is part of the continuing debate — growing pains, if you will — which we all hope will arrive one day at a higher and more humane ideal.

TROUBLESHOOTING CHART

HOOF STRUCTURE	ISSUE	PAGE	FIGURE #
TOE LENGTH	EXCESSIVELY LONG	278	1,2
QUARTERS	"SCOOPED"	278	3
SOLE	EXCESSIVELY THIN	280	4
BARS	REMOVED	280	5
HEEL-BUTTRESSES	REMOVED	282	6
SEATS-OF-CORN	BLEEDING	282	7
FROG	EXCESSIVELY THINNED	282	8
MUSTANG ROLL	NO ROLL GIVEN	282	9
CORONARY BAND	COLLAPSED HOOF WALL	274-5	-

(*Overleaf*) Note: the following images were taken of cadaver hooves, as I would not subject any live horse to the trimming methods employed to create the final results shown. [all photos by *Cindy Sullivan Images*]

1,2   EXCESSIVE TOE LENGTH

Excessive toe lengths, or "long toes" as the issue is referred to among professional natural hoof care practitioners, are common among beginners who still lack experience and confidence to shorten the hoof safely without quicking the sole. Happily, this shortcoming is easily remedied by further practice while remaining diligently faithful to the natural model, and by attending natural hoof care clinics staged by skilled professionals who are competent at capsule reduction.

But long toe syndrome also reflects the belief among some farriers and barefoot trimmers that either "more capsule is better" (more hoof = stronger hoof) or that there is some particular relationship between toe length and some other hoof dimension that must be arrived at in strict correlation. Often these two beliefs are tantamount to the same thing — long, unnatural toes.

An example of this is the theory that the length of the toe from coronet to ground at the center of the dorsal (toe) wall [1] should match the diameter of the hoof measured at the coronet when the hoof is viewed from the front [2]. The foot here (*facing page, top and bottom*), trimmed according to this criteria, has assumed a 4 inch long toe! This toe length is not at all natural, and, in my opinion, creates dangerous lever forces at the laminar corium and within the navicular pulley system. I've never found this relationship to be the case in the 1,000 or so wild horse hooves I have sampled, nor would I ever trim a domestic horse hoof to "fit" this fantastic claim. Most wild horse hooves are at least an inch shorter down the toe wall than they are across the coronet, and naturally trimmed hooves are only slightly less than this.

Creating artificially long toes to meet such criteria is arguably a prescription for fatigue, gait obstruction, and aching feet. And it flies in the face of what we know to be natural for horses.

Remedy: Learn how to properly trim a hoof to its natural length. Chances are very good that if your toe lengths are equal to or greater than the diameter of the hoof's coronet, you need professional guidance from a bona fide natural hoof care practitioner.

3   SCOOPED QUARTERS

The quarters are relieved or scooped [3] based on the theory that the lateral expansion component of hoof mechanism (Chapter 3) cannot be properly achieved if the quarters are not passive to the rest of the hoof. Such quarter treatment is believed to be needed standard fare for all horses regardless of their natural wear pattern. Additionally, it is believed that the lack of passivity in the quarters is a primary actor in the development of quarter cracks.

The problem with this is that not all wild horse hooves have "scooped" quarters, and those which do not, in fact, do not develop purported quarter cracks. The hooves of the robust stallion seen in Figure 4-6 of my book, *The Natural Horse*, had no such quarter cracks and I was unable to pass a piece of typing paper between my impression board and the lateral quarters of either front hoof. Moreover, many horses shod year after year never develop quarter cracks. Wear patterns in the wild are complex and variant, each depending upon the conformational idiosyncrasies of the horse. Thus, if a quarter, or any segment of the hoof wall, is rendered passive through "formula" trimming practices, such as the hoof here (*facing page, top/bottom*) and in so doing conflicts with what might naturally be an active support point, then the hoof, by definition, is imbalanced.

Clearly, the hoof mechanism is adaptable to all natural active and passive wear configurations. Therefore it is not judicious for a conscientious natural hoof care practitioner to fight nature by relieving the quarters according to any fanciful dogma unfounded in the ultimate testing ground of the horse's natural world.

Remedy: No credible studies ascertaining the relationship of body and hoof conformation to active/passive wear patterns have been conducted, nor has any such investigation been conducted in the wild. This research is badly needed (Chapter 18). Until this happens, I advise that natural hoof care practitioners follow the trimming protocols in this *Guide* and simply render a reasonably natural and balanced hoof capsule. Natural wear is then our greatest ally to finish the job, although we must remain ever vigilant to the prospect that, in domestication, opposing forces are always at work.

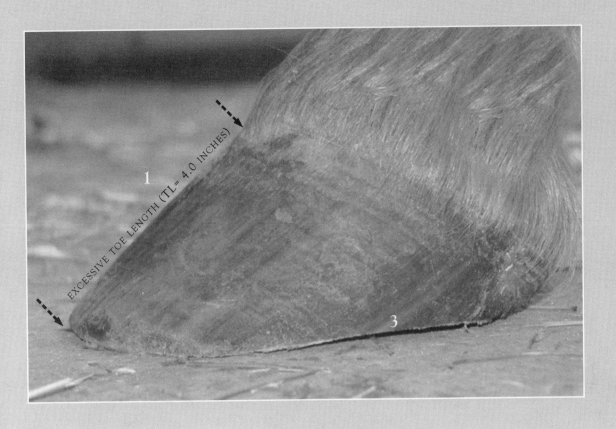

EXCESSIVE TOE LENGTH (TL = 4.0 INCHES)

1

3

Coronet = 4.0 in.

2

4 THIN SOLE

The sole is carved out excessively [4] in the belief that solar concavity must be created to mimic the assumed concavity of the coffin bone. It also reflects the belief that not doing this will leave the sole too thick and inflexible to allow proper hoof mechanism.

Proper and natural reduction of the sole, like hoof wall reduction, can be challenging and problematic for novice trimmers. Once more, attending clinics, exercising common sense — removing too much of anything can cause hypersensitivity — and diligent practice, should enable the dedicated practitioner to overcome the obstacles inherent in inexperience.

At issue here too, unfortunately, is that "sole thinning" among some practitioners has been elevated to a belief system and corresponding methodology. Their argument that the solar dome must conform closely and precisely to the concaved volar aspect of the coffin bone must be tempered however by the inclusion of a sufficiently thickened armor of hardened epidermal horn — demonstrated by all wild horse hooves and genuinely naturally trimmed domestic hooves. This mass of epidermis is visible in Figure 2-11 (top) and Figure 8-5. Removing this buffer, as in close-cropping it to the coffin bone itself, therefore is an infringement upon what is clearly a growth defense mechanism against hypersensitivity and injury to the sensitive structures within the capsule.

Further, it is principally the flexible frog and digital cushion (Chapter 2), and secondarily the relatively flexible epidermal striations of the solar vault[*] — all of which are imbued with moisture from blood gases and the environment — that impart resilience to the hoof — that is, the hoof mechanism. The flexions of the mechanism, in turn, aid in the lubrication of the naturally thick epidermal horn. According to Emery, "The sole, frog, and bars are . . . constantly growing downward. In a natural state, they also are being worn away by continual movement. The friction that causes the wear also preserves their proper form. It maintains the most efficient thickness of sole, prevents the frog from becoming too prominent, and keeps the bars in the shape to support the heels. The horn not worn away is highly elastic, its moisture being provided through constant expansion and contraction. Flexion of the sole during movement also contributes to shedding excess horn. Such flexion is often inhibited by unnatural hoof shape."[*] Hence, it is not really the thickness of the sole that inhibits the mechanism — clearly proven by our wild horses — but pain: pain from constrictive horseshoes, pain experienced by hooves yet adapted to their environment, and in the case of the hooves shown here, from pain caused by excessive thinning of the soles.

Remedy: Once again, learn how to properly trim a hoof to its natural length. Diligently follow the rules of relative concavity (Chapter 2), and you will stay out of trouble. If you harbor further doubts, seek guidance from a bona fide natural hoof care practitioner, or attend a natural hoof care clinic based on the wild horse hoof model. And remember — a thickened sole is perfectly natural.

5 BARS REMOVED

Excessive paring of the bars [5] is thought to be necessary by some in order to 1) create the believed mandate of straight bars running from the heel-buttresses to the mid-point of the frog where it ends at sole level; and 2) aid in the de-contraction of the hoof. Some de-barring procedures are tantamount to surgical ablation.

De-barring the hoof for these or any other reason violates the natural integrity of the hoof in many ways. First, ablating or close trimming the bars is tantamount to removing a vital structure that nature intends to be there for structural purposes — namely, to form the heel-buttress. Such procedures also open the hoof to bleeding, infection, and abscess. Long term and permanent damage to soft tissue structures cannot be ruled out. Second, the bars of most wild horse hooves I sampled do not parallel the frog, nor, as I wrote in Chapter 8, do they always lay with their tubular ends oriented towards the ground — rather many fold over and are pressed and fused into the solar dome near the seats-of-corn. Third, many, possibly most, hooves are naturally contracted by conventional hoof care industry standards; thus, de-barring healthy and naturally contracted hooves to de-contract them establishes a dangerous precedent.

Remedy: Never surgically de-bar or excessively trim the bars for any reason. Nature put them there, so leave them alone. At most, trim the bars even with or just above the sole. Or simply let them fold over and wear naturally if natural boarding and riding strategies are geared to this.

*Emery, et al., in Horshoeing Theory and Hoofcare, p.77-78.

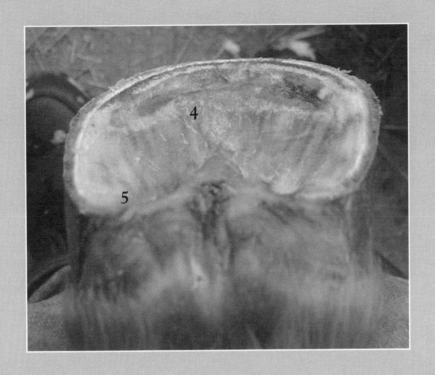

6   REMOVAL OF HEEL-BUTTRESSES

The entire heel-buttress structure is trimmed to its core [6], or growth matrix. This ablative procedures is believed by some to be necessary to de-contract hooves.

Removing or close-trimming the heel-buttresses, called an "opening cut" in some circles, violates the natural integrity of the hoof in precisely the same way that de-barring does. The hoof will bleed, and likely become infected and abscess prone. Internal soft tissue structures may become permanently damaged and your horse lamed indefinitely.

Remedy: If your horse has been subjected to an opening cut, his state of soundness and possibly his very life is at stake. This is an emergency. I advise that you immediately seek licensed veterinary medical intervention. At the same time, solicit the services of a genuine natural hoof care practitioner.

7   BLEEDING AT SEATS-OF-CORN

The seats-of-corn are naturally protected by the heel-buttresses. If the seats are close-trimmed, almost assuredly so if the heel-buttresses have been ablated, they will bleed [7], once more opening the hoof to infection and recurrent abscessing.

Remedy: Bleeding the seats-of-corn in effect creates an open wound and is tantamount to surgery. Call your vet at once for potential anti-biotic and tetanus therapy. Solicit the services of a natural hoof care practitioner for future hoof work.

8   OVER-TRIMMING OF FROG

The frog, like other members of the volar dome, may be trimmed down excessively to its growth matrix. One reason for doing this is to bring it into the same volar concavity as the solar dome [8], that is, to make it conform to the volar aspect of the coffin bone. Another reason is to render it passive during ground contact until the volar arch of the hoof "flattens" out, in other words, to prevent it from obstructing the hoof mechanism.

An important observation I made of wild horse frogs is very relevant here. In the wild, frogs may lay very flat and indeed conform to the natural concavity of the volar dome. But this is only true when the hooves are subject to dry and very abrasive ground — not always the case in wild horse country. I have observed frogs that are very moist and protuberant during the winter months; such frogs hardly conform to the concave base of the dome. The wild horse hooves held by the wrangler's ropes in the beginning of Chapter 2 are an example. Wild horses do not become lame during winter when their frogs are swollen with moisture. And this is evidence enough that naturally worn frogs, whether dry and flat, or moist and swollen, do not imperil the hoof mechanism. There is no credible evidence for such a thesis.

Remedy: It is not necessary to over-trim the frog. Trim it back if gets obviously long and raggedy. Or, if the horses is ridden and boarded on suitably abrasive ground, don't trim it at all. Eventual it will wear off on its own.

9   NO MUSTANG ROLL

The mustang roll — a centerpiece of naturally trimmed and worn hooves — is believed by some to be contraindicated if the horse is boarded on soft ground. Every bit of hoof wall, proponents argue, is necessary to prevent the hoof wall from collapsing back in on itself and the hoof from becoming contracted.

This nonsensical belief is difficult for me to acknowledge, let alone dignify with a response. There is absolutely no evidence for such a statement, either from wild horse country, the laws of physics, or even the worst alleged "contracted" hoof in the domestic horse world.

Remedy: Roll the hoof wall and don't worry about it.

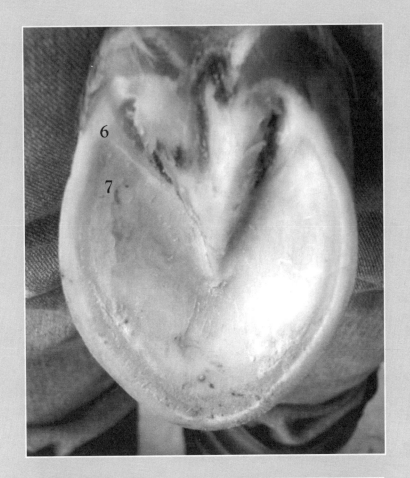

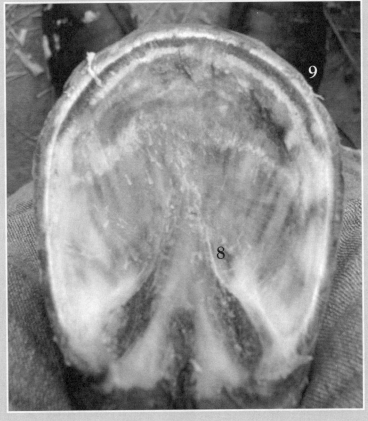

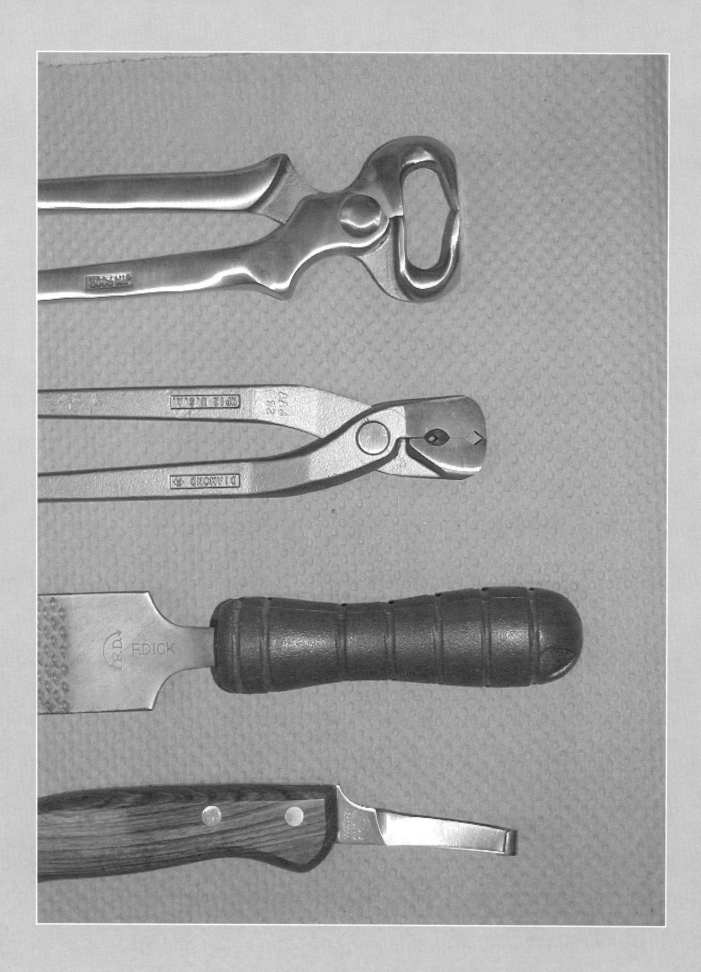

RESOURCES

As this *Guide* to *Natural Hoof Care* enters its fourth year, and first major revision, I've had ample feedback from many readers and natural hoof care practitioners to justify updating this Resource section. All have been grateful for its inclusion because it's a way to learn more and to locate the tools, equipment, and accessories hoof care "do-it-yourselfers" want and need.

As in the earlier edition, this Resource section is a marketplace. Here, readers can order directly the kinds of things they tell me they want. Many of the things I've recommended in this book. You don't have too travel to far off farrier supply houses or local hardware or feed stores to try and locate equipment I've suggested, but which, in many instances, they don't stock. A lot of these places emphasize shoeing, and don't really understand the needs of natural hoof care providers, particularly amateurs. Some may try to sell you junk that's not fit to use, simply because they've learned you're a beginner. You won't find any junk in this little storefront! Nor will you find stuff you don't need. Or that's excessively expensive. Just high quality, good-value-for-your-money equipment that gets the job done right.

BASIC TRIMMERS KIT

When you turn the page, the first thing you'll discover is my "Basic Trimmers Kit." This is new. If you're new to trimming, or have invested in poor tools, or the wrong tools, now's the time to get it right. I've selected specific tools to get you not only started, but "armed for life."

The kit is simple and includes a quality hoof nipper, hoof knife (left or right-handed), hoof knife sharpener, trimmer's rasp, and rasp handle. These are the "basic" tools of the natural hoof care practitioner.

Included are the quality brands that I use myself to do the job efficiently and correctly. They are professional level tools — not cheap "amateur" stuff. Even though you may be an amateur, you don't want to use second-rate tools often handed-off to beginners, because all you will accomplish is a second-rate job. You don't want that, do you?

As you gain more experience you will probably discover other brands that may fit your technique better. That's to be expected. However, don't fall into the expensive and self-deluding trap that many amateurs (and professionals) fall into: changing brands to compensate for lousy technique. Or worse, to enable you to do things to the hoof (like over-trimming the sole) you shouldn't be doing anyway.

I've picked these tools to keep you out of trouble and able to get the job done right. With them, as I wrote in Chapter 5, I can trim any hoof on the face of the earth in just a few minutes. I've heard more than once (usually from neophytes that have only been trimming for two or three years – I've been trimming 25 years) that unless I use such and such tool, I won't be able trim as efficiently or effectively as they are able to. Okay, show me. Now, if they're at the hoof longer than 3 minutes – five at the most – they're in for a shocker. Because that's what I'll have the job done in, using the tools in the Basic Trimmers Kit. Correct technique and quality tools is the difference.

In selecting these tools, I've also taken into consideration the fact that many women are trimming their horses. Their grip may not be as large or powerful as a professional male farrier. No worry, the tools and equipment I've picked, without exception, will work for both men and women with less than farrier grips. Besides, you don't need a farrier's grip or strength to do natural trimming (or de-shoeing). Like I said at the outset of this *Guide*, all you need is proper technique and the right tools and equipment.

TRIMMING ACCESSORIES: OTHER ESSENTIAL TOOLS

The next section includes a few extra tools and accessories that professionals are apt to keep around. I do, and I recommend that you do too. Read the recommendations closely and see if you don't agree.

DE-SHOEING TOOLS

Flip the page again, and you'll arrive at a different set of tools and equipment. These are de-shoeing instruments. They are not the most expensive "highest quality" tools money can buy, but they are high quality professional tools to get the job done quickly, efficiently, and correctly. I don't want to see you wasting your money on high-end farrier tools to get the shoes off, even if you intend to pursue natural trimming professionally. It isn't necessary.

The de-shoeing tools you see me using in my trimming video (see later in this Resource section) have been in my tool box for over 20 years. I don't know how many horses I've de-shod with them, because I can't count that high! But if you intend to pull shoes, you will need these tools to get the job done. They are worth the investment.

TRIMMER'S APRON AND WORK GLOVES

These two items are truly indispensable. A law ought to be passed to make the trimmer's apron and leather work gloves mandatory. If you don't wear an apron, you are going to injure your legs and ruin your clothing. If you don't wear gloves, your hands will be cut to ribbons; moreover, with the abundance of harmful microbes inhabiting the bottom of the average hoof, wounds will be predisposed to infection.

I've selected the apron shown because I've used it for many years. The current design is actually a big improvement over the one I originally purchased for myself 20 years ago The knee area is now double-reinforced with a second band of leather for added protection and padding for comfort. The rivets and adjustment clips are industrial grade and the belt is now heavy and durable. The adjustment straps enable a range of sizes, so this apron fits women as easily as men. It protects the thighs, knees, and lower leg.

Included also are a range of sizes for the type of leather glove I use personally. Beginners may feel that wearing gloves prevents them from feeling the hoof closely and that their work will suffer. Not with these! I used to shoe horses wearing them, and I could roll a thin horseshoe nail between my thumb and index finger. There was plenty of "sensitivity." As they break in, the feel will increase. So use them and protect your hands from injury.

HOOF STAND:
ALL-PURPOSE WORK CENTER

This is a "biggy" with me. My "work center" is also "misnamed" by many, including myself for years, as a "hoof stand." It is anything but just that. It is a work station, where many things happen, including supporting the horse's foot.

First, it is an important way to protect your legs and back. The horse is fully capable — and will if you let him — of bearing his weight down on your legs when supporting his hoof. In a moment of resistance or in trying to find his balance, he can flick his hoof and take you with him. This is potentially very dangerous. You can ruin your knee joints and lower back for life. Learn to use the hoof grip when finishing the hoof, and you will thank me one day. Countless farriers have been forced into early retirement because they failed to take protective measures via the hoof stand–work center. You may get by for several years, or even a decade or more, but when that moment arrives — that unforgettable "twinge" of pain in the joint or lower back — it's the "beginning of the end." Use the hoof stand–work center like it were your guardian angel.

But it is more than a hoof stand. It is also a very convenient place to keep your tools at hand while you work. Remember the photo of the young man in Chapter 5? His tools are all over the place, and ready to be ruined when the horse steps on them. The dirt will dull his blades and he will waste time having to re-sharpen them. Worse, having to reach to the ground will harm his back and render his work incredibly inefficient. By the time he's reached for his hoof knife on the ground, assuming he can find it, Jaime Jackson will have finished and gone home.

My "work center" has a tool caddy that spins around the support base. So you can spin the right tool into position for use. This is one reason why I am able to trim so quickly and efficiently. My tools are right there where I need them at all times.

The "grip head," by the way, is perched upon a telescopic base. You can set the support grip high enough to make your job easier for both you and your horse. Set the grip head at or higher than your knees. It will be easier on your back, and I've discovered that horses balance themselves more easily than if set lower.

Besides the grip head and tool caddy, which come with the work center, there is an optional "hoof cradle," to secure the hoof in instead of holding it between your legs. I don't use it personally because I love to feel the hoof between my legs, and I have developed powerful leg muscles to grip the hoof with. But if it makes your job easier, use it.

I've also designed an optional "mini-anvil." Like the hoof cradle, it is interchangeable with the grip head. You will need the mini-anvil if you are going to boot horses professionally for others. You don't need it if you are just going to use boots — although it comes in handy if you need to re-seat a rivet, cut a toe slot, or heat fit the boot. Come to think of it, the mini-anvil probably has other possible uses too. Just use your imagination!

The "work center" also breaks down in less than a minute. You can pack it away if traveling and space is an issue — especially if you'll be taking an airplane.

The center is also zinc-plated to prevent rust.

So, there you have it. Many good reasons for owning and using a "hoof stand work center."

BOOKS AND VIDEOS

Next, we come to what are the foundational learning materials of the natural hoof care movement. Some of this information goes beyond the hoof, but, as every natural hoof care practitioner learns sooner or later, what happens above and beyond the hoof — holistically speaking — affects the hoof. So, it is important that you keep this information close at hand as you assume more and more control over your horse's hoof work.

I expect this section to expand as other natural hoof care practitioners begin to publish their experiences and knowledge base for others to learn from.

CATALOGUE/INTERNET RESOURCES

For a number of reasons, this Resource section is not completely comprehensive, nor can it ever be entirely up-to-date. Consequently, I've created a mail order catalogue and internet site to meet your growing hoof care needs. This section describes what the Star Ridge Catalogue includes beyond the resources provided here, and, for those of you with internet access, where to go on-line to order products and gather additional information.

AMERICAN ASSOCIATION OF NATURAL HOOF CARE PRACTITIONERS

Learn more about this new organization dedicated to the advancement of natural hoof care practices.

NATURAL HOOF CARE PRACTITIONER CERTIFICATION PROGRAM

As the natural hoof care movement has gained momentum, the importance of providing horse owners with qualified trimmers and hoof boot fitters has become increasingly obvious. This training program is a national effort to recruit, train, and promote competent professional horse booters.

ORDERING

You can order any of the hoof care tools, equipment, and learning materials by mail, telephone, or internet from the Star Ridge Company. Contact information, including an order form (if you wish to order directly from this *Guide*), can be found on the last page of this *Guide*.

RESOURCES - CONTENTS

BOOKS AND VIDEOS

ESSENTIAL LEARNING MATERIALS

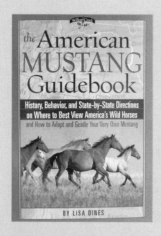

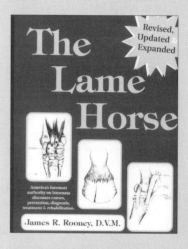

THE AMERICAN MUSTANG GUIDEBOOK

BY LISA DINES

This book is a combination travel guide, gentling and training guide, resource book, natural history, and American history • Detailed state-by-state directions and maps show where to best view America's wild horses in their native pastures • Contact names and addresses of the state BLM offices, a list of wild horse handlers, local and national wild horse organizations • 152 pages, soft cover.

$19.95

I have had many requests from readers to tell them where they can go and see wild horses in their natural habitats. Author Lisa Dines has come to our rescue, providing a very precise guide to locating America's mustangs from coast to coast. Also an excellent resource for adopting a mustang. — JJ

THE NATURAL HORSE
LESSONS FROM THE WILD

BY JAIME JACKSON

Vivid accounting of wild horses and their natural habitat, the model for true natural horse care • Most complete description of naturally shaped hooves to be found anywhere • In-depth discussion of the horse's natural gaits • Numerous illustrations • Jackson's original trimming guidelines for natural hoof care • 192 pages, soft cover, perfect bound.

$24.95

The original work that started it all! Jaime Jackson's unforgettable foundation for the natural horse care movement . . .

THE LAME HORSE

BY JAMES ROONEY, DVM

Explains anatomy and biomechanics of the horse • Explains why horses "break down" from abuse of their natural capabilities • Hundreds of photos, drawings, and x-rays of pathologies facing horses due to abusive practices • Advocates barefootedness, balanced riding, and natural trimming • De-bunks numerous veterinary myths • 264 pages, soft cover, perfect bound.

$29.95

Most veterinarians today are completely unfamiliar with the burgeoning natural hoof care movement. What they know about it they have learned from their horse owner clients — not their schools or professional symposiums. Help temper this pathetic reality by referring your vet to Dr. Rooney's landmark book above — the first and only book by a U.S. vet who embraces the natural hoof and barefootedness. — JJ

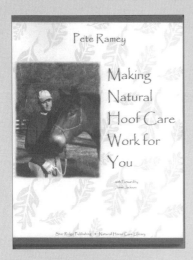

CREATING THE PERFECT HOOF (VIDEO)

WITH JAIME JACKSON

MAKING NATURAL HOOF CARE WORK FOR YOU

BY PETE RAMEY

Pete Ramey is a skilled, full-time natural hoof care practitioner from Georgia. Pete has written his first book about the many horses, both shod and lame, he has brought successfully into barefootedness and soundness since then. Written in down-to-earth language, and chock full of photos and drawings, *Making Natural Hoof Care Work For You* is Pete's unique spin on natural hoof care. A perfect companion to Jaime's HOG, horse owners will find countless bits of useful information in Pete's book to make their hoof care programs more successful • 192 pages, perfect bound, soft cover.

$26.95

FOUNDER: PREVENTION AND CURE THE NATURAL WAY

BY JAIME JACKSON

Founder kills thousands of horses every year, and leaves tens of thousands of others debilitated in its wake. In this startling revelation and guide to the natural, holistic cure and prevention of founder, author and hoof care expert Jaime Jackson brings an entirely new perspective to the treatment table. This may be the most controversial book yet written on the subject . . . and the most useful. 156 pages, soft cover, perfect bound.

$19.95

Founder is a time bomb ticking away in every domestic horse on every continent of this planet. No horse is exempt. It explodes into the horse owner's life like a terrible nightmare. You have two choices: ignore Nature's stern warnings until it's too late. Or get with the program now. – JJ

Learn what a "natural trim" is by watching hoof care expert Jaime Jackson in action. Close-up footage gives you the trimming detail horse owners want. Excellent sections on non-violent horse handling, balancing the horse, selection and use of tools, exercises to condition your body, securing the horse's hooves, using the hoof stand, and much more! Includes remarkable close-up shots of wild horse hooves. 2 hrs. 40 min, Stereo, VHS.

$39.95

I created this video to show you how we do it. All the principles, methodology, tools, etc., that I've laid out in my companion book, Horse Owners Guide, are brought to life here. Short of an actual hands-on clinic, this is the next best thing. And maybe better, since you can refer to it as often as you need to. As I point out in this video, trimming is the easy part of a much bigger picture. And it's all the rest that really makes the trimming so easy. This video spells out the rest of the story. – JJ

STAR RIDGE VIDEOS AND BULLETINS

ESSENTIAL LEARNING FOR ADVANCED TRIMMING

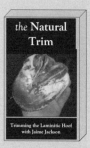

NATURAL TRIM:
TRIMMING THE LAMINITIC HOOF
WITH JAIME JACKSON

Learn how to trim laminitic hooves with master trimmer Jaime Jackson. Jaime brings to bear his entire arsenal of information and technique to put laminitic hooves on the road to healing and soundness. Use with companion bulletin. VHS, NTSC, 1 hr. 30 min.

$39.95

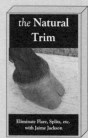

NATURAL TRIM:
ELIMINATING FLARE, QUARTER CRACKS, AND RUN-UNDER HEELS
WITH JAIME JACKSON

Jaime receives more questions about dealing with wall flare, cracks, and run-under heels then any other facet of trimming. Here's his step-by-step presentation of solutions to these and other aberrations of normal hoof growth. Use with companion bulletin. VHS, NTSC, 1 hr. 30 min.

$39.95

GUIDE TO BOOTING HORSES
FOR HOOF CARE PROFESSIONALS (book)
BY JAIME JACKSON

Complete how-to guide for the fitting and use of the Swiss Horse Boot • Meticulous descriptions of every aspect of booting: from fitting & modifying, to quick mounting and easy removal • Illustrations, photographs and diagrams • Resource section for obtaining boots, tools, and equipment. • 192 pgs./softcover

$26.95

GUIDE TO BOOTING HORSES FOR
HOOF CARE PROFESSIONALS (video)
BY JAIME JACKSON

Shows how to measure and fit hooves with the Swiss Horse Boot • Action footage shows boots being put on, removed, and used by clients • How to modify boots with inserts, toe slot, heat fitting • Repairs • Sections correspond to chapters in companion book of same name • 2 hrs. • NTSC • VHS

$39.95

These unique educational bulletins by Jaime Jackson are published as pdf documents to give you the highest quality photos and diagrams. They present the most up-to-date information available on natural horse/hoof care. Shorter bulletins are available via email, longer on CD.

E-MAIL **$7.95**
CD **$12.95**

See our website for current special
for buying all bulletins on one CD

STAR RIDGE
BULLETINS

Bulletin No.	Article Title	Format
100	hgc: Hoof Growth Cycle	e-mail
101	Trimming for Natural Toe Angle (T°), Toe Length (TL), and Heel Length (HL)	e-mail
102	Supercoriaitis: Laminitis Redefined	e-mail
103	The Supercoriatic (Laminitis) Pathway	e-mail
104	Trimming The Supercoriatic (Laminitic) Hoof	CD
106	Rules of Rasping: Eliminating Wall Flare, Splits, and Run-Under Heels	CD
107	The Correct Mustang Roll	CD
108	A New Mechanistic Theory: Time and Mass In A 4th-Dimensional Hoof Mechanism	CD
109	The Whole Horse Trim: Finding the Natural Hoof Within	e-mail
110	The Supercorium	CD
111	Does Horseshoeing Cause Hoof Contraction?	e-mail

BASIC TRIMMER'S KIT

TRIMMING TOOLS

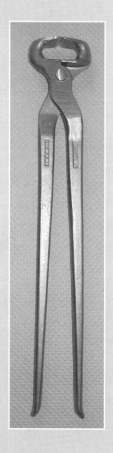

STAR RIDGE HOOF NIPPER

ESSENTIAL TRIMMING TOOL

We added this superior professional hoof nipper last year, which was upgraded by its manufacturer (Cooper Tools). 12 and 15-inch models with beefed-up jaws and sharp cutting blades will get you through the toughest horn, eliminating the need for compound nippers. 12 in. model is suitable for ladies and men with smaller hands.

15 IN. (HIS) $74.95
12 IN. (HERS) $71.95

F. DICK RASP HANDLE

ESSENTIAL TRIMMING TOOL

This is an excellent rasp handle by F. Dick in Germany. It is light, durable, and offers superior grip. It is a screw-on type which adapts excellently to both the "his" and "her" F. Dick rasp sizes.

$5.95

F. DICK HOOF RASP

ESSENTIAL TRIMMING TOOL

I gravitated to this professional level German product for several reasons. It is consistently sharp, and properly cared for will enable a full year's worth of trims for six horses at 4 week intervals. What separates this rasp from others is the layout of the coarse cutting teeth (chisels), which span the entire width of the rasp — which I've not seen on any other professional rasp. This translates to less work for each swipe of the rasp. Offers superb bite and will render a beautiful mustang roll. "His" (large, 14") and "Her's" (small, 12") sizes.

HIS $20.95
HER'S $19.95

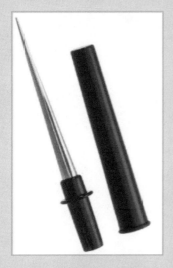

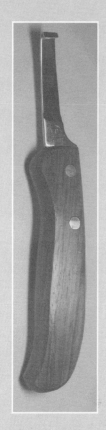

ISTOR HOOF KNIFE SHARPENER

ESSENTIAL TRIMMING TOOL

As sharpeners go, this Istor Sharpener from Switzerland is unparalleled. There are two models, the "Professional" (*above*) and a smaller version, the "Regular." Both work well, one difference being that the Professional model has a protective handle with thumb guard to prevent accidental cuts if you slip. The smaller model is a little easier to work near the crook of the hoof knife. Both are excellent for sharpening other implements (e.g., kitchen knives) and make for wonderful gifts for the non-horsey minded set too.

ISTOR PROFESSIONAL 18.95
ISTOR STANDARD $11.95

BUCK DIAMOND HOOF KNIFE CROOK SHARPENER

ESSENTIAL TRIMMING TOOL

Use this high quality tapered diamond sharpener manufactured by the Buck Knives Company to sharpen the crook (curved portion) of your F. Dick hoof knife.
$16.95

F. DICK HOOF KNIFE

ESSENTIAL TRIMMING TOOL

This is the favored European hoof knife, which sports a handsome Rosewood handle and a super sharp blade made of the finest steel. I've selected this model because the cutting blade is neither too "flat" nor too "curved." I'm particularly concerned about hoof knives with the latter conformation as they facilitate excessive scooping of the hoof's solar dome — a dangerous practice with potentially devastating consequences for the hoof. This is an excellent, highest quality professional knife that can enable you to do a superb natural trim quickly and efficiently.

F. DICK GRIP MASTER $23.95
F. DICK ASCOT $19.95

TRIMMING ACCESSORIES

OTHER ESSENTIAL TOOLS

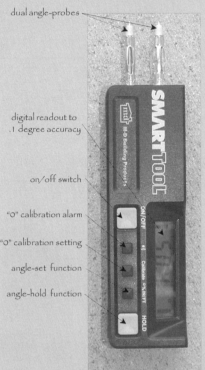

dual angle-probes

digital readout to
.1 degree accuracy

on/off switch

"0" calibration alarm

"0" calibration setting

angle-set function

angle-hold function

STAR RIDGE
RASP CLEANER

ESSENTIAL ACCESSORY

It is a characteristic of rasps to pick up hoof filings between the teeth (chisels) and hold them there. Use this 10 inch rasp cleaner to keep the cutting chisels free of such debris, and you will add on to the trimming life of your rasp.

$10.95

ELECTRONIC TOE
ANGLE-FINDER

ESSENTIAL ACCESSORY

This is a pretty sophisticated electronic toe angle-finder (adapted from the building trades) — the most accurate hoof gauge on the market. Measures all variations of T° (toe angle) described in my bulletins (p. 301) for advanced trimming — a must for the serious natural hoof care practitioner:

$124.95

STAR RIDGE HOOF
METER READER

ESSENTIAL ACCESSORY

This is my invention. It's a simple and inexpensive way to measure your horse's feet for Toe Angle and Hoof Width — important measurements for ascertaining changes in the hoof capsule due to adaptation or pathology, for fitting horse boots, and gauging the consistency of your trimming work.

$9.95

LUFKIN METRIC TAPE MEASURE

ESSENTIAL ACCESSORY

This quality tape measure, calibrated in Metric and U.S. Equivalents, complements the Hoof Meter Reader (*facing page*) and enables you to take accurate measurements of your horse's feet. Important for determining hoof balance and fitting horse boots.

$10.95

HOOF PICK

ESSENTIAL ACCESSORY

I was shocked when recently I went on the internet to check out suppliers for hoof picks. The variety of hoof picks was staggering, each claiming to be "the" answer to cleaning out the hoof. Many were fancy, gimmicky and expensive. The good news is that the one here, the simplest of them all — and the least expensive — is all you need. I've used the one above for over 20 years, and I've yet to run into a hoof I couldn't "unload" with it in 5 seconds.

$2.95

JV ALUMINUM RASP HANDLE

ESSENTIAL ACCESSORY

The best rasp handle I've ever gotten my hands on. A favorite among professionals.

LARGE (HIS) $16.95
SMALL (HERS) $14.95

TRIMMER'S APRON AND WORK GLOVES

ESSENTIAL APPAREL

(above) AANHCP practitioner Richard Drewry of Arkansas puts hoof cradle to work on Star Ridge Hoof Stand.

STAR RIDGE DELUXE TRIMMER'S APRON

This superior leather apron is the one I've used for over 25 years. Double-leather pads to protect your knees. Heavy duty belt and leg straps adjust to fit all sizes, men and women. Right knife pocket. Made in the USA.
$84.95

Adjustable leg straps render good fit for all sizes.

Prevent cuts, bruising, and infection by using these SRP work gloves. Choose between cowhide, deerskin (buckskin), and latex-coated knit or Kevlar. We feature hard-to-find smaller sizes for women.

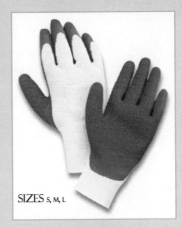

KEVLAR

Excellent cut resistant Kevlar shell with blue high-flex latex coating for superior grip and moisture resistance.

$13.95

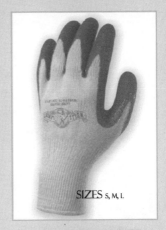

KNIT W/RUBBER-COATED PALM

Premium knit shell with blue high-flex latex coating for superior grip and improved cut, abrasion puncture & moisture resistance.

$5.95

BUCKSKIN

Premium grain leather, same qualities as cowhide gloves, but super-supple.

$12.95

COWHIDE

Premium grain leather, very supple, durable, washable, with adjustable straps.

$10.95

GLOVE FITTING CHARTS ARE AVAILABLE ON OUR WEBSITE:
www.star-ridge.com

HOOF STAND: ALL-PURPOSE WORK CENTER

ESSENTIAL EQUIPMENT

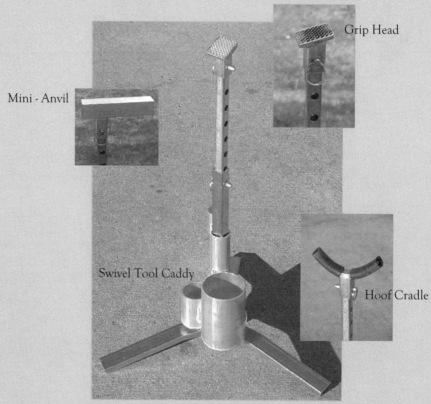

Grip Head

Mini - Anvil

Swivel Tool Caddy

Hoof Cradle

STAR RIDGE HOOF STAND
AND WORK CENTER

Here's the low down on this incredibly important piece of equipment that is indispensable to efficient professional natural hoof care: Zinc-plated, super strong steel core is lightweight for easy positioning under horse • Stand takes all the horse's weight — you concentrate on your work, instead of back or knee pain • Handy Aluminum tool caddy swivels into optimal position for accessing your tools • Telescopic shaft is adjustable so stand height can be set for you and your horse's comfort and balance •

Work center breaks down into component parts, including three detachable legs, for compact storage and traveling • Comes with serrated grip head to secure horse's hoof, optional hoof cradle to support hoof and save your back and knees, and optional mini-anvil for modifying horse boots.

HOOF STAND $150.00*
HOOF CRADLE $14.95
MINI ANVIL $19.95

*Note: add $12^{00} shipping within
U.S. (UPS Ground). No additional
shipping charges apply to cradle or anvil
if ordered at the same time as the stand.

DESHOEING TOOLS

FOR REMOVING HORSESHOES

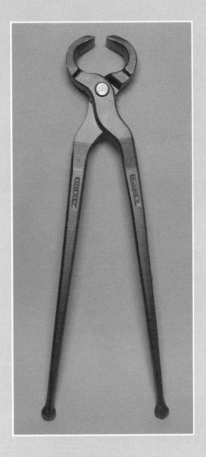 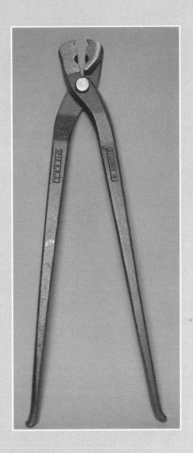

STAR RIDGE
SHOE PULLER

ESSENTIAL DE-SHOEING TOOL

I've used this shoe puller for 25
years. It's going to outlast me —
ditto the nail puller at right too.
This is an essential tool for de-
shoeing, and if you think you might
be helping a fellow horse owner get
started with natural hoof care, then
make this quality professional tool
part of your basic kit.

$57.95

STAR RIDGE
NAIL PULLER

ESSENTIAL DE-SHOEING TOOL

Sometimes it makes de-shoeing easier to yank out a few nails before
using the shoe puller at left. Shoers
use them to pull astray nails in the
hoof wall, but you can use them to
help you get the shoes off! I would
not think of de-shoeing without
having this handy tool in my hoof
stand work center.

$49.95

STAR RIDGE CATALOGUE OF NATURAL HOOF CARE SUPPLIES

FULL LINE OF TOOLS AND EQUIPMENT, EDUCATIONAL MATERIALS, HOOF CARE SUPPLIES

 SHOP ON-LINE 24/7

VISIT OUR
STAR RIDGE INTERNET MARKETPLACE

www.star-ridge.com

JAIME JACKSON NATURAL HOOF CARE CLINICS

NATURAL TRIM AND FUNDAMENTALS OF BOOTING

JAIME JACKSON CLINICS

Jaime is the official Orientation Clinician for the AANHCP. Whether you're thinking about becoming a certified practitioner or just wanting to learn how to do natural hoof care, attending one of Jaime's "hands-on" trimming clinics is a great way to learn. Jaime provides a complete overview of natural hoof care principles, and then shows you how to conduct "precision trimming". Clinics are kept at no more than four participants to insure ample individual attention. Go to Jaime's website for complete details.

SCHEDULE & SIGN-UP INFO AT:

www.jaime-jackson.com

AMERICAN ASSOCIATION OF NATURAL HOOF CARE PRACTITIONERS

SERVING THE WILD HORSE HOOF MODEL

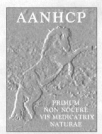

"Cause no harm ... respect the
healing powers of nature"

AANHCP
Certification Program
P.O. Box 2181
Harrison, AR 72601

www.AANHCP.org
info@AANHCP.org

American Association of Natural Hoof Care Practitioners (AANHCP), a non-profit organization, is dedicated to the promotion and practice of humane and natural hoof care in the United States.

AANHCP conducts a training and certification program to render the highest possible professional standards for its members.

AANHCP embraces fully the wild horse and its exemplary hooves for its natural hoof care model.

Join the AANHCP

The American Association of Natural Hoof Care Practitioners (AANHCP) was founded on the belief that genuine natural hoof care deserves a systematic approach to training and evidence of competence. The AANHCP Certification Program is the culmination of combined efforts and continuing dedication to this belief. Students are systematically instructed in an intense, hands-on, and step-wise program designed to build technical skills and theoretical knowledge. The clinicians, instructors and examiners of the Association are highly skilled and experienced practitioners who "mentor" each candidate to provide individual guidance while ensuring the successful graduate's competence. All certified graduates enjoy the full recognition and support of AANHCP officers, staff, and membership.

If you are interested in participating in the AANHCP Certification Program, please visit our website for complete details and downloadable application forms.

QUALITY HORSE BOOTS

ESSENTIAL HOOF PROTECTION

The AANHCP: On the Importance of Hoof Boots

To the professional natural hoof care practitioner, no hoof-related product is more important than the hoof boot. For many horses coming out of metal horseshoes (called "transition"), and suffering its deleterious effects, the hoof boot may mean the difference between success and failure. They cushion and protect the weakened and hypersensitive sole during transitional conditioning (i.e., rehabilitative) exercises, and they enable horse owners to keep riding without harmful consequences to the foot's sensitive dermal structures. Indeed, *movement* is the principal force driving natural healing. Hoof boots, hence, give the underlying growth corium (dermis) time to build a new and powerful protective armor of callused, epidermal horn — growth stimulated by barefootedness, natural trimming and natural horsekeeping practices.

The AANHCP encourages the manufacturing sector to aid the natural hoof care movement by creating new, and better hoof boots. *The demand is there.* In recent years, AANHCP practitioners have evaluated a number of hoof boots in the marketplace (most are of European origin). To date (2004), two boots that have been thoroughly tested stand above the rest in terms of their quality, adaptability to the hoof, user-friendliness, and — of vital importance to the AANHCP — apparent harmlessness to the horse and his feet. The AANHCP wishes to make the following endorsements:

"The American Association of Natural Hoof Care Practitioners (AANHCP) has evaluated the Boa Horse Boot and Swiss Horse Boot and has found them to be safe, reliable, and quality hoof boots for most equestrian purposes, when fitted properly and used in conjunction with a responsible regimen of natural hoof care and natural horsekeeping practices."

For more information about the Boa Boot and Swiss Horse Boot, please visit the manufacturers' authorized websites:

www.boahorseboot.com

www.swissboot.com

Boa Horse Boot

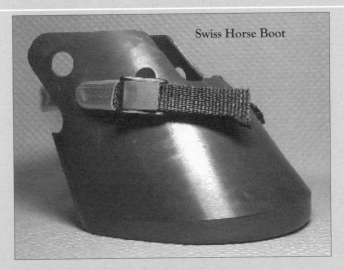

Swiss Horse Boot

GLOSSARY

This glossary focuses exclusively on hoof care terms used by natural hoof care practitioners. It does not include most veterinary and farrier definitions as there are ample sources devoted to those disciplines.

active hoof wear: Abrasion of the hoof capsule caused by direct contact with the ground. *In naturally shaped hooves, the hoof wall endures mainly active wear, while the frog undergoes passive wear.*

active support: The portions of the hoof capsule that actively support the weight of the horse. *The naturally shaped hoof wall actively supports the weight of the horse on hard ground.*

angle-of-growth: The angle at which the hoof wall grows down from the coronary band.

barefoot hoof: An un-shod hoof. *All natural hooves are unshod, but not all unshod hooves are natural hooves.*

barefoot trim: A generic term for any trim that does not including fixed shoeing. *A natural trim is a barefoot trim, but not all barefoot trims are natural trims.*

callus: The hardened and thickened state of the hoof capsule resulting from natural wear.

coffin bone rotation: Separation of the hoof wall from the coffin bone, caused by laminitis.

compressional forces: Pressure within the hoof capsule caused by descending body weight.

concussional forces: Shock caused by the hoof's collision with the ground.

contraction: The natural state of the hoof during its flight (airborne) phase. Pathology: the shrunken state of the hoof due to shoeing, hoof pain, and close confinement.

de-shoe: Removal of the horseshoe in preparation for natural trimming and high performance barefootedness.

feral hoof: Existing in a natural state; wild not domesticated; the result of a horse having reverted back to the wild state, as from domestication: *America's wild horses are feral equids with wild hooves.*

flare: Excessive outward growth of the hoof wall beyond what is natural.

flight phase: The airborne phase of the hoof during a stride.

founder: Coffin bone rotation caused by diet and unnatural hoof care and veterinary practices.

frog pressure: Weight-bearing forces squeezing the frog in the direction of the ground.

hairline: The lower edge of the hair above the coronet of the hoof capsule.

heel: The segment of the hoof wall between the quarters and heel-buttress.

heel-buttress: The segment of the hoof wall between the heels and the bars.

high performance barefootedness: The ability of a horse to move naturally without artificial hoof protection.

hoof balance: A dynamic equilibrium between the hoof and the whole horse marked by total soundness, locomotive efficiency, and optimal health. *A natural hoof is a balanced hoof and conversely, a balanced hoof is a natural hoof.*

hoof capsule: All of the hard, horny structures of the hoof below the hairline.

hoof color: The pigmentation of the outer wall.

hoof length: The length of the underside of the hoof from the toe wall to furthermost supporting surface of the hoof capsule.

hoof mechanism: The natural contraction and expansion of the hoof during flight and support respectively.

hoof size: The measurable dimensions of the hoof. *Hoof Length, Hoof Width, and Toe Angle* are examples of hoof size.

hoof wall: The entire hoof wall below the coronary band.

hoof width: The width of the hoof from quarter to quarter.

horse boot: As opposed to a medicinal boot, a boot that horses wear temporarily for riding purposes.

lameness: The inability of a horse to move naturally.

laminitis: Lameness caused by unnatural diet and other factors.

long toe: (Pathology) A toe which is excessively longer than normal ranges for naturally shaped hooves.

medicinal boot: A non-riding horse boot intended for treating wounds and infections.

mustang roll: The radius or curve to the hoof wall at its ground bearing surface. *The mustang roll is a characteristic of all natural hooves.*

natural boarding: Horse stewardship based on the principles of nature.

natural diet: The diet of healthy wild horses.

natural healing: Allowing the hoof to heal itself by restoring it to its natural state in conjunction with natural boarding.

natural hoof: Existing in or formed in accordance with the principles of nature. *All wild hooves are naturally shaped hooves, but not all naturally shaped hooves are wild.*

natural hoof care: The care of hooves based on the principles of the natural hoof.

natural hoof care practitioner: (Professional) A person who trims and boots horses according to the principles of natural hoof care.

natural trim: Hooves trimmed according to the principles of nature. *Unshod naturally trimmed hooves are natural hooves.*

natural wear: Locomotive forces necessary to create naturally shaped hooves and which are the product of high performance barefootedness.

navicular: (Navicular Syndrome) Lameness attributed to pain in the back half of the hoof.

outer wall: The hoof wall visible to the naked eye.

passive hoof wear: Abrasion of the hoof capsule caused by indirect contact with the ground. *In naturally shaped hooves, the sole undergoes passive contact with the ground,* while the hoof wall endures active wear.

passive support: The portions of the hoof capsule that passively support the weight of the horse. *The naturally shaped sole passively supports the weight of the horse on hard ground.*

relative concavity: The relative natural positions of the hoof wall, sole, frog, and heel bulbs to each other. *The sole is passive to the hoof wall in the hoof's concaved volar dome.*

run-away hoof: (Pathology) A hoof whose toe wall has grown or "migrated" too far forward, even though the toe wall may be naturally short.

run-under heels: (Pathology) Condition of the hoof capsule in which the position of the heel-buttresses is too far forward under the hoof, caused by excessive growth.

sidebone: (Pathology?) Ossification (calcification) of the cartilages. There is evidence that sidebone may be perfectly natural and non-debilitating to the horse.

support phase: The weight bearing phase of the hoof during a stride.

thin sole: (Pathology) A sole too thin and which is hypersensitive, caused by unnatural hoof care practices.

thrush: (Pathology) Fungal and bacterial infection of the frog.

toe angle: The angle of the toe wall relative to the ground.

toe length: The length of the toe wall from the hairline down the center of the hoof wall to the ground.

transition: The period of time between deshoeing and adaptation of the hoof to its environment.

trimming to the hoof: Trimming according to the natural conformation of the hoof.

White Line Disease: (Pathology) Serious condition of the white line characterized by widespread necrosis and detachment from the coffin bone. Probably a secondary complication of laminitis — if there is even a difference between the two.

wild hoof: Existing in a state of nature; not tamed or domesticated: *a wild horse hoof.*

wild horse trim: See "natural trim."

INDEX

ABOUT JAIME JACKSON

A SHORT HISTORY OF THE NATURAL HOOF CARE MOVEMENT AND THE AUTHOR'S ROLE IN IT

by Holly Harrison

*The wild horse adoption program actually began under the auspices of the International Society for the Preservation of Mustangs and Burros, founded by Velma Johnston ("Wild Horse Annie") — seen here in this rare photograph from the 1950s (BLM archives). ISPMB is still active today, 50 years later! I've been on the organization's Advisory Board for several years.

Jaime began his professional career as a farrier 25 years ago. In 1978 he met Les Emery, fellow farrier and author of the critically acclaimed text, *Horseshoeing Theory and Hoof Care* (1977). Jaime and Les began a serious dialogue about hoof lameness issues and the possibility of a "natural" hoof form or model that might be essentially lameness free. This speculation continued until 1982, when an event occurred that would alter both men's careers as "shoers" forever.

A client of Jaime's had at that time purchased a wild horse ("mustang") through the Bureau of Land Management (BLM) adopt-a-horse program.* Asked to look at the mare's hooves with an eye to trimming, Jaime was staggered by what he saw: perfect hooves as he had never seen before.

Within a week, Jaime related to Les that he was going immediately into wild horse country (Nevada) to learn more about what he had just witnessed. At this time, the early 1980's, the Reagan Administration was in place and the BLM was anxious along with conservative (cattle ranching) interests, to remove wild horses from the government rangelands. Tens of thousands of wild horses were swept up in "gathers" and removed to vast holding paddocks located near Palomino Valley, Nevada, and Litchfield, California.

Jaime split his time between the open rangelands of Nevada, California, and Oregon, and the Litchfield holding facility. From 1982 until 1986, he observed wild horses in their native haunts and studied their hooves up close at Litchfield as they entered the paddocks. The BLM aided Jaime in his efforts. "As a horseman," related Jaime to Rick Lamb ("The Horse Show" radio program) years later, "it was the greatest experience of my life."

From this first hand accounting of equine life in the wild, Jaime eventually wrote his first book, *The Natural Horse: Lessons From the Wild* (1992, Northland Publishing), hailed by Emery as "the most important contribution to horse care in the 20th Century."

During the 1980's, working alone, Jaime began to experiment with his findings on domestic horses. Armed with a consummate image of the wild hoof, now etched indelibly in his mind, he adapted his trimming skills as a farrier and the statistical framework of the wild model to the task of rendering naturally shaped hooves among his

(Continued on page 314)

I'm reaching for my Star Ridge nippers. Let's review some points I made earlier in the HOG: my toes are pointed inward (why?); my tools are carefully organized in the Hoof Stand—Work Center (can you remember the special feature of the tool caddy seen here?); the horse's head is tied loosely in what position (do recall from Chapter 6?); and the horse is supporting herself mainly on what two legs? I'm also wearing a trimmer's apron and gloves (why?). Natural hoof care is very rewarding when things are done right consistently — study this Guide closely and you'll discover why.

clients' horses. On one breeding ranch, Jaime applied his new method of trimming to over 300 horses over a four year period. All the riding stock were ridden shoeless. The result: hundreds of sound, barefooted horses. Inspired by his success, Jaime then turned to his other clientele, "de-shoeing" and adapting his "mustang trim" to their horses if they were willing to go with the program. By 1988, Jaime had come to the conclusion that horseshoeing was as unnecessary as it was harmful. In 1990, he terminated his horseshoeing business forever. He had become America's first born "natural hoof care practitioner."

Backing up a bit, Emery and Jackson were invited to report jointly on Jaime's findings at the 1988 Annual Convention of the American Farriers Association. An audience of 1,000 farriers at Lexington, Kentucky scratched their heads in bewilderment at Jaime's four hour barrage of hoof measurements and statistics, slide show, and array of hoof biospecimens collected from the rangelands. No one knew what to do with the information, and his call for a "natural hoof" model of soundness fell on deaf ears.

A few years later, in 1992, The Natural Horse was published by Northland Publishing of Arizona. Whisper quiet, and without any cognizance of the fact by the horse using community, it entered the marketplace as a "coffee table" type book of the Southwest genera. Only a few horse owners, through sheer chance, happened to stumble upon it. But those who did were emphatic about its powerful message, writing letters of support to the publisher, thence to Jaime.

But the book failed to reach mainstream horse owners, and in 1995, Northland, selling out its first run, decided to vacate the title from their book list. TNH had been "dumped" and with it, Jaime's wild model for soundness.

Forward thinking editors at the American Farriers Journal, however, encouraged Jaime to write a series of articles about his findings. This occurred over the next 5 to 10 years. But by and large, professional farriers ignored what was published, and the valuable information hidden within Jaime's writings never reached their horse owner clientele. The natural hoof model was still virtually unheard of.

Around the same time, in 1993, Jaime was invited by Dr. Barbara Page, an equine veterinary practitioner from Denver, Colorado, and avid supporter of Emery's book, to speak before the Denver Area Veterinary Medical Society's annual convention at the Denver stockyards and fairground. Response to Jaime's talk was very enthusiastic from the vets and the few farriers and horse owners who were present. But, as with the farriers five years earlier at the AFA convention, the imaginations of those present were insufficiently fired to

(Across) I'm showing client Cathy Drewry how to sight a hoof for balance. Can you recall from reading this Guide what Cathy is looking for? [Hint: How do the heel-buttresses line up with the toe wall?]

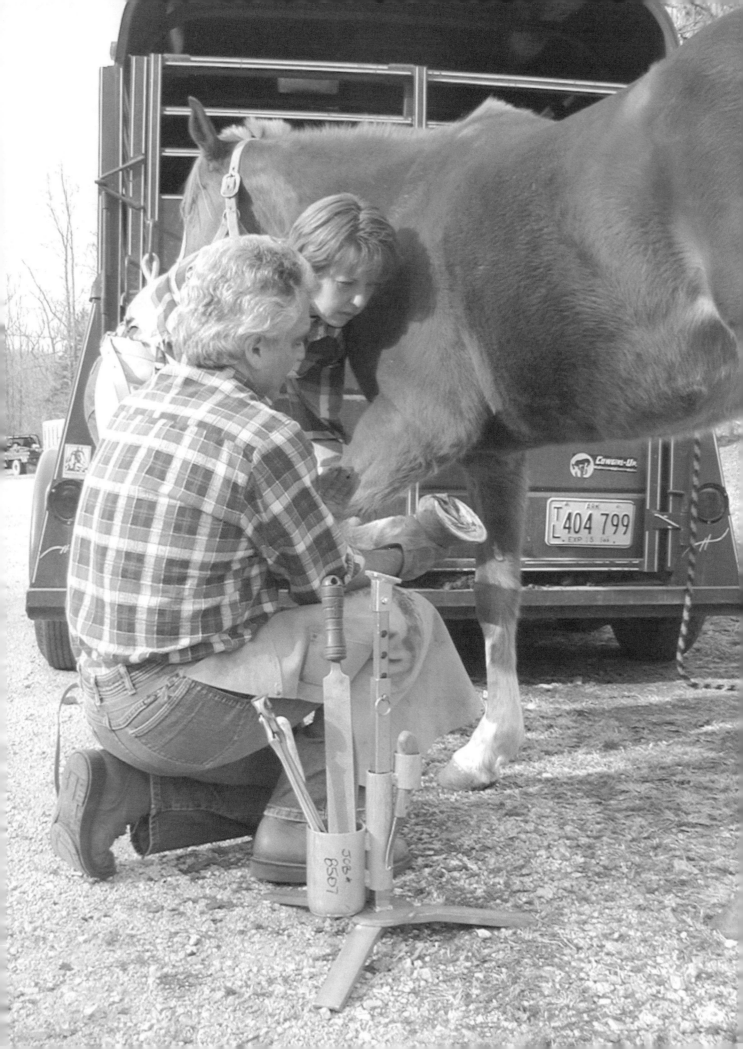

take the message back to their clients. [Dr. Page, however, did several years later form a research group with Professor Robert Bowker (Michigan State University) to conduct their own research on wild horse hooves.]

By 1995, Jaime had all but abandoned any hope that the wild model would ever be brought before horse owners. Other publishers were contacted to take over his book, but in each case, it was met with rejection. *TNH*, seemingly destined to oblivion, went "out of print."

Then, one night in 1995, Jaime received an unexpected call at his mountain farm from an elated Dr. Ric Redden, founder and host of the prestigious Bluegrass Laminitis Symposium held annually in Louisville, Kentucky. Redden, an equine vet and farrier, had just discovered an old copy of *TNH* and was now eager to have Jaime come to his convention and speak for four hours. The deal was struck and Jaime went before another packed house of veterinarians and farriers that winter. This time, response was considerably better than at previous talks, and Redden himself related to Jaime, "We will make this model the industry standard."

Bolstered by the obvious acceptance by many of the wild model at the 1995 Symposium, Jaime and his wife Nancy, decided at the suggestion of Dr. Redden to re-publish *TNH* themselves. They formed Star Ridge Publishing for this purpose. During 1996 - 1997, SRP began to push *TNH* before the horse using community, and, with much effort, began to make inroads. Horse owner response, to say the least, was enthusiastic.

Ironically, it soon became evident that horse owners — not vets or farriers, who continued to ignore the model — would lead the way to acceptance of the natural hoof model. Accordingly, Jaime wrote three new books (*Horse Owners Guide to Natural Hoof Care, Boot Your Horse!*, and *Founder: Prevention and Cure the Natural Way*) and created two videos ("Creating the Perfect Hoof" and "Boot Your Horse!") to help horse owners bridge the gap between conventional shoeing and the burgeoning new natural hoof care movement.

Writing apocalyptically in his 1999 newsletter, The *Natural Hoofcare Advisor*, "We will bypass the farriery community, and teach horse owners themselves to manage their own horses' feet the natural way." By 2001, SRP could count some 10,000 horses that had been brought into barefootedness without any support from the traditional veterinary and farriery communities. Change indeed was not only in the air, a new hoof care revolution had been launched.

Not one to simply hold ground, Jaime in 1999 traveled to Europe to lay the foundations for yet another epoch change in the natural hoof care revolution. Recognizing that many horses are rendered tender footed by shoeing, Jaime believed that a quality hoof boot for riding was needed to transition horses through the early phases of deshoeing.

Jaime's answer was to be the Swiss Horse Boot, the brain child of Hubert Rohner — a fellow advocate of barefootedness from Switzerland. Jaime calls it the "ultimate boot," due to its many features which enable it to adapt to naturally trimmed hooves. By 2000, the Star Ridge Company was formed to introduce the new boot to U.S. horse owners in the natural hoof care movement.

Today — 20 years after he first entered wild horse country — Jaime continues his mission in life: "Helping Horses Naturally!"

Jaime's most recent undertaking, and a mammoth one at that, is the creation of the American Association of Natural Hoof Care Practitioners (AANHCP). "This is the natural hoof care movement's answer to the traditional farrier organizations. It will represent a systemized approach to developing the natural hoof care alternative into the mainstream *standard*." The principal objectives of the AANHCP are training, certification, wild horse research, and liaison with the horse using community.

Jaime, in conjunction with Star Ridge Publishing, is also publishing the works of fellow natural hoof care practitioners. "I'm certainly not the only person doing this kind of work out there with a message. Others have their own insights and unique contributions to make. SRP will do everything it can to bring their important messages into the mainstream natural hoof care movement. In 2002, three new books are in progress: an inspirational story about booting horses (a collaboration between Jaime and one of his clients and hoof care practitioner herself, Cathy Drewry); a detailed trimming guide by Pete Ramey (see Chapter 17, "Natural Hoof Care Practitioners") that will work very well with Jaime's *HOG*; and, with Charles Hall (see Chapter 17), a specialized guide for trimming foundered horses. "These are very exciting developments in the natural hoof care movement," explains Jaime, "because each book adds more important knowledge to the information base that horse owners, hoof care providers, and vets can readily access and put to good use.

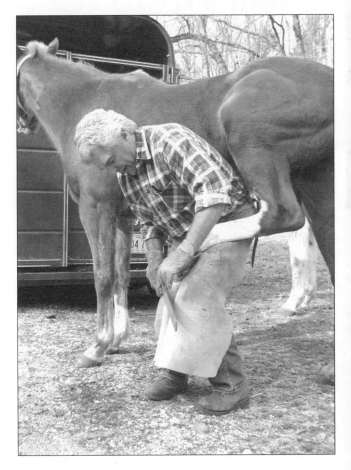

*   *   *

Jaime Jackson lives with his wife and two children in a small town nestled in the Boston Mountains of north Arkansas.

[Note: Holly Harrison is Managing Editor for Star Ridge Publishing]

NOTES

HORSE OWNERS GUIDE TO NATURAL HOOF CARE

NOTES

ORDER FORM
PRICES SUBJECT TO CHANGE

Product Description	Qty.	Price	Subtotal

SHIPPING

	TOTAL	ADD
$0	$9.99	$1.50
10	29.99	3.95
30	59.99	5.95
60	79.99	6.95
80	99.99	7.95
100	149.99	9.95
150+	-	11.95

Order total: _____

(AR res. add 6.0% tax): _____

Shipping: _____

Total: _____

U.S. PRIORITY MAIL: Add $1.00 per item
CANADIAN ORDERS: Add $2.00 to the amounts listed in the chart at left.
FOREIGN ORDERS: Please see our website or contact us for rates.

Name (please print): _____

Address: _____

_____ zip: _____

Phone: _____ e-mail: _____

Method of Payment: ☐ Check/M.O. ☐ Visa ☐ MasterCard ☐ Discover ☐ AMEX

Credit Card #: _____ Exp. date

Signature: _____

STAR RIDGE COMPANY   P.O. BOX 2181   HARRISON, AR 72601
1-870-743-4603 (phone)   1-870-743-1637 (fax)   star@star-ridge.com (e-mail)

FOR SECURE ON-LINE ORDERING GO TO:
www.star-ridge.com